To Triska's
family —

It's all about being
KIND. —

I'm sure you already are ☺

Adrienne Palzon

LIVE
LIKE
PAUL

ADRIENNE FALZON

BLUE NOTE
PUBLICATIONS, INC.

FIRST Printing

Melbourne, Florida

Blue Note Publications, Inc.

1-800-624-0401

bluenotepublications.com

Library of Congress Control Number: 2020941419

ISBN No.: 978-1-7338019-4-2

Cover Design by Paul Anthony Maluccio

The stories in this book are the author's own personal experiences, reported as she saw them. The opinions of the author on the people, places and events are only the author's observations and opinions.

Printed In The United States of America

This book is dedicated to all who are committed to making this world a better place to live.

To all those who understand that the title *Live Like Paul* means not only to live without prejudice and hostility but it also reminds us to spread kindness and generosity.

It is the intent of this book to show that the lack of empathy has disastrous results, whereas love conquers all.

May that message resonate with all who read this.

Books By Adrienne Falzon

What Is An Angel?
By Adrienne Falzon
Illustrated By Helen Salzberg • ISBN: 978-0-9855562-2-8
Hardcover, Full Color • Children/All ages

The Search For The Perfect Shell
By Adrienne Falzon
Illustrated By Helen Salzberg • ISBN: 978-0-9903068-5-6
Hardcover, Full Color • Children/All ages

Selfish Sally
By Adrienne Falzon
Illustrated By Helen Salzberg • ISBN: 978-0-9963066-9-0
Hardcover, Full Color • Children/All ages

It's Not Fair!
By Adrienne Falzon
Hardcover with Dustjacket • 32 pages/full color
Illustrated By Debbie Waldorf Johnson
ISBN: 978-1-878398-33-8 • Children/All Ages

All available at www.bluenotepublications.com
Info: 1-800-624-0401
bluenotebooks@gmail.com

www.AdrienneFalzon.com

— ✳ —

Acknowledgments

THERE ARE SO MANY PEOPLE to recognize in the process of writing this book. So many people to thank for their input and participation in one way or another.

First and foremost, I want to thank God for giving me my son Paul for 43 years. It's in the spirit of gratitude where we will be happiest as we go through our lives. I write about this very subject in this book

I choose to be grateful for the time I had with Paul, as opposed to the time I didn't have.

I also want to thank Paul for allowing me and choosing me to be his mom, giving me 43 years of immeasurable joy along with anyone else he came in contact with.

Thank you, Paul, for being that beacon of light in the hope and comfort of knowing there are good, selfless people in this world.

It seriously took a village in getting my hand written book onto computer files for the simple reason that I don't type! It took a series of available typists, beginning with Julia Shilen, a college student who was home in the Hamptons for the summer. Whenever I had a chapter done, we would meet at some location so I could give her my handwritten pages in return for the typed ones she just finished. This went on until she had to go back to school in Utah. Thank you, Julia!

My next typist was my granddaughter Olivia, who was then free from some of her US SKI TEAM training schedules. I would take photos of my hand written pages and email them to her. Upon receiving them, she would type and send back to me in a labeled file. This went on even while she traveled with her team to Switzerland.

In between, it became necessary to have one of my son's secretaries, Veronica Lisboa, pitch in.

My goal date for completion was coming up quickly and there was so much to type up!

Organizing these various files from various sources was a huge job in itself and eventually they all found their way to my publisher, Paul Maluccio, at Blue Note Books. Paul published all four of my children's books and our experience working together has been just wonderful. I am so grateful that he was introduced into my life so many years ago! Thank you, Paul, for your patience, professionalism, and guidance.

Of course, as always, there's my dear husband Manny, making every effort to see that I have everything I need. In those writing months, I would be at it for 10 to 12 hours a day nonstop, rarely leaving the house. Manny made all that possible in picking up groceries, supplies, etc. He is truly the best.

And then there's my son Frank, along with daughter in law Erin, grandchildren Olivia and Frankie, as well as sons Richie and Bobby, who were always there to listen and commiserate all those months as I would cry my heart out in writing certain chapters. They knew that saying "I know, mom" was all I needed to hear.

And, finally, thank you to all my fabulous friends who kept encouraging me to keep writing, remembering the good times and also kept reminding me that they were there for me whenever or however I needed them.

And that is how this book got written.

CONTENTS

—— ✳ ——

INTRODUCTION

I CHOSE TO BEGIN THIS MONUMENTAL TASK of writing Paul's story in my Rancho Santa Fe, California office. It's my happy place. The bright California sunshine illuminates pale yellow walls adorning framed family and friends' photos, along with my dad's oil paintings he made many years ago. Bookshelves are at their limit with both read and unread books, interspersed with my huge collection of angels, cards, and even more photos. Dad's stained glass creations line the window seat, transposing sunlight into various colored shapes and sizes. And, the love and peace in this space is also augmented by the view of mountains with a hint of the Pacific Ocean.

Some of these embellishments needed to be reorganized and relocated on Thanksgiving Day 2018 to accommodate one new addition—my son Paul's wooden box of ashes, along with two of his favorite shirts—the ones he wore all the time, and especially on the last two times we were together.

Those two shirts. They are neatly folded and rest on my treasured box.

This is all I have to physically hold on to.

I will begin my journey here, surrounded by all of this, where I will hopefully receive the spiritual guidance, wisdom and courage to say what needs to be said. I'm confident that in being embraced by so much love and beauty, I will be strengthened and energized to do so.

I never imagined writing a biography, especially a biography on one of my sons. Usually, but not always, a person's biography is written after they die.

So yes, my son Paul died, and here I am.

The thought that any of my four sons would predecease me was unthinkable. And, actually, still is.

I struggle with the fact that my dear son, Paul, is no longer on this earth. I can't call him. Can't text him. Can't see him. Ever. Where is he? Where did he go? What mother can deal with that?

I had no idea how to begin this "biography-book." I am the published author of four children's books, but never wrote for adults. Not that I didn't want to. What's interesting, and curious at the same time, is that there are parts of this book that begged to emerge from my thoughts out onto paper for 35 years. But it never happened. They just stayed in my head. I kept pushing these ideas aside. Instead, I wrote more children's books that I never got around to getting published, which are still sitting in a file drawer in my office.

The "other" book was sitting on the back burner, waiting for me to light the flame. People say "it's all about timing," and that "everything happens for a reason."

I now see the wisdom of that, and how patience plays a huge part in letting God, the Universe, fill in the blanks in divine order, not ours.

Paul died. These words reflect a hard reality for me. One I still can't wrap my mind around on most days. But there it is.

And, when Paul died, interestingly, that "35-year-old-in-my-head-book" haunted me all over again. I saw in my mind's eye that it was all somehow connected.

Paul's life journey, coupled with all my prior observations, concerns, and disappointments about the destructive behavior of so many of the world's inhabitants, gave me the final push I needed to get that mental script on paper. It became an opportunity to tie up loose ends, while showing the senseless conduct of so many. I now had someone to use as an example that certain thinking is wrong; absolutely wrong, criminal.

Criminal in the way that people have been bullied, tortured, and, even killed, because of senseless ideologies.

Thank God none of those horrific things ever happened to Paul. But, they COULD have! Deep inside, Paul knew that. And, at one point, he felt that he couldn't deal with what might be in store for him in the future. More on that later. What "saved" him? The sincere declarations of love and acceptance from his closest friends.

Had they not stepped forward, this beautiful life of loving and giving that you are going to read about here in this book, would not have existed. Pure hatred would have and could have prevented a life such as his to reach its natural fruition. All his incredible accomplishments, experiences, and generosities towards others never would have happened.

Hatred has no reasoning, logic, or moral compass. It's blind madness. Hatred has taken the lives of so many like Paul and from so many others because of senseless excuses—lives that could have also brought joy to the world as Paul's life did.

And that's part of the reason for this book.

It's to show how pure love saved a life that had every right to be lived and respected. And how hate has unjustly taken that opportunity from so many.

May that stop once and for all.

It's heartbreaking that it had to be my own son's story to give substance to my points presented, but what could ever have a larger effect? It was probably the way it had to be. Was that all pre planned? Do we sign up for reasons to be here? Are we born for a purpose attached to an expiration date? Was Paul's final unselfish act to die, designed to be the impetus to get certain messages out, as they already have in so many ways, even as I write this?

Such questions brought me to research other areas of interest I knew nothing about. And, now I am obsessed with all of it.

Yes, lots to talk about here. You can expect some thought-provoking, and, possibly, controversial ideas from my personal observations.

This actual *Introduction*, as it was taking form, started in my mind for several months, immediately following Paul's funeral service on Wednesday, November 21, 2018, in Atlanta, Georgia. Hearing how Paul positively affected so many people as they recounted their testimonies at the Chapel's microphone, several feet from where Paul laid in peace, the decision was made. Further "love stories" followed on Facebook, social media, texts and emails. I have included many of them in a separate section in this book.

And, on the plane returning to San Diego, California, the following day, words bombarded me as I cried constantly, staring out my window.

It was actually Thanksgiving Day, the day Paul was to be at our home, along with his brothers and friends having Thanksgiving dinner.

Ironically, he did come, but not the way I could have ever imagined when I set the table a week before, but in a wooden box of ashes.

I didn't have the strength to put those relentless words and sentences on paper. At least not yet.

I was so deep in grief for days, then weeks. All I wanted to do was lay on the couch and be quiet. No talking. No phone. Manny took all my phone calls, opened my mail and packages, (and there was much of that) fed me, and pretty much breathed for me. There were times I wished I didn't breathe at all, so that the unfathomable truth would just disappear, along with myself.

It's a truth no mother can reconcile with. Or make sense of, or remove. I would have gladly given my own life to get back his, as I would do for any of my sons. In a heartbeat.

So, NO, I couldn't bring myself to start writing in those early painful weeks. But, then I had to, because words would follow me as in thought balloons above my head. Related, and unrelated sentences.

I couldn't even take a hot bath in peace, which I took many of to calm and relax myself amongst the lavender bubbles, soothing my swollen eyes with warm washcloths. It was my total alone space where I would just lay quietly, fixating at the vibrantly beautiful green California trees outside my bath window, getting me to think about the color green itself—its tranquilizing quality. I'm glad God didn't choose any other color for nature's palette. Can you imagine the colors of black, red, orange, yellow, etc., adorning mountains, hills, front and backyard lawns?

Nothing can do it like green. Funny how I never thought of that before.

It's interesting how such random ideas pop into your consciousness when alone and in total distress. Well, maybe not as alone as I thought. I was upstairs and far away from any activity on the lower level of our home, but, somehow, my dear, loving husband always seemed to be upstairs when I took my spa retreats. I know he probably always worried I would drown in my sorrow somehow, accidentally falling asleep. I must say he was (and always is) the most caring and devoted husband ever. He would hear me crying in the jacuzzi and ask "Are you okay in there?"

"Yes, I'm okay," I'd answer.

But, let's face it. I'd never be "okay" again.

Taking any kind of drugs (antidepressants) was never an option for me.

I managed to stay away from that for 71 years and wasn't about to start now. I figured if I got through a difficult divorce 30 years ago (and the nightmare years before that) I could manage with all the coping tools, armor, and willpower I learned at that time.

However, there was never a battle like this one. This was all out war on the mind and body.

My grief was raw and very, very deep, but I still didn't want any chemicals to interfere with the process. It was my own personal choice. I didn't see how masking or postponing my grief would work for me. But I completely understand if sometimes it's imperative that people need such assistance!

Everyone is different! No judgment here!

Eventually, I slowly came around to making the first step in my project at hand, and that was to get notebooks out from my supply closet. That alone was an effort. Everything seemed to be an effort, including getting out of bed and getting dressed.

Opening the cabinet door to see what was inside was a start.

As a teacher for many years, I was always in the habit of having plenty of pencils, pens, envelopes, construction paper, loose leaf paper, spiral pads, notebooks, binders, markers, etc. on hand because "you never know when you will need them."

That didn't change even after having been retired for 23 years!

And, so, with blank notebooks and sharpened pencils strewn on my desk, I was ready. Notice there was no mention of a computer. Old fashioned as I am, I need my paper.

I have a confession. I actually purchased a brand new gorgeous MAC computer when I was starting this, and, I'm embarrassed to admit, went to all of Apple's classes for 2 weeks, in the hope of learning how to use it. At the end of 2 weeks, I was like a deer in headlights. I went straight home from that last class and packed up the MAC computer where I couldn't see it so I could pretend I never bought it.

Confession over.

So, now that I had the notebooks in front of me, where in the world do I start? It all seemed overwhelming.

I then went to my trusty inner circle of friends, to tell them my intentions. Their questions followed, and it was those questions that gave me a roadmap to where I was going and how to get there. It looked like it would be a long journey, with lots of side trips, forks in the road, and even some U-turns.

Many times I ran out of gas with no fueling station in sight. I never lost hope. I persisted. I kept a focus on those questions for direction:

"Why are you doing this? What do you hope to accomplish? Who is your audience? Will there be personal, controversial subjects and stories revealed, or will it be cleaned up?"

That last question made me laugh because nothing I say or do is ever "cleaned up", because I believe in saying the truth and not holding back. What you see and hear is what you get. So, no, there will be nothing held back because of what "people might think". If it's my truth, it is what it is. I think more and more of us feel that as we get older (and wiser).

Their provocative queries inspired and coaxed me to move along with organization and purpose.

I love my friends. I've been so, so blessed with so many of them, too.

Yes, the title *Live Like Paul* gives one a clue that this book will be acknowledging and celebrating the love, generosity, good works, and forgiving nature of its namesake. But, that's only part of the story.

The motto LIVE LIKE PAUL would become a mantra, adorning bracelets, sweatshirts, tee shirts, Facebook groups, a Foundation for two Georgia Tech scholarships, concerts, 5K annual marathons, dedications, etc.

And, all of this was created to spread kindness, compassion, and love to all, encouraging everyone to do the same. ALL—meaning everyone. EVERYONE—meaning all colors, religions, sexes, financial or social statuses.

So, yes, this book is about getting to a higher level of humanity, or "enlightenment" so to speak (well, maybe not that high) but, again, there is so much more to talk about before we even talk about that. To make certain points clearer, to be more digestible, I had to dig deeper.

I think background information is crucial in setting up a story, so the intended effect can be better experienced, or realized by the reader. Having such a backdrop, as you may sometimes experience in movies or books in the way of flashbacks, gives one that eureka moment of "Oh! Now I get it! Now I see why!"

Once a person is aware of the genesis of what is present in the now, there could be a fuller understanding, or appreciation, or empathy.

Just as one values the historic details in a novel, the same applies here in nonfiction, a biography, if not more so. Why? Because it's a true story and it all really happened!

So, therefore, you will either be reminiscent, or informed, depending on your age, of events that occurred up to 30 years before Paul was even born. And, because of these events and existing sentiments infiltrating the world he was born into, Paul, like many others I am sure, was a conflicted soul in grappling with such unwanted, different struggles.

You see, Paul was gay.

There will be much more about this in the Reflections and Connections Chapter, so stay with me here for now in the Introduction. It will then be easier to connect the dots to see where all this is going.

My first intention in writing this book was to show how Paul overcame his struggles and turned things around for the common good. He had a happy and fulfilled life in his 43 years, as will be shown in a myriad of ways in his Biography section as well as throughout other sections of this book.

Hopefully the happiness and contentment of his life can ultimately be viewed as attainable for anyone going through hopeless or despondent times in their own unique circumstances.

One's physical or mental health is compromised if one allows for negative energies to enter in.

On the heels of that, it's my next intention to shed light on all the mundane, senseless ideologies and opinions that people have collected and carried around for years (centuries).

I call these people who go around pontificating such judgments "the bullies". They come in all forms with many disguises, be it in the name of religions or "do-gooder groups". And, we, as citizens of the world, have victoriously set the stage for disaster because we haven't really, really acknowledged these systemic, inherited, and contagious viruses as detrimental. As deadly and as detrimental as the Covid 19, which is currently affecting us at this very moment of time in my final editing of this book before publication!

We haven't truly successfully confronted and rectified the evidence of such antagonistic, destructive acts—just lip service.

So, there lies my second intent, along with, and related to, Paul's life story. Prejudice, in all its lowly forms, whether it be for color, race, sex, social status, etc. never ends well.

The attack on one individual affects the universe as a whole. It's like the Butterfly Effect, which simply states that the flaps of the tiny wings of a butterfly become part of the conditions leading to a chain of events, which then leads to a larger chain of events.

In other words, everything we say or do (and even think!)

matters. Whether it be positive or negative, it all results in this rippling effect on the world we all live in.

It's a sobering thought, isn't it? Especially if we look around us as the present moment.

In a world full of chaos, violence, and economic upheaval, it's more important than ever to commit to one small positive action as often as possible, knowing its impact.

A compliment. A smile. Holding the door for the one behind you. Letting someone in your driving lane.

Each one of us was created to make a difference.

As Ghandi said, "Be the change you want to see in the world."

Well, fear not! This certainly won't be all gloom and doom!

Although the brokenness of some of society's detrimental perceptions will be highlighted and challenged, one can take solace in knowing there are many good people in this world, on the right path, supporting and respecting others, like Paul did.

And, more will do the same.

Hopefully, this book will be the jump-start towards spreading kindness to all.

The benefits are too significant to ignore. That really is the purpose of writing all this. To not only chronicle and celebrate Paul's life, but to wishfully set the stage to put all prejudices at rest once and for all for the sake of our world's future peace.

Reviewing Paul's 43 year life span was the most difficult process of all in the organization of this book. But, in that process of reviewing all that he was, I became ever so grateful to have been his mom, although the time, for me, was so short. Once I turned my attention to what I HAD as opposed to what I lost, healing began.

That realization brought me to the study of Gratitude. I would have been negligent if I didn't share all that. I learned not only about the importance, but the actual need of daily gratitude in one's life. It's been shown that having gratitude, in even the worst of times, gives one peace, while encouraging acceptance of what is.

I also became aware that in getting in the mindset of gratefulness for everything that is present in our lives (the good, bad and ugly) there could be complexities to deal with.

Intermittently in life we can find ourselves in difficult situations that are not our fault. Many of our heartaches or disappointments are sometimes caused by the irresponsible or evil actions of others. I know. The frustration of being in the midst of unfortunate or devastating circumstances because of the deeds of another, can easily and understandably lead to depression, anger, or even the need for revenge.

And, yet, we're told (by research), we have to be grateful for all of it, no matter what? That conundrum led me into the study of forgiveness.

That word forgiveness is still a bit elusive for me.

I say elusive because although I know how healing the power of forgiveness is, so they say, I have not mastered it myself. I am, as I said, a work in progress.

However, Paul, on the other hand, was a master of it. And, in following his lead, in *Living Like Paul*, I hope I arrive at the Forgiveness Station one day. I see several stops ahead, but the train is moving, so that's a good thing!

While discussing powerful life tools as in gratitude and forgiveness, I am adding *The Power of Positive Thinking* to the list, referring to the title of one of my favorite books. Positive thinking is so dear to me, and, I must say I have used THIS tool throughout my life. So did Paul. And, you will read, in full detail, my favorite story of Paul, where, at the age of 10, he won a trip to Hong Kong. It's such a testimony to the force of positive thinking, that I told it at Paul's funeral service and I've told it here in this book in a separate section.

Yes, it's so hard to think "positive" when you are in the deep dark dungeons of grief.

Grief is an unwanted and, too often, unexpected house guest that arrives and doesn't want to leave.

Grief, whether it be for the loss of a child, husband, parent, friend, pet, house, money, etc. is real. It's a loss that can never be found. Grief can literally make a permanent home in one's heart, head and soul if we let it—IF we let it.

Along with all the intents and purposes already mentioned, sharing what I learned about grief became another, hoping to give comforting validation and counsel to anyone who may need it at some time in their life.

Unfortunately, none of us can escape losing a loved one as we go through our life's journey.

As I expressed earlier in this Introduction, Paul's passing encouraged me to research areas of interest I not only didn't know much about, but also didn't think about.

Consequently, in searching for answers and any comfort I could find, I suddenly became obsessed with learning about the "Afterlife". There may be some eye rolling going on right now after reading that, but stay with me. I will be sharing some really, REALLY amazing personal stories that happened to me. So, take your skeptic hat off for just a little while and keep an open mind.

The final section in this book includes many testimonies (there were literally hundreds) that were sent to me by his friends, through Facebook, emails, cards, texts, phone visits and personal visits.

They were too heartwarming and meaningful not to be included. There's so much love and positive energy in every account and who wouldn't want to be filled with that? It also demonstrates how we all leave a legacy in one way or another when we die. So, why not leave a legacy that leaves those left behind happier to have known us?

It's in our power to do just that.

Adding these stories and comments by his amazing friends was also my way of thanking them, on behalf of Paul, for giving him the love and camaraderie of their friendships. I know how much Paul's friends, their families, and their children, meant to him and I am so grateful they were all in Paul's life. There's that word GRATEFUL. I'm using it often these days.

Paul will never be forgotten in my mind. I selfishly needed to write his story for my own healing.

But, I also had altruistic motives in the hope that in offering my journey along with his, others could be encouraged to make better choices—and, that, in these printed pages, Paul will not only have permanent evidence that he lived, but that he mattered.

He would want you all to know and truly understand that EVERYONE matters. EVERYONE deserves a full, happy, and respected existence.

He did what he could to make that happen every day for not only himself, but others. And, as it's already underway, as shown, those positively touched by him have picked up the baton to continue his work.

THIS is the kind of virus we want to spread.

LIVE LIKE PAUL

Knowing I've done my part in being his final voice, I can also now rest in the peace, acceptance, and comfort I was hoping for.

I found a way to turn tragedy into some higher good.

And, in the final analysis, isn't that the best we can ever do?

—— ✳ ——

Reflections and Connections

"Be kind, don't judge, and have respect for others. If we could all do this, the world would be a better place. The point is to teach this to the next generation."

—Jasmine Guinness

A s I mentioned in the introduction, part of this book has been on the back burner for many, many years. I started to look around and noticed things that just didn't make sense, and actually seemed wrong. I do believe there is a right and there is a wrong.

I always loved studying philosophy and psychology in college, and always thought I would be a psychologist or psychiatrist one day, having majored in that field. Life, however, took me in another direction. I wanted to get married.

So, education beyond my Master's degree never happened. Instead, I became a Reading Specialist and pursued a teaching career that I absolutely loved. It was a very rewarding position that encompassed various populations of students. That could actually be a whole other book! But, it was through those years that I started to see how important it is for children to begin life with a clean slate. By that I mean with no outside influences about race, religion, or any other judgements. Children are so innocent when they are little. It's when they get older that they start to like or dislike people from what they hear or observe.

Perhaps my observations started back when I was a child myself, unconsciously filing away certain covert and overt messages.

I began my education attending Our Lady of Mt. Carmel School in the Bronx, followed by St. Catharine Academy, also in the Bronx. My College and Master's degrees were completed at the College of New Rochelle, also a Catholic institution. That was 17 years of Catholic school teachings.

But, what I remember affecting me the most was what was being taught way back in that elementary school. That was the doctrine that if one weren't Catholic, he or she was not going to heaven. This had a very traumatic effect on me because my parents never went to Church! Nor did my Aunt Rose, who I loved like my second mother. As an only child, I went to Church alone every Sunday, and sometimes, during the week when I would go over to the convent and join the nuns in their private chapel.

At one point, I thought I would be headed for the convent myself! I was so afraid of going to hell, which was constantly put over our heads on a daily basis. I can still visualize those pictures of flames with people screaming around them that were put before us. The fear of committing a mortal sin, like missing Church on a Sunday or holiday, or eating meat on Friday (God forbid!) consumed me. I guess you can say it was all fear-based devotion. I was overcome with worry that my parents and Aunt Rose wouldn't make it to heaven, even though they were the kindest, most loving people! I just couldn't accept that a loving God would do that.

As I got older, and met people of other faiths, my worry extended to them. They all seemed like good people. So, why would God not want them in heaven either? These thoughts plagued me, and, sometime in my graduate school years, I basically discounted all that was presented to me as fact. I started to think and read on my own, studying other religions, appreciating their views. But, then it started to become clear in my research that following certain religions did not always bring peace. As a matter of fact, they brought wars, hate, abuse, separation, and fear. And, that God existed in spite of religion, not because of it. We may have different lamps, but the light is the same. Too often religions are manipulated by people to justify anger, bigotry, violence and hatred, and, if you think about it, they are at the root of too many wars, suicides and cruelty going back as far as you can research. Religion winds up separating us from one another, as one interprets and theorizes. Faith is between you and God. He is the only One to answer to as you become a better version of yourself each day. It's our responsibility to love for the right reason, which is love of God and our fellow man. Not fear. Not fear of committing a sin by eating meat on Friday (which is no longer a law) or missing Mass on Sunday. Suddenly, things weren't as they appeared and there were lots of holes in the fabric of my life. And this would be only the beginning.

Right. That would only be the beginning of my disillusionment with the Catholic Church, after being a devout Catholic all those years, bringing up my four sons as participating Catholics, with all the Sacraments, Confraternity of Christian Doctrine (CCD) classes each week and taking them to Church each Sunday, while I sang in the Church Choir.

My life took an unfortunate turn with a necessary divorce. I say unfortunate because no mother wants her children to be brought up in a divorced situation with all the circumstances surrounding it, such as losing their family home and split holidays for starters. But, it had to be. And, it really was the best in the long run. The other new reality, besides being a single mom with no alimony or child support (another book) the Catholic Church informed me that I would no longer be able to receive Holy Communion as a divorced person. Yes, you read that right in case you were reading late at night and thought you dozed off. True. After 17 years of Catholic school, and not missing any Sunday or holiday Masses, I was ostracized. That bothered me. Of course, the Catholic Church had a solution. I could always get an annulment to get "cleared". There was a huge charge and wait time if I decided to do so.

No, thank you.

Church attendance became difficult for me, yet I was so conflicted. I thought I still needed to have my four sons go, so I took them as usual and would even sneak in Holy Communion whenever I could without a second of guilt.

And, while I thought I was doing the right thing in taking my sons to Church, in keeping their faith, little did I know what was going on in Paul's mind while praying in Church. I will eventually get to all that. I know it's taking me a while to get to the reason for all this, but it will all make sense for you (I hope) at the end. All of the disclosure in this chapter does have a purpose.

So, time went on, and, in 3 years, I met the man of my dreams. (Story included in the Biography section). After a few years of courtship, we decided to get married. But, it wouldn't (couldn't) be in the Catholic Church, because of my divorce status and so we had a Presbyterian Church service, which was lovely and welcoming.

I was pretty much done with the Catholic Church at this point, and within a few years, I was totally sure I would never step foot into a Catholic Church again when I heard about the priests' sexual abuse cases against children, sometime in 2001. I was totally ignorant that such conduct was going on for many, many years all over the world. The Church did a fine job paying off all the families in hush money. They also did a fine job moving all of the priests around so that no one would find out. Of all the injustices I had been monitoring concerning the Catholic Church, this was the worst. Such disgusting cover ups at the expense of the physical, emotional, and psychological care of children.

And they were worried about my receiving Communion as a divorced single mother?

So many memories then flashed into my mind from when I was a child going to Church. We were given a box of envelopes in school each month that we had to bring home to give to our parents. These envelopes had to be filled out each Sunday with our names and amount of money enclosed, to be put in the basket at the Offertory part of Mass. The people from my old Bronx neighborhood were poor, hardworking immigrants, and yet, you can be sure they never missed that basket drop. All I can think of is how that hard-earned money went to the families of the victims to keep them quiet. That bothered me. A lot.

This Church, with all its pomp and circumstance, and high expectations for its parishioners, was a fraud, ruining countless lives forever. And no one seemed to care to do anything about it.

It seemed everyone within the Church, including the biggies at the Vatican, were turning a blind eye.

It was all so hypocritical. So destructive. This religion, the Roman Catholic religion, which should, in God's name, bring peace, love and acceptance to all, preached and displayed anything but. It was not only mind abuse, but physical abuse as well.

Disillusionment with religion wasn't the only thing unsettling my mind.

Flashbacks to my 1950's childhood, watching the Holocaust images on our tiny black and white television in our Bronx, New York two room apartment, would perpetually haunt me. I remember asking my dad what was going on as I looked in horror at the skeletal remains in the death camps. I don't remember a clear-cut answer since there couldn't possibly be a viable explanation to a 10 year old. I vaguely remember a long hesitation, and the word hate. I recall thinking who could hate and kill like that?

I would later learn that what I was seeing was anti-semitism, which, when you think about it, was part of that "my religion is better than yours" mentality.

This mentality still exists today as exemplified in the deadliest attack in the United States on a Jewish community in Pittsburgh, Pennsylvania in October, 2018, where 11 people were killed in their synagogue. And that was followed by the Poway, California shooting on April 27, 2019 at the synagogue there, where one person was killed.

I was starting to connect the dots and the picture being formed wasn't pretty.

All those years ago, the Holocaust realization into my small world was soon followed by other unimaginable events showcased on that same TV screen. More violent eruptions. Only this time, it was about the segregation of white people from black people, in the Martin Luther King riots in Alabama in 1963.

Once again, I asked my dad about this.

He just shook his head in sad disbelief. My parents were both so accepting of everyone. I never heard an unkind word said about anyone in my home. Growing up in an exclusively Italian neighborhood in the Bronx, New York, I never saw a dark-skinned person although I knew there were people of color. I guess you can say I was somewhat sheltered. Well, actually, now thinking back on it, I was very sheltered. Not purposely. It was just the way it was. My neighborhood was primarily made up of families who came over from Italy in the early 1900's. They worked in the market and small shops as bakers, butchers, seamstresses, etc., and pretty much no one ever left the area. Children played outside their apartment buildings or in the school yard. The men who served in World War II, like my dad, came back to their old neighborhood where their families came from Italy, settled down, and had families of their own. So, the neighborhood became one big family.

There really weren't too many people we didn't know.

However, one day, when I was about 11 years old, a tall dark-skinned girl, about my age, walked right by where we were playing jump rope. I smiled as she passed and asked if she wanted to join us. I could tell she was very shy when she said she lived several blocks away and was on her way on an errand at the nearby shopping area on Fordham Road.

I suggested she come by another time, but, unfortunately, I never saw her again.

I now realize she knew what I didn't. The segregation meme was already part of her psyche.

As I became more and more aware of this, the more questions I asked. Why are people being tortured, ridiculed and discriminated against because of their skin color? A skin color that they were born with? What makes one skin color better than the next? Why are people doing this? And, STILL doing this? There was just an incident on Long Island, New York where a 15 year old boy was cyber-bullied (because of his race) by 3 of his classmates. Incredibly, the school did not take disciplinary action against his bullies, so this young man had to go to class alongside them for the rest of the year, unprotected. On his own, he started an anti-bullying organization to help get new laws to help fight bullying. He's also working with local legislators to get a law passed to hold schools accountable in bullying situations. He's also hoping that schools can host mandatory anti-bullying classes that teach students and educators how to handle and identify bullies.

Why hasn't the educational system initiated anything before on its own?

When I was growing up it seemed every time I turned around, I was running into unanswerable questions, as I am now. Questions no one can answer.

Years ago, "social media" was your television, if you were

fortunate enough to have one, with just a few available channels. You also had newspapers where one could keep up with the news, which seemed to have a lot to do with hate. How much has changed in 60 years? When are we going to turn the corner on all this?

As mentioned earlier, I grew up very sheltered given where I grew up and went to school. So, therefore, I never heard of or knew about homosexuality until I was about 18 years old. I know how remarkable that sounds even as I write this, but it was just never spoken about. My friends never knew about it either.

Around the time I graduated high school, there was some whispering going on about a distant cousin. I knew who they were talking about, but couldn't put the pieces together as to why there was this intrigue about this person. It would be later on that year when I finally asked what was going on to learn he was gay. Honestly, that didn't help because I didn't even know what that meant. Hard to believe, but in those days you didn't have such topics discussed at the dinner table. I did a little asking around on my own to get my answers, and, quite frankly, it didn't make any difference to me. I knew him to be a nice person and that was all that mattered to me. I then heard that gays were not accepted by the Church and were considered sinners. That DID make a difference to me. It added to the existing disappointments about the Church and its teachings.

Soon after finding out about the hushed existence of homosexuals, there were the Stonewall riots in Greenwich Village in 1969. Evidently police raided and arrested people known to be homosexuals while in bars and in other places they would congregate. The gay, lesbian, and bisexual communities banned together to demonstrate against such activities. They demanded their civil rights to be who they are, while protesting exploitation and police harassment. The result of these riots was that they served to be the most important event leading to the gay liberation movement and the modern fight for LGBT (Lesbian,

Gay, Bisexual, Transgender) rights in the United States.

Any time I hear of any group being ostracized, I am not happy. As long as a person is kind, generous, and law-abiding, that's good enough for me. I really don't care about your color, religion or sex preference. Actually, I hardly notice those things when I meet someone. What I will notice is how they treat others. Or how they treat me.

Most recently, in 2015, there was a big hoopla about when Bruce Jenner became Caitlin Jenner. He is a trans gender. Now, I ask you, is this our business what he does, or what anyone does with their life? I applaud him becoming her if that is what his journey had to be. I can only think in terms of empathy for someone like him who was born a certain way physically, but was conflicted mentally. What torture these people must experience every day being uncomfortable in their own skin, (literally) not knowing why. Just for the record, people, they do not choose this! Who would choose a life of utter physical and mental chaos? I cannot wait for the day that scientists finally announce that gays, lesbians, etc. are born the way they are, as we all are. It is not a choice. It is not because of psychological or emotional issues, although dealing with prejudicial people can lead to such. The suggestion of going into therapy or participating in techniques to change sexual orientation is ludicrous. The consensus of the behavioral and social sciences is that homosexuality and bisexuality are normal variations of human sexual orientation. There is no scientific basis for regarding them as disorders or abnormalities. Even suggesting treatments to change one's sexual preferences can and does create a setting in which prejudice and discrimination can flourish.

There is that word again. Prejudice. It is that word that has taken the lives of thousands of individuals who were born LGBT, by either suicide or murder. It is still going on today. As far as I'm concerned, anyone who is openly prejudiced can be considered a murderer, taking into account its effects.

Leave people alone! Unless people break the law, they are citizens of this world just like you and me, and have to be treated with respect.

I think if there's ever to be a study, it should be on bigots. What is their problem? They are the ones who need intervention.

Yes, homophobia is also alive and well along with all the other prejudices. There's always a story somewhere in the media about an altercation against an LGBT individual. Just recently, again on Long Island, a local gay couple was "gay bashed" while leaving an eatery by several employees. The owner of the restaurant apologized profusely when he heard about the incident, and offered to terminate the employees when he spoke to the offended couple. Intelligently, the couple refused the offer and instead suggested teaching and coaching the employees instead, spreading awareness to foster change. Ignorant people can learn and views can change. Hopefully.

Something has to be done...now. The negative energies circling around are worse than ever before. Children have been exposed to the worst examples from adults.

And, I haven't even touched on the political prejudices going on at the present moment. That's a whole other situation! If one doesn't agree with a certain political party, or has different opinions on issues, all hell breaks loose. People think nothing of slamming one another or the politicians themselves on all forms of social media. Families have been torn apart, friendships broken, because of opposing viewpoints. There's blame, shame, and finger-pointing all over the place.

I was shocked when a dear old friend seemed to drop out of touch. When I finally reached her, she said she dropped all of her friends who she thought were of a different political party than hers, and she thought I was one of them! First of all, I'm the least political person out there. I vote for whomever I think has the best intentions for my country, and that has spread all over political parties in the past. That statement left me cold. This is what we are dealing with. Hate in all forms. It's probably why so many children, young adults, and adults are self- medicating with drugs and alcohol.

I don't think things have ever been this troublesome right here in this country.

I know other countries have their own issues to deal with, but I was just reading about the Island of Mauritius in the Indian Ocean, east of South Africa. It's a role model for all religions, colors and cultures, living together in harmony. There's a respect for "the others". They enjoy and realize the importance of having diversity. A question can be answered in many ways and that's how they see themselves expand, instead of confrontations. Islam, Buddhism, and Hinduism and Christianity all flourish together through tolerance.

Tolerance. Now, there's a word I like.

They pride themselves on looking beyond physical appearances, and, instead, into all the hearts of all they come in contact with.

Sounds like a peaceful way to live, don't you think?

With all the above being said, bullying, as we know it today, is prevalent in overwhelming ways. It's the resulting culminating behavior of those who are prejudiced against anything and everything. It doesn't matter. It could be because a child is poor, rich, unattractive, overweight, underweight, shy, wears glasses, studious, popular, unpopular, etc. The list is endless.

Bullying is a tactic used by people who have no moral compass, self-esteem, empathy, or hope. They have been tainted by the universal energy of hate for just about anything and anyone.

And, right now, it's systemic after all the years of the atrocities of prejudice, which were never rectified. There you have it.

So, back all those years ago, approximately 30, when I sat back and saw the horrific cruelties against our fellow humans, as in the crimes of sexual abuse in the Catholic Church, crimes against the Jewish faith (Holocaust and present massacres), race wars, or hate towards anyone being anything other than heterosexual, I did some soul-searching.

This was hatred. Pure, fanatical hatred.

But, how does one begin to hate? I truly believe that no one is born with hate in his heart. If you observe babies, they love everyone and don't see beyond how a person treats them. They are not born with biased attitudes. Those views are collected along the way.

Only recently, His Holiness the 14th Dalai Llama said,

"Young children don't care about differences of nationality, faith or race, so long as their companions smile, they play together happily. It seems it's only as we grow up we focus on secondary differences between people, creating trouble."

Exactly!

So, those many years ago, with all the above recognitions in mind, I thought perhaps I could create a school curriculum that would celebrate and discuss the varied differences we are born with. I designed an outline using a whole language approach from Pre-K through high school students, exposing children, age appropriately, to the positive aspects of our individualities.

I was really excited and enthusiastic about such a project at the time. Unfortunately, sometimes our roads are paved with good intentions that never get realized for whatever reasons that pop up. I hesitate to make excuses, because it sounds so lame, but I had plenty. Taking care of a large family, basically alone, had to come first. So, I never saw it through, but never forgot about it, because I saw the ultimate need and value.

And, then, ironically, during the writing of this book, I came across a video of His Holiness the 14th Dalai Lama speaking to a group of medical students from Tulane University at his residence in Dharmsala, India. It was surreal. He offered the importance of teaching the hygiene of emotion to kindergarten children through the university years of education. He went on to say that we have created a lot of problems stemming from our education which is not adequate because it's oriented to material values. Children don't care about nationality or religious faith. Once they join school, they are not taught the importance of inner peace or our emotions. An attitude of US versus THEM develops. Here he's saying what I thought all along. The answer lies in how we are taught from the beginning. He goes on to say, out of the 7 billion people alive, no one wants to suffer or have problems, yet we have them because of our ignorance. And the one solution for ignorance is education. We need to educate our children from the very beginning through our school system. Not just lectures or a class here and there. There has to be a mandated formal curriculum built into the studies.

So, you might be wondering why I chose to expose all the faces of prejudice, and its consequences in this chapter.

What does this have to do with Paul? Everything.

I needed to set the stage of the world that Paul, as well as everyone, is born into. How the negative energies surrounding us affect our lives in a detrimental way.

But, how the power of love and acceptance can positively alter the course of one's well-deserved destiny.

Remember when I said Paul would pray for a special intention when I took him, along with his brothers, to Church every Sunday?

I would find out what that prayer was when Paul was 20 years old. His constant prayer was to not be gay.

He wanted to be like "everyone else."

He told me how he feared the rejection not only from his

Church, but from his friends and family.

He knew and observed what people thought of gays. Hushed comments. Some not-so-hushed comments. Sidelooks. Eyerolls.

He couldn't face what laid before him for the rest of his life. Shame overtook him.

He wanted to end his life and had plans to do so.

He purchased a gun and set the date. He (fortunately) told a couple of his close friends of his intentions.

They (fortunately) in turn, went immediately into action behind the scenes. They arranged an intervention of Paul's many friends who subsequently drove and even flew to Atlanta, Georgia. They surrounded him in pure love and acceptance.

There was no way that "being gay" was changing how they felt about him. They loved him for who he was.

It took a lot of convincing, as I heard, but they would not give up. It worked.

And that's why Paul was able to go on and live his following 23 years in a happy, productive life.

How many other gays (or anyone feeling "less than") could have been saved if only someone reached out to them with such love and acceptance?

The power of prejudice may be strong, but the power of love is stronger! It's what the world needs, and, it's up to every one of us to show it.

Not only to save a life physically, but mentally and emotionally as well.

Each and every one of us, in our thoughts and actions, is responsible for the well-being of others, as well as ourselves.

Each and every one of us, in our capacity for love and acceptance, can literally change the world. A world filled with peace and harmony, instead of shame and guilt.

Paul was victorious because of a group of friends who loved unconditionally.

It shows that when people think rationally, and are not consumed with all kinds of unnecessary and illogical discriminations, love prevails.

How tragic it would have been to have lost Paul at that time? I can't even have my mind go there, as his mother. My grief in losing him because of the effects of a flu shot is overwhelming as it is, but to have lost him in a senseless suicide would be incomprehensible.

And, yet, there have been lives cut short because they "couldn't go on," because, perhaps, no one convinced them "you're okay."

What about those moms?

Could it be that Paul's mission on earth was to be an example of the power of love? Love conquering all?

Hopefully, at some time in the duration of reading this book, you will find it in your heart to remove any prejudice you may have regarding anyone or anything.

It's really what LIVE LIKE PAUL is all about.

Paul loved everyone. He helped everyone. His entire life. He didn't see color, religion, social status, etc. He didn't care.

His life was about love and giving, asking nothing in return.

That will be shown throughout his biography as well as in the countless testimonies. His example of love affected and changed so many lives for the better.

"What counts in life is not the mere fact that we have lived. It is what offer we have made to the lives of others that will determine the significance of the life we lead."

—*Nelson Mandela*

In Steve Maraboli's *Life, The Truth And Being Free*, he talks about how we are perfectly imperfect.

This is my exact message in one of my children's books, *The Search For The Perfect Shell.*

But, I love his analogy with snowflakes. We all have heard that no two snowflakes are alike...each snowflake takes the perfect form for the maximum efficiency and effectiveness for its journey. While gravity gives them all a shared destination, the expansive space in the air gives each snowflake the opportunity to take its own path.

Some snowflakes may collide and damage each other, some may collide and join together, some are influenced by random winds. But, no matter what, the snowflake finds itself perfectly shaped for its journey.

The parallel here is with snowflakes and us. We too are all headed in the same direction, driven by a universal force, taking a different journey. Along the journey, we sometimes bump into each other, cross paths, become altered, taking different physical forms. But we too are 100% perfectly imperfect. We are perfect for our journey. You are perfect for yours. I am perfect for mine. We can't be perfect for someone else's journey. We're heading to the same place, taking different routes, exactly perfect the way we are.

Understanding this could help in our relationships. People are headed to the same place, and no matter what they may appear like to you, they have taken the perfect form for their travels.

If we realized this, our relationships could become stronger with more respect in that we are all perfectly imperfect for our life here on earth.

Perhaps you will never look at a snowflake the same way again—or each other.

Soren Kierkegaard, the famed 19th century Danish theologian, remarked, "Once you label me, you negate me."

The process of putting ourselves and others into neat little compartments on the basis of any label, and then making judgements on the basis of those labels is dehumanizing. We all have the same colorless insides, and yet we allow what we see on the outside to give us permission to hate.

And, now on to his Biography where you will get to know Paul from birth. An incredibly sweet, happy child.

A pure soul.

We are all born as a pure soul.

"HATE. It has caused a lot of problems in the world, but it has not solved one yet."

—*Maya Angelou*

The Biography

And, in the end, it's not the years in your life that count;
it's the life in your years.
　　　　　　　　—Abraham Lincoln

USUALLY A BIOGRAPHY STARTS from when a person is born, or, from the present time, with flashbacks to the past. At least those were my experiences in reading biographies, although I didn't read many I have to admit.

I chose to commence from the day my son, Paul, was born and proceed chronologically through his 43 years.

This journey, in looking back at Paul's life, was challenging, and raised so many questions about life itself—when and how we are born, for starters.

Why are children, born under the same roof, with the same parents and extended family, so different?

There are so many variables in one's developments, and they became clearer as I wrote and researched.

It seems that in families with two or more children, an underlying competition exists in wanting to suppress the standard.

I heard it once compared to a vineyard where the vines are planted very close together, creating a rivalry for the nutrients in the soil as well as the sunlight.

That stress causes the plants to put more energy into their reproductive process, increasing the quantity and quality of the grapes.

Siblings seek and need to establish a unique identity and position of their own in their family. If an older brother excels at school, attracting the attention and admiration of his parents, another sibling may try to excel in sports. Or, that same sibling may not be sports oriented, along with knowing he could never achieve the high grades of his competitions. That child may get lost altogether by doing neither.

All this could be happening in the life of a child, without the parents being aware, especially if there's a few children in the family.

Life gets hectic in dealing with toddlers, changing diapers or going to little league games.

Children are quite aware of their parents' differentiation among their children, and pick up on those differences, ultimately powerfully shaping their personality.

We all come from a unique lineage with inborn characteristics that shape the way we approach different experiences in life from childhood, therefore affecting who we become as adults.

My four sons were all different, and it was a wild ride at times. I would do it all again in a heartbeat, as long as I could with the knowledge and wisdom I have now. Wouldn't we all?

Parents were not supplied with "How to Be a Parent" handbooks years ago. It was learn as you go and, acknowledging how each child is so different, having very different needs, I probably could have done better. But, then again, people say I'm really hard on myself in being a perfectionist. Actually, I do know I did a good job in raising those four beautiful sons seeing them as adults, and especially since I did most of it on my own.

I am very proud of all of them.

I took being a mom very seriously. At some time before they arrived in this world, I had decided to document everything about them.

I just loved writing, I guess. Writing was always a comforting outlet for me, perhaps because, as an only child, it kept me occupied. I was constantly writing essays from my elementary school years and, unbeknownst to me, while in the sixth grade at Our Lady of Mt.Carmel in the Bronx, an essay was entered by the nuns into the New York City Fire Prevention Week writing contest and it won.

My entire class joined me, along with the Pallotine nuns and my parents to receive the Fire Prevention medal from NYC Mayor Wagner. I still have it in its original box from 54 years ago.

I continued writing throughout college and graduate school at the College of New Rochelle, in New Rochelle, New York, where most of my writings were termed "utopian" in nature. I was always anticipating (or hoping for) a world where everyone got along and was at peace. I always visualized a society whose social conditions, laws, government, etc., were harmonious.

So, with the background understanding of how I loved to write all my life, it would not be as surprising to see how or why I undertook the meticulous chronicling of the lives of all four sons.

When Frank, my first born, came home from the hospital in 1973, I started a little notebook (which I still have) making accounts of how many ounces of formula he consumed at each feeding, along with the times. And, yes, diapers contents as well throughout the day were recorded. I did this with all four sons for about a month.

I hope I have a few readers left after that last sentence!

I know—a bit obsessive. I took the care of those little lives very seriously.

In 1965, Parents' Magazine Press published *The Baby Book* in order to observe and record child development from birth to the tenth year.

These 9x12 hard covered books were filled out constantly throughout the ten years of all four sons. Each had their own.

The questions in each month of development were thought provoking and laborious to answer. It took about an hour each time they were filled in.

I guess I could have given these books to the boys as they became adults, but I really don't know why I didn't.

Perhaps it was meant to be so I would have access to Paul's baby book now.

Who knows why things happen? I ask that a lot lately. Sometimes I find myself looking at all this, and all that I've gone through in life and think it was all "supposed to be".

But, more on that in another chapter.

So, along with filling out these development books, I took on the task of keeping a *School Days* binder once they entered Preschool.

Published by Win Graft in 1966, this was a file system to retain important school records and memory keepsakes from preschool through twelfth grade. Names of teachers, classmates and report cards were filed in the provided folder sleeves.

How great to look back on one's school days!

I knew the boys would appreciate it when they got older for themselves and possibly their children.

But there were still more record keeping devices!

In 1975, ironically the year Paul was born, I purchased a monthly calendar that became a short version diary. I filled in each box with the events of the day. I have continued this practice to this present time, which is a total of 43 years! And, yes, I have every one of them!

Interestingly enough, my mother did the same thing in a different way. My boys told me that Grandma Mary would write, on her big oversized calendar, every time they would call her, which was often. She would mark down "Paul called," "Bobby called," "Frank called," "Richie called," "Adrienne called", etc. It was mostly for remembering when she spoke to anyone last. My parents had moved to Cape Canaveral, Florida from New York and she was feeling very isolated, lonely, and missed her family terribly.

So, in keeping a log of who called when, she would know when to make a call back. I guess. Or else it was a way to put someone in the penalty box if she saw she didn't hear from them in a while. Only kidding. She was a loving, kind grandmother, and my boys loved her and my dad, their grandfather, Pepa Frank.

Mom also saved every greeting card that my boys and I ever sent her. Not surprising, I have also saved every card from my boys, Manny and my parents.

And, as I will mention later in the book, Paul did as well as I found them in a binder of his.

I'm starting to think this is a genetic thing!

So, in case you are wondering, I inherited her calendars and cards as well, and still have them too.

By this time, I have probably lost any reader who might have hung on since the diaper notebook.

I probably do sound a bit neurotic, I will concede.

Actually, I know it does sound neurotic, but I have to admit I would do it all over again. I wanted to make sure their lives would not be forgotten by me or my boys when they grew up.

I simply had to hold on to every memory.

But, sorry, there's still more. I have over 100 photo albums, plus scores of videos from their childhood years. Each album is categorized by year written on each spine.

They are stored in a huge 4' x 8' fire proof safe in our garage which had to be delivered on a special forklift truck because of its weight.

When we moved to California 7 years ago, we heard about random fires, usually set by pyromaniacs, in San Diego, and other nearby locations. I went into panic mode, not because of our home, which could always end up replaced, but those photo albums!

So, my dear sweet husband, Manny, arranged getting that safe ordered and delivered to put my mind at ease. And, there they stay.

You might be wondering where all these mementoes have been stored all these 46 years from the birth of Frank, my first born.

Everything has been packed in secure boxes and moved with me exactly 8 times from one home to another covering three states.

I really am grateful to have all this, especially now.

I could never have relied on my memory to fill in the details of Paul's life in putting this book together. My memory was never good to begin with, but since Paul's passing, it's much worse. So much so that it started to concern me recently. However, I read that grief can be such a shock to one's system that memory can definitely be affected.

The process of opening boxes, retrieving and reviewing Paul's personal effects was grueling and painful. I had not looked at anything I had written or saved for the 43 years.

It was like having him born all over again, but sadly knowing there would be an unexpected halt.

Instead of the joy I was hoping to experience amidst all the memories, I felt overwhelming sadness and even anger at times. Like, why did this have to happen? And, why did this happen to me? Those thoughts were fortunately replaced with healthy productive ones which will be discussed in the scope of this book.

Looking at photos and watching videos was especially hard.

I thought to myself, as I looked at his smiling face through the years, and thought "if we only knew what was to come".

But, would we really ever want to know even if we could?

I think not.

If he hadn't passed away, going though those keepsakes with him would have been so enjoyable, since he, too, liked to keep records.

I found that out when I went through a gigantic box of scrapbooks, spreadsheets and a binder of saved greeting cards. Paul documented everything (surprised?). He was the ultimate file keeper. The "memento gene" was definitely passed on to him from me and my mom. Actually, I just remembered Richie has that gene too!

Paul and I were very much alike in so many ways. Except for all his extreme sports activities like jumping out of planes, running, mountain climbing and swimming, we shared a love of people, puzzles, hiking and scrapbooking.

We both loved friends and loved introducing our friends to other friends. We found enjoyment in getting people together.

Again, it's sad we didn't get to review his life and stuff together. He could have seen my pride once again in the newspaper articles about him in our hometown papers *Lewisboro Ledger* and *Patent Trader* as well as when he was at Georgia Tech.

Who would ever think we would run out of time?

Who would ever think we wouldn't get the chance to finish the puzzle we started on his last visit, planning to finish it at Thanksgiving?

I remember starting that 1,000-piece puzzle and working on it for hours together at my kitchen table in California. We set a huge cardboard mat down first to work on, so the puzzle could be easily moved from place to place.

It was just the two of us that day in the house when everyone was over for Easter. The rest of the gang went off doing other things, and Paul and I just stood around the puzzle and talked, while finding homes for the puzzle pieces. I should say he was the one putting most of the pieces in because all I heard was that clicking sound as he clicked each piece in the correct spot. I laughed, asking him, "how do you do that so fast?"

But that was Paul. He was quick and smart in everything, yet so humble—ever so humble.

That puzzle remains undone. I am crying (again) as I write this. It's strange how certain memories trigger my tears.

This was one of them.

I can't decide if I should leave it undone—the way he left it, or finish it in his memory.

Tears again.

Who would ever think we would run out of time to finish a puzzle?

But we never know, do we?

Just that thought.

Not finishing a puzzle.

Who would ever think he would go before me?

And, if only we got to watch that whole set of family videos that he made years ago from our ancient VHS tapes. He gifted each one of his brothers and myself a set one Christmas.

These were videos that he originally took himself starting at 10 years old, carrying that huge cumbersome video recorder on his shoulder. He took it everywhere we went and was in sole control of the tapes, labeling them, etc. All of the original VHS tapes have his printing on the label meticulously describing the contents.

If it weren't for him, we never would have any videos of his brothers' games, etc.

That was Paul.

No, no one ever knows what will happen next, and that's another reason for writing this book.

Don't wait until tomorrow, next week or next month to look at your family's photos together, in celebration of your lives together, reminiscing the good times.

Don't wait to play that game. Do that puzzle and finish it.

Time is precious and unpredictable with all our loved ones, family and friends together.

Put a date on your calendar right now for that one thing you've been wanting to do with them.

This is not a story of grief and sorrow, but a celebration of a special human being filled with love on this Earth plane.

*　*　*

Where It All Started

WE WERE LIVING IN WEST NYACK, New York, a suburb of Rockland County at the time of Paul's birth on September 25, 1975.

Our home was a simple, adorable 1950's, 3-bedroom ranch style home with pink appliances, on about an acre of land. It was an idyllic little neighborhood. We had a park like backyard where we had barbecues with family and friends. It was a happy home, surrounded by wonderful neighbors and friends who also moved nearby when we made the exodus from the Bronx, a borough in New York City.

The school where I was teaching before I gave birth to Frank, Paul's older brother, was walking distance from our home. My classroom teacher's aide, Phyllis, who had been with me for years, would sometimes walk over at lunchtime and visit Frank and I as we anticipated Paul's birth. Frank was about 2 ½ years old when Paul was born. Frank was an active, bright little boy who looked nothing like me with his very blond hair and big blue eyes. Adorable. Frank was way ahead of his expected development in completely walking at 7 ½ months, knowing the complete alphabet and numbers by 15 months. His pediatrician would always be amazed at his abilities. He was a very happy little boy who looked so forward to the baby coming.

In those days, few (if any) people found out what baby they were having. It was always a surprise. Today I smile at the gender revealing big affairs going on.

Times have certainly changed.

I decided to take La Maze classes for Paul's birth.

Frank's birth was very difficult because of his position, giving me terrible back labor for many hours. So, therefore, I was quite sedated during his birth so much so, I mostly slept for a couple days. Those were the days when a mother could stay in the hospital until she was ready to go home.

I needed those days to get out of the stupor I was put in.

Actually, the funny thing is that Frank was born on my father's birthday, March 3, 1973. He was 2 ½ weeks late from my predicted due date. It was quite a surprise that not only was he born in a totally different month, but on dad's birthday. Of course, he was named after my dad, Frank.

Being a girl, and an only child, my dad always had a special bond with Frank, but as the others arrived, Pepa Frank was close to them all.

I started La Maze classes in preparing for Paul's birth in July 1975 at Nyack Hospital with Jean Tripichio.

The Le Maze method of giving birth (naturally) was starting to get popular at that time. It was a six week course and ended three weeks before Paul entered the world on Thursday, September 25, 1975 at 11:20 pm, delivered by Dr. Droga.

He was 6 lbs. 13 oz. It was an easy delivery and Paul and I were back home on September 28.

Paul occupied the crib that his big brother Frank just vacated. Frank was now in his big boy bed in the room next door to the nursery.

Their crib had been custom made with painted images of Ralph, our Yorkie, created before the babies arrived. It was very cheerful and colorful.

From the day we brought Paul home, Paul laid in that crib with his mouth wide open in a smile, his eyes glittering with such joy! We would find Frank lying next to Paul in the crib some mornings at 5 am. Paul would have his face turned towards him, his mouth open, so excited while kicking his legs in those onesies.

Paul, like all my babies, slept through the night by three weeks old! Of course, this took discipline and planning on my part, but it was good for everyone.

I gave the bottles on scheduled times of the day, factoring naps, etc., and then I would wait as long as I could to go to bed at which time, I would wake them up around 11 pm, feed and change them and back to the crib.

This guaranteed a good night's sleep to at least until 5 or 7 am.

I didn't know many moms that breast fed in those days and know it's so different now.

The only thing with Paul is that he started projectile spitting up when I would burp him during and after a feeding.

As gentle as I would be in putting him to my shoulder to burp, he would spray anyone within 2 feet with formula. The doctor could not figure out why, although we did change formula.

Perhaps he would have been a great candidate for breast feeding, after all.

He eventually got better after about 8 months. Only in writing this now did I realize that perhaps the spitting up as a newborn was the genesis of his hiccups. Paul was known for his hiccups throughout his life.

They were extremely loud and sudden. He had no control over them and there seemed to be no medical explanation.

Those that knew him wouldn't flinch, but, if he was in a store or restaurant, heads would turn in shock.

Actually, one of his friends wrote on Facebook "To only hear one of those hiccups again!"

Birth To One Year

PAUL'S FIRST FEW MONTHS were as smooth as can be. All he did was eat, sleep, and laugh. It's all I have written down.

He was baptized on November 23, 1975 at St. Anthony's Church in Nanuet, New York. His sponsors were Nancy Connelly, my husband's sister, and Frank Giaccio, my husband's brother.

I started the tradition of having Sundays at our home with both sets of grandparents as well as whoever else could come from the family.

Being an only child, I loved company. Most holidays were always at our home, so Paul and his brothers experienced a close upbringing.

Paul had his first Christmas photo with his brother, Frank in 1975. Christmas photos of the boys together would become a Christmas card tradition.

Every couple of years, another little face would be added.

As I read my notes, it was so repetitive.

"Paul is such a happy baby."

Unlike Frank, who was walking at 7½ months, Paul was content to be "just laying around and playing with no symptoms of crawling or sitting up".

"Still not holding his bottle," is what I wrote down.

Paul had this adorable crop of curly, medium brown hair with reddish highlights.

It's about this time we started calling him Fozzie Bear, one of the Muppet characters. I have no idea how or why we called him that unless it was because Fozzie Bear was hairy and so lovable.

Paul was such a cushy little mush.

Paul started to crawl at 8 months, exploring and vocalizing along the way. He was able to sit up well at 10 months, picking up objects to look at and play with.

I write:

"So far no attempts at saying words or imitating sounds".

Frank was his constant entertainer and laughed at everything he did.

They were very connected to one another.

"His attachment and love of Frank, his older brother, is so evident. Frankie is like a mother with him."

Those were still the days of the playpens. I don't know what I would have done without playpens. It was a safe place to put a baby while a mom "got things done".

Many times, Frank would be right in there with him, playing ever so gently.

Throughout Paul's first year, my comments are the same.

"Paul is such a doll, excellent baby, happy with anything, never whines, always laughing at everyone and everything, excellent baby, calm, too good to be true, never fusses about anything, good natured."

These were my exact comments.

The summer before his first birthday I was in the backyard with Paul, a good friend and a couple of other little children.

I filled up our little kiddie pool in the morning, so the water wouldn't be so cold by the afternoon. Paul loved to splash into the water while holding onto the sides of the plastic pool rim, while he stood on the grass.

He got himself so excited splashing that he leaned too far forward, and his head went down into the water. Of course, I was right there and scooped him up in a second, but it must have been frightening for him. He never cried even though his little head was wet. I must have held him in my arms for an hour after that. I was realizing that freak things can happen in a matter of seconds and what if my head was turned, even sitting right there? That experience never left me and probably why Manny calls me "the safety officer". No matter where we go, I always point out what could be a hazard for either adults or children. I do that constantly. However, as I would find out 42 years later from that pool incident, there are some things you cannot control or protect your children from.

Some things you can—some things you can't.

And that's just the way it goes. My final comment at one year old is:

"Paul is still a doll—the happiest baby around. No problem all day—I forget he's around! Still has only 2 bottom teeth."

NYACK HOSPITAL CRIB IDENTIFICATION CARD

SURNAME *Giaccio*

SEX *Boy*

MOTHER'S GIVEN NAME *Adrienne*

NURSERY *I*

MOTHER'S ROOM & BED *257^w*

DATE & TIME BORN *Sept. 25, 1975 @ 11:20 p.m*

WEIGHT *6 lbs. 13 g.*

OBSTETRICIAN *Dr. Draga*

PEDIATRICIAN *Dra. M-R-L-S*

Wall hanging in Paul's room.

proclaim the birth of
Paul Christopher
child of
Adrienne and John Giaccio
born on
September 25, 1975
in the city and state of
West Nyack, New York

Paul's Paternal Grandparents, Sal and Ann

Paul's Christening on
November 23, 1975

Paul at one month old with brother Frankie

Christmas 1975. Paul's first Christmas. Three months old.

Paul at two months old with his Dad.

Paul's First Birthday.
West Nyack, NY.

Frankie, Paul's older brother with Ralph, our Yorkie

Frankie loved visiting Paul in his crib. Three months old.

Always, always happy!

Paul eight months old with Frankie.
I was always taking them to photographers.

Paul, nine months.
Day of the pool incident.

Paul at ten months with Grandma Mary

One To Three Years Old

PAUL'S ONE YEAR BIRTHDAY PARTY WAS SPECIAL. Actually, there were two celebrations, as I did every year for each of the four boys.

Paul's first was on Friday, September 24, 1976 at 1 pm with about 10 children and their moms.

Then, on September 26, 1976, Sunday, all four grandparents came, along with Paul's great grandmother, Pauline, who died at 103 years old!

Paul started to walk a little at 14 months. In my notes, I read how close he was with Frankie. He had little interest in toys, but loved to push my yellow basket around the house, which I have no recollection of, till reading this. No interest in blocks either, even though "The book" said children at this age like blocks.

Vocabulary consisted of two words at 14 months. Mama and Dada, and he showed no interest in repeating in what we said.

At 16 months, he still only had 4 teeth. They were coming in very slowly!

Christmas Eve 1976 was spent at home with my parents. Mom and I always prepared their traditional Italian 7 fishes, and they would stay over for Christmas morning.

I was so grateful that my parents were able to drive to Rockland County from the Bronx, New York to visit every week.

It was about an hour's drive over the Tappan Zee Bridge. Many of my friends' parents did not drive, so moving away as we did would have been difficult if my dad didn't.

Sometimes, in good weather, I would drive down to the Bronx with Frankie and Paul in their car seats, to pick up my mom and her sister, my Aunt Rose, who was like another mother to me, and another grandmother for the boys.

I would then take them to Rockland County for the day. Then, my dad, after work, would take the trip up to Rockland County, have dinner, and take mom and Aunt Rose back home.

When I think back at what they did, it was quite amazing. And, I'm sure it's why my sons were so close to them, seeing them all the time.

I've added in so many details and stories about my parents, Aunt Rose, etc, because I truly believe every childhood experience and observation (both positive and negative) makes us who we are. Children are the greatest observers, even if you think they are not watching.

My boys were witnesses to total unselfishness and compassion by my parents and Aunt Rose. Aunt Rose lived in the same house as my parents, on the upper floor. When the boys would visit, they were showered with attention and mom and Aunt Rose would "argue" who was making the chocolate pudding and fresh whipped cream for them. (Their absolute favorite).

It seems so different today. It's rare that one's children stay in the area that they grew up in, raising their families.

Often, they move to a completely different state, either because of the housing costs or job opportunities.

There's something to be said about parents, children and grandchildren living near each other. Unless, of course, the families are dysfunctional. In that case, it's best to move as far away as possible!

Besides family, I had a wonderful group of friends that were like family.

When he permanently moved to Atlanta, Georgia, after graduating from Georgia Tech, Paul would develop a framily of his own, as he called it. They were a very large committed group of friends that did everything together and supported one another. They are still a huge part of his life, even now that's he's gone. They are the strongest and largest group of comrades I have ever witnessed, other than my own! Another way Paul and I were alike.

We love our friends and somehow we were both blessed with so many faithful ones. What do they say about relatives and friends? Friends are the ones we choose.

That's how Paul grew up. I always had friends and their children over. We would have tuna, peanut butter and jelly sandwiches, coffee and Entenman's cake. If it was nice outside, we'd be in the backyard with playpens, strollers and baby swings strewn about.

It was casual and relaxing even with everything going on.

We are all still friends to this day, and talk about "those old days" when life was simple and happy.

I think it's important for young mothers to have such a circle of support. Being isolated raising babies is very hard, and, not only lonely for the mom, but the children as well.

Even though I was a "stay at home" mom, having put my teaching career on hold, I still felt it was necessary to participate in some meaningful charity work.

I chose the Rockland Auxiliary for Retarded Children to donate my time to because of my degree in special education, and became the Membership Chairperson. This was a good fit for me since I was able to hold prospective member lunches at my home, whereby moms could bring their children. It was easy and I met some lovely ladies who ultimately joined the organization, spearheading many fundraisers.

Yes, our little home on Marcus Road was filled with relatives, old and new friends and neighbors at all times celebrating one thing or another. Great memories.

Paul, one and one half years old, Christmas, 1976
Notice the plastic covers on the furniture.

Paul and Frankie, College of New Rochelle Strawberry
Festival, May 1977

West Nyack backyard. They loved their Pepa.

Jones Beach, 1977. Paul's happy place.

Christmas 1977

West Nyack backyard.
Mother's Day 1977

Unfortunately, our time in West Nyack, New York, was abruptly coming to a close. My then-husband, Paul's dad, received an employment opportunity that would take us back across the Tappan Zee Bridge and north to Westchester County to a small little hamlet called Waccabuc. We purchased 12 beautiful wooded acres and began to build our home in the summer of 1977. Paul was almost 2 years old.

It was noted in "the book" that developmentally, children this age like to imitate either their parents or siblings.

Well, I was about to see Paul's imitation in action!

In September, 1977, we had a garage sale in preparation for our upcoming move. We had a very long driveway from the street that people had to walk up to in order to get to the sale.

Some children were playing on the front lawn, where I sat watching everything unfold. All of a sudden, I saw Paul behind a crippled lady who was bent all the way forward, holding a cane. Paul was right behind her walking the same way! I couldn't believe my eyes and jumped up to scoop him in my arms before anyone else saw.

Actually, my friend did see and was hysterical laughing, but I didn't think it was funny!

So, yes, Paul was in "Imitation mode"!

At 19 months, I write "Paul has no interest in talking, but, at 24 months, he would repeat the ABCs, yes, no and Paul. He understood everything but did not want to talk in sentences. He "plays well with Frankie and all other children, giving up his toys to share with no issues"

Not surprised. He never changed.

At 2 years, 1 month, I wrote he had about 12 words in his vocabulary.

Some of the words noted were MONEY, ball, puppy, dog, Ralph, mommy, daddy, eat, no, yes, eight, Rose, Paulie.

Our new home in Waccabuc, New York.
Twelve beautiful acres of woods.

I think the word MONEY might have been his first word. I didn't remember that at all until I read what I wrote. Interesting word considering the businesses he was in!

Our new home in Waccabuc was to be ready in the late fall of 1977.

It was sad and a bit exciting at the same time. I knew absolutely no one in what seemed to be a isolated area. However, challenges or the unknown, never concerned me. I was always up to the task and always knew it would work out.

After some research, I heard that the Pinchbeck nursery School was by far the best. It was in Ridgefield, Connecticut, 15 minutes from where our new home would be, but 1 ½ hours from the house we were still living in until late November!

I registered Frankie in that school immediately and wanted him to start will all his little new friends that September so he wouldn't be the "newbie".

Yes, I drove that 1 ½ hours twice a week with Frank, and Paul in the car as well. While we waited for Frankie during his 2-½ hours in preschool, Paul and I would drive to the construction site of our new home or go to the library, or Friendly's. We would then pick up Frankie and go back home.

Crazy, I know, but it was only twice a week and I saw how much Frankie loved it. I was young and energetic in those days

Paul had his second birthday and what would be his last in West Nyack. Lots of parties at our home, and then it was time to start packing.

There was so much to do along with the "good-bye" get togethers.

On moving day, November 19, 1977, my parents came to Rockland County to help me pack the car with personal items along with Frankie, Paul and our Yorkshire Terrier, Ralph.

The plan was to follow me in the car up to Waccabuc along with the two moving trucks behind us.

While the moving men packed the trucks, all the neighbors came to say goodbye. My mom was crying, hugging everyone. She really loved that house and all my friends. It was an emotional departure.

It was finally time to start the excursion with the four vehicles.

My then-husband was working and did not participate in this monumental event. Not saying anything else about that. Keeping this book as positive as possible.

So, off we went to our new home in the woods, which I thought would be completely done. Wrong. It was a nightmare. The 1,000 foot dirt driveway leading to the house, through the woods, was muddy and partially caved in and the trucks could not make it up. We almost didn't as well. The movers had to carry items from down the driveway and everyone, and everything was covered in mud. But that was only an iota of the disasters we were facing.

The house was freezing cold. The heat didn't work. Nor did the oven and stove. Every cabinet in the kitchen and bathrooms was covered in dust. The bathrooms were not ready for use. Thank God for my parents! My mom and I put on our rubber gloves (we both always wore them while cleaning) and got to work scrubbing and washing down everything. Dad stayed with Frankie and Paul, out of the way, but also trying to help. I wondered what I got myself into.

The moving date I mentioned, by the way, is also the date Paul passed away. November 19. I never realized that until I began writing this book, reading my notes. That date will always get my attention.

Somehow, my mom and I got everything cleaned up in days and I even shopped for Thanksgiving although I still didn't have a working oven until the day before! I pulled it all together and we had our first Thanksgiving there.

It took months to get the house in working order. The driveway was a huge problem. I would wind up carrying Frankie and Paul up and down wearing big rubber boots, because my car would always get stuck below.

There was a constant problem with the water in the basement, which no one seemed to be able to fix.

We were always cold.

I don't even want to remember those days. I felt like a frontier woman.

The good news is that, even with all the inconveniences, the boys settled in nicely. They absolutely loved the woods as boys would. I walked through them alongside Frank and Paul, while they blazed their trails, which would eventually be the pathways for the go cart my dad would build them.

To help with the incompetent (almost nonexistent) heating situation (it was all electric with pathetic heating elements at the bottom of walls) we got a wood burning stove. My dad designed and built a gas powered log splitting machine to cut all the wood needed to constantly fill the stove. I mean constantly.

My dad was an absolute genius. He could design and build anything. He was also an accomplished artist. I have most of his oil paintings, some rather large. He also sculpted, and created many stained glass masterpieces, adorning windowpanes as well as lamps and vases. These were all his hobbies that he enjoyed after working all day at his business as a machinist. He started his business when he was very young.

It seems there was nothing he couldn't do. A kind, patient, brilliant man, devoted to his family. That was my dad. My sons' grandfather. Paul's grandfather, who was a big influence on him his entire life, (and all of ours').

And, life went on in the woods. At least we were warmer with our newly installed stove.

It wasn't long before I met some wonderful ladies, I joined a Bible group and was able to bring Paul. Basically, I could bring Paul anywhere because he was such a good little boy.

Things were beginning to fall into place, little by little.

At 2-½ years old, Paul still wasn't talking too much. He started putting 4 word sentences together. I wrote that he was an incredibly calm child. No temper tantrums ever. He adjusted very well to our move. With all the snow storms that winter, my favorite thing to do was to take Frankie and Paul on a sled around our property. They just loved it.

There was so much to do, as I would find out, in our area, even though it was so country-like.

Library events, mom-toddler groups, community get-togethers, etc became ways to meet others. It wasn't long before our house became a home, filled with friends and children once again.

Paul would love to hear the front doorbell ring. He would run

October 1978 Danbury Fair - Paul on Camel. Frank on Elephant.

Christmas 1978, First Christmas in Waccabuc home.

to the entry hall, along with our Yorkie, Ralph, barking all the way. He particularly loved one of my new friends, Georgine, and when she came, he would shout her name so excitedly—Georgine! Georgine! Of course, she loved it, and would pick him up for hugs. As I'm writing this, I just realized she does not know of his passing. I am sure there are many others that don't know since some moved away and we only connect once a year. I will have to let her know at some point. Not the call I want to make.

Georgine also had four sons, and we had great times through the years.

Well, what did they say about new house, new baby?

Paul would no longer be the baby in the house come September, 1978, when he would be almost 3 years old.

By the summer of 1978, our little family was well established in our little Waccabuc home.

We were anticipating the birth of Frankie and Paul's new sibling, sex undetermined. But, they both made it clear—they wanted a baby brother.

Those were the days before "Gender Reveal" parties. No one knew what sex the new baby would be. It was always an exciting surprise. Any gifts at a baby shower would be either yellow or mint green and rooms were decorated in the same colors. Then, once the baby arrived, the pink or blue accessories would indicate girl or boy.

There were many fun experiences going on in our daily lives with play dates, Church, sports (Frankie playing soccer), town swimming pool and recreation center, etc.

It was a good distraction from the persistent annoyance at home. We were always cold and walked around the house bundled up in sweaters. The only relief we got was the woodburning stove installed in the fireplace, so we congregated in there most of the time. But, the wood stove brought its own issues since it constantly needed to be filled with wood! Once the wood was split by the log splitter my dad made, it needed to be stacked outside, and then eventually brought in the house.

Fortunately, living on 12 acres of forest, there was plenty of wood, but it was a full time job. Even at their young age, Frankie and Paul helped.

A wagon of cut wood went in the garage, up a few steps, through the kitchen, to the den where each piece had to be placed on the log hoop on the side of the stove. Then, the wagon was rolled back out the way it came in, leaving an absolute mess of wood chips everywhere. So, then, the broom came out, followed by the vacuum.

Paul with his Pepa Frank, great grandma Pauline and me, pregnant with Bobby.

Baby Bobby has arrived! September, 1978. Paul loved holding his hand..

Baby Bobby 3 months old with his Dad. Paul holding his hand as usual..

Paul glued to Baby Bobby. April 1979

Paul and Frank with Great Grandma Pauline in
Waccabuc, NY backyard, 1978.

Frankie and Paul, Halloween, 1978

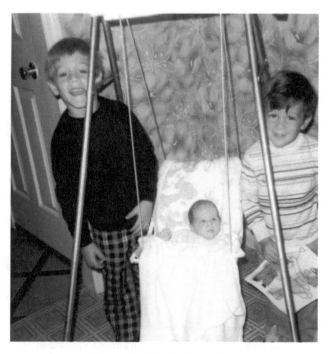

Thank God for baby swings

Halloween 1979. Always had lots of children and fun at the house.

This was THREE times a week, at least, depending on how cold winter was, or how long.

Can anyone understand why I loved spring and summer so much?

I have to say, Frankie and Paul were always helpful and cooperative from the beginning and continued to be, along with their other two brothers.

We just learned to live with things, like the water in the basement (we just never used it) and a difficult driveway. Getting stuck in the middle of the driveway, or other people getting stuck, having to call a tow truck, was part of our life.

We basically tried to concentrate on the positive. And, there were many positives living there.

Isn't concentrating on the positive the best way to live?

Especially if things are unsolvable? Or unfair? I actually wrote a children's book on that, entitled *It's Not Fair!* and you'll read about that elsewhere in this book.

There was a section in Paul's baby book entitled Meals and Eating. In reading my input, I have to smile. I wrote that Paul's appetite, at three years old, was good, and he ate almost anything. And, I wrote, even though he loved chocolate and cookies, he would readily accept and eat the fruit I substituted. That was Paul. Never a problem. Funny how that memory hit a nerve for me. Now that he's gone, I wish I allowed him those few extra chocolate bars or cookies.

Another food rule I had was to just offer soda on a Sunday, (same rule I had growing up). Actually, they rarely wanted it.

Paul was completely toilet trained that August, 1978, when he was almost 3 years old. He then went into his own room and big boy bed, relinquishing his crib and nursery for the new baby the following month.

Paul had a cute saying at three years old. "Big Deal!"

And, interestingly enough, all his life, Paul would always say:

"It's not a big deal!" to anyone annoyed or whining about something. That was Paul. He was always looking at the big picture—what was really important, and what was necessary to give one peace.

My husband, Manny, suggested that sentence as a title for this book. Haven't decided yet. I'll just keep writing and will see what happens.

But, if you are reading this now, you will see if I did so or not.

And, if not, you'll know the title chosen.

I write, finishing three year old notes:

"Such a pleasant little boy."

"Always smiling."

Cape Cod,
1979

South Salem Nursery School, 4 years old.

Abby Pribus	Brian Carr		Mike Bolard	Brad Hess		Christine Allen
Winnie Barry	Emily Patek	Kate Wagner		Ed Kolowski	Eric Zamft	
	Kathy Murray			Tammy Donahue	Paul Giaccio	

Pete Heisen		Scott Budich		Barbara McCann	Michele Kaplan	Jeff Brickman	Christine Allen
				Eric Zamft	Paul Giaccio		
Dennis Gaudenzi	Ivy Sheibar	Gretchen VanEyte		Jani Pacchianna	Abby Pribus	Alisha Soderland	

Age 3–6 years old

It was a big year for Paul with lots going on.

He got the baby brother he wanted—Bobby, named after my first cousin, Aunt Rose's son. Paul rarely left Bobby's side, if he was awake. He was absolutely in awe of his baby brother.

With the new baby on the scene, Paul became more mature in dressing himself.

I write:

"Paul is just a very happy child and he'll go anywhere with me."

I remember that sentence to be true in all the years to come. With all the food shopping I needed to do with ultimately having four sons, I could always rely on Paul to come with me to push the second cart, which would also be totally full.

Baby Bobby was in his baby seat in the cart, with food items tucked all around him. Sometimes he'd be sleeping, and sometimes awake, but he was always a good baby as well.

Paul loved grocery shopping because it was always an adventure. It's probably why, later in life, he could be so successful working at the grocery store. More on that later.

The whole excitement for Paul, even at that young age, was how much money we would save with our coupons. You see, my Aunt Rose and my mom were really into coupon clipping. Really into coupon clipping—organized into all categories of foods in envelopes.

Every week they would present me with a huge packet of these, spanning many years.

Paul loved to see the final amount saved at check out time at the register. Sometimes it was double coupon day! That dollar amount saved led to a phone call when we got home. Yes, we had to wait until we got home to tell Aunt Rose and mom the great news. There were no cell phones. We couldn't take photos of us shopping (selfies) to send to grandma, or a photo of the amount saved from the receipt. We had to go home and dial the number on a rotary phone. And, if no one was home, we had to call again and again. There were no answering machines to leave a message.

How did we ever live?

Actually, we lived very well, with a lot less stress and with more patience.

But, in our case, Grandma and Aunt Rose were always home.

We would tell them the amount of money we saved on coupons, which was recorded, trying to beat that amount the next week.

I enrolled Paul in the Spring 1979 session of the South Salem Presbyterian Nursery School. He went twice a week in the morning. Having the newborn baby, Bobby, it would have been difficult to do the winter session. It was so cold and usually snowing and I didn't want to take them out in that. Also, I saved some time with taking Paul to the South Salem nursery school, since it was a little closer. I was looking for any help I could get to make life just a bit more manageable.

Both of his teachers, Mrs. Berg and Mrs. Richardson, would always rave about him.

This is the year Paul really started talking, and became extremely verbal and inquisitive, asking questions about everything.

Notes from his teachers: "Everyone loves Paul."

"He has a great personality."

Paul's 4th birthday party was at home on our deck with nine of his friends. I barbecued hot dogs and hamburgers, served with the usual party favorites, cupcakes and ice cream. I orchestrated lots of easy games in the backyard. The children were always so good.

Three of the four boys' birthdays were during great months for outdoor activities, so I was always able to have the parties outside on our property. Many times I would hire a couple of teenagers to help me play games, baseball, hand out food, etc. They would dress up as clowns to make it more festive. I would oftentimes have up to 15 children, and the party could go on for hours. Sometimes the moms would stay because it was so much fun. Every year was a different theme. One of the favorites was the year I set up an obstacle course.

As I mentioned before, all the holidays were spent at our home, which I loved.

The Christmas Eve tradition was that my parents would shop on Arthur Avenue in the Bronx to buy all the fish, mozzarella, bread and Italian pastries before coming to us. Mom and I would bake and fry fish most of the day, in preparations for the Eve dinner. We would usually eat around 6 pm, clean up and then I would get the boys ready (whoever was old enough to go) for Church to leave around 9 pm since I sang in the choir. Eventually all four sons were old enough to go with me.

My parents would sleep over to be there the next morning. I just had the visual of my mom bundled up in the morning, saying how cold she was, which was followed by her ice cold hands on my arm to prove it. Like I needed proof or more coldness on my body.

It was such a treat for us when they stayed over, which was seldom, except for Christmas Eve.

As an only child, these four grandsons meant the world to my parents and my boys knew it. They loved them right back until the day they both died. More on that.

There were always health questions in the Baby Book, and I kept answering over and over how Paul, along with his brothers, were all very healthy pretty much all their lives, rarely even getting the cold or the flu. Maybe living in a cold house was the reason! Either that, or maybe it was all my Italian meals of macaroni and meatballs, chicken cutlet parmigiana, eggplant parmigiana, minestrone soup, broccoli rabe, and lots of garlic. Lots of garlic!

When it came to the questions about "athletics," I wrote that Paul didn't run too fast and was cautious going up and down the stairs. However he loved to dance and sing from a very young age.

As he got older, he still loved to sing, being in all his school Chorus groups, but dancing, no, definitely not.

Sports and exercise became his life, as it turned out, as much as he tried to stay away from it earlier. It was a complete reversal.

The summer of 1979 found us at Lake Truesdale in South Salem, a lake close to our home. It was a safe water area to bring young children where they could play at the water's edge in the rocky sand.

Paul loved it there. He met up with all his nursery school friends, and I would set up the playpen for Bobby where he could play and nap safely near me, while I could be with Paul by the water. It was so convenient for young mothers because you could park your car very close to the sand to unload everything.

Our summers were full and happy.

Reading on in my notes, I stated, "Paul is starting to assert himself."

I forgot all about this time, but from hardly talking, he went to nonstop talking. And, if anyone else tried to say anything, he could become frustrated and start to cry, saying "I don't like you! I just don't! Now I forgot what I was going to say!"

This phase didn't last long, but I felt so badly reading it. Perhaps we weren't sensitive enough to his newfound need for expression. Perhaps we could have been more patient giving him all the time he needed, more respectfully. I feel so sad now reading that he felt he needed to just keep talking and couldn't get it all out.

If only I could hear him speak now. It was also a time, as I read on, that he loved baby Bobby so much, he would not leave him alone. He was obsessed with holding his little hand and making him laugh. It was very endearing (he always loved babies) but baby Bobby would start to fuss because he wanted his hand back—the hand that Paul was kissing nonstop.

It was also annoying at times when he was holding Bobby's hand while I was trying to feed or dress him.

Looking back now, it really wasn't a "big deal."

It's during this 4th year that Paul showed a keen interest in numbers, and Frank would teach him adding and subtracting.

How interesting, since his whole life was devoted to numbers!

Although he never stopped talking, he never had "bad language" as "the book" said; many 4 year olds will experiment with it. I wrote that I said the words "shut up" (don't know to whom or why) and Paul said, "that's a bad thing to say!"

Very healthy year for all. Not even one cavity.

February 1980—

Paul is approximately 4-1/2 years old.

My exact words in entry:

"Paul is a real character and comes out with some funny remarks. He's very perceptive and a philosopher. He loves me dearly and he's very affectionate." (Yes, that brought a meltdown of tears for me).

He always liked to lead prayers before dinner, and then end with Jesus Christ! Lord!

I have no idea where that came from, unless he heard someone yell that out in frustration.

I end the section with:

"Paul is a happy child who loves life. It shows on his face. He's easily pleased"

The above statement remained true his whole life.

In the summer of 1980, Paul went to the Kindergarten camp at the Lewisboro Day Camp three mornings a week. All other times and days we all could be found at the Lewisboro Town Pool. We switched over to the Pool venue from Truesdale Lake because it became more convenient as the boys went to the day camp on the Pool grounds.

I would prepare and cook dinner in the early morning and store away for heat up later on. I then would leave for the Pool at 11 am with baby Bobby, meeting Paul and Frank as they were dismissed from their camps. We would all be there together until 5 or 5:30 pm, go home to shower, have dinner, relax and in bed by 7:30 pm. That summer routine went on for years.

We rarely went anywhere. We really didn't need to. We had so many amenities around us, but, that summer, we rented a house on the beach with another family in Surf City, Jersey Shore.

It was a great time and so convenient, being right on the beach. Paul and his brothers absolutely loved the beach. Always did. Also, it was my passion.

September 1980—

As one of the youngest in his class, Paul started Kindergarten in the morning. He went to Lewisboro Elementary School, with Mrs. Hostetler as his teacher. A small class of 16 children. Paul did very well.

He dressed himself completely before school, brushed his teeth and hair (different brush, I hope).

He was totally independent and organized. He always made his bed! And nicely!

Frank and Paul, the oldest brothers, had definite chores. One of Paul's chores was to straighten up the playroom.

Paul was a real kidder. He used to play this game with me where he would say, "Don't look in the playroom! It's a big mess! I didn't clean it!"

Of course I knew he really did, but I would always play along, so, on the way to the playroom, (which he wanted me to do in the first place to see how neat it was), I would be stomping my footsteps on the way, mumbling that I can't believe that the playroom is a mess and that I'm so disappointed he didn't do his job, etc. I would then open the door and then act totally surprised and happy to see it absolutely spotless! And, it truly was spotless and neat! Paul thought this whole scenario was hysterical and he would be beside himself laughing. This went on for a long time, and, to this day, I can picture that whole scene played out in my mind's eye.

Rhinebeck Fair, 1980

Paul's 5th birthday party, Waccabuc back yard.

Kindergarten 1980-1981

Jim Kehoe	John Ryan	Craig Shurtleff	Dennis Grady	Jason Blairs	Raymond Pagnucco	Mrs. Hostetler
	Brian Mongillo	Paul Giaccio	Patrick Wayland	Ed Kolowski		
Tammy Donohue	Winnie Barry	Sanna Smyth	Lisa Lusk	Kathy Murray	Maryellen McQuade	

Spring Soccer

First Grade, 1981-1982, Mrs. Geddes

Paul Giaccio	Brian Mongillo	Jason Blair	Greg Clark	Kipp Beltramello	Craig Shurtleff	Jared Green
Sharon Mayor	Kate Wagner	Tammy Donahue	Abby Pribus	Sanna Smyth	Winnie Barry	
		Jim Kehoe	Tommy Constalatto			

Surf City
June 1980,
Always loving
the beach.

I was so happy when I found some of his written paperwork from when he was very young.

This one here is from Christmas 1980, in Kindergarten, 5-1/2 years old. I have translated it the best I can.

"Dear Santa,

I want for Christmas is this: I want boxing

I would like an electric train set

I would also like four ET Posters for Richard and James Norten.

(He crossed out Bobby and Frank who were originally on the list which is so funny. I guess they did something to him.)

Is Rudolph the red nosed reindeer real?

Can I have a lot of puppets?

Please, a watch

I want all of my friends phone numbers

A black night rider car

Hungry Hungry Hippos

and a nice picture of your helpers and if Rudolph the red nosed reindeer is real, a picture of him. If not that — no picture

I would really really want a 3 feet tall Robot that does all the work for me and I will write it all down and put it inside the robot."

This was all on one side. Then he wrote: (other side) and continued listing… *"a little pad that has superman on it*

a E.T. sweatshirt and the watch that I told you already it should have E.T. on it

a Rubix cube that has print on it

and a magnet it can hold for the highest amount of weight is 6000 pounds

an invisible squirt gun a nice 200 page pad

I would like ET Jacket and an ET hat and a ET magic marker and a ET pencil and ET red and blue pen"

I just hope Santa got this list. I never remember reading all this. I hope he got some of this that Christmas!

I will never know now.

And, here's another note I loved. Paul would write notes to me if I was on the phone because I told the boys not to interrupt me.

Loving the game that he would tell me the playroom was messy (when it wasn't) and I would stomp over looking annoyed only to see it wasn't. I have the original note from a kitchen note pad. He wrote:

read mom

boy o boy

is that playroom messy

you want to see it

close your eyes

closed   yes or no — circle it

My heart breaks when I read these.

He was always there to help, without my even asking. Even at such a young age, he was a strong quiet influence in the family, which was, unfortunately, filled with drama many times.

I promised myself that I wouldn't get into any negative talk in this book, although it was tempting. I wanted to keep the sharing positive and productive. However, I would be remiss in at least "hinting" that family life was not exactly smooth sailing. After all, this book is about Paul and who he was. So, the circumstances as to how he grew up, without being specific, needed to be out there in some way.

Let's just say that home life could be compared to a slow, constant, unwanted faucet drip that could be fixed at times, to get some relief. And everyone is happy for a time—for a short time. And, then the drip starts again, and eventually it can no longer be fixed because the inner hardware is stripped.

So, all the "dripping" finally led to my filing for divorce many years later.

Uneasiness and insecurity in a home has its effects on children, as I was so aware of as I watched certain behaviors unfold. I mustered every ounce of strength I had to "keep it together." I know this happens in many families and it usually does fall on the mother to keep an emotionally healthy atmosphere for the sake of the children. I did the best I could for many years, as I'm sure many women do. We never know what people are going through, and why we shouldn't judge. It's not easy to break up a home.

My mother would always say "no one knows what goes on behind closed doors."

But, before it all "went down," there were years still left at our Waccabuc home, and I was doing what I could to fix the drip.

The year Paul turned 5 was tumultuous. There were just way too many things going on. I was once again pregnant. With my fourth child. The responsibilities were mounting everywhere.

During that pregnancy, an event on January 1, 1981, rocked my world. While Frankie and Paul were playing outside, Frank fell on a pile of wood in the backyard and was taken to the Northern Westchester Hospital for immediate surgery.

I had just made a beautiful New Year's Day breakfast and was upstairs changing Bobby in his room, when I heard the screams from down below. It's a morning I will never forget, nor did Paul. Feeling totally frustrated and useless at home while I waited to be taken to the hospital, I called my Bible Group to pray for Frankie.

As I was to find out later, the prayer requests went statewide through networking. Prayers were answered.

Upon coming out of anesthesia, the nurse asked Frankie if he wanted a new brother or sister, and he said "brother," and, from that moment on, I prayed for another son to make my Frankie happy. And, that son, Richie, arrived on August 1, 1981.

It was very frightening for Paul to see his brother go through such an ordeal. He had seen the entire event happen, and had dreams he told me about. He was extremely close to his older brother and remained so until Paul's last day on earth.

Fortunately, Frankie recuperated well but it left me very shaken as to the vulnerability we all live with, not knowing what can happen one day to the next.

I was on high alert for accidents or disasters to occur. As a mother, and a mother who was expecting her fourth child, I could not get it out of my head that "something" could happen at any time and that I wouldn't be able to protect my children from it.

Well, they say that we attract what we are afraid of. Sure enough, that happened.

Several weeks after Frankie's accident, Frankie was invited to a friend's house nearby for a play date. I drove him there on that cold, snowy day with the plan to pick him up in three hours. For some reason, the whole family was in the car when we went to get Frankie, perhaps because we were on our way somewhere else after. So, we all got out of the car and walked around the back of the house to the back door. There was snow everywhere and it was freezing cold, the middle of winter 1981. Somehow, Paul walked onto an in ground hot tub jacuzzi that had a flimsy cover on it, but was invisible to the eye because it was covered with snow. Right before my eyes, I saw Paul fall into this water hole and I screamed and screamed. His father ran to pick him out immediately but he was drenched in his snow suit. I took off my coat and put it around him and the adults from inside ran out with a blanket. We rushed him home and into a warm bathtub.

Freak accidents, I know, happen every day. I shudder with the thought, "What if we weren't there?"

Yes, a person's life can change in seconds. For stupid, makes-no-sense reasons. It was to be the second scariest time while I was pregnant with my fourth child. Thankfully, we got through the rest of that school year without any more frightening events.

In April, 1981 Paul and I took an unexpected trip to Mission Viejo, California.

We stayed with our friends Wanda and Lynn Yeazel, who we met in Waccabuc when we moved there. Wanda and Lynn became like family. They didn't have any children at the time and they loved coming to our home with all the activities and holiday dinners. Lynn would entertain Paul with his amazing train set at his home.

Sadly, Lynn's job took them to California, but we stayed in touch constantly. They then had a baby, Laura, and, with missing them all so much, I decided to take a trip to visit them with Paul. It was our first time in California and we both absolutely loved it. I remember thinking how lucky they all were to live there. Never, in my wildest dreams did I think I would have residence there 30 years later, with Paul coming all the time to visit me and his best friends.

Paul and I had the best time, and he was treated like a little prince by everyone. We were treated to a day at Disneyland, and all sorts of fun excursions, lunches and dinners. Paul was always the perfect little traveler and companion, and everyone would remark, no matter where we went, on how good he was.

He loved their little girl, Laura, who was so sweet, and was ever so gentle with her.

Paul with Laura Yeazel,
April, 1981,
California trip.

(Paul always loved small children, as seen in the photos throughout the book.)

Even though I was pregnant, due in a few months, we all managed the trip extremely well.

I realized then, as I always did thereafter, how important it is to have quality time with each child so they don't get lost in the shuffle.

Paul made us laugh with his antics all the time.

He loved the song "You've got the look I'd like to know better, you've got the look that's altogether. Working, playing, day or night, Jordache has the fit that's right!"

Of course, this drove his brother Frankie crazy, but baby Bobby, 3 years old at the time, would sing along with him.

Disneyland California, April 1981

This "show" went on for a few weeks until another took its place. It was a real circus at the house many times.

At the end of that 1981 school year Mrs. Hostetler wrote:

"Paul is a pleasure to have in class—eager and very willing." I wrote:

"Paul has a good feeling about himself and everything he does."

In looking back at what I wrote in my observation at my 5 year old son, it was so totally true.

He WAS happy with his little life, and enjoyed every minute of who he was in that life. Writing this now, I have the advantage of reflection in being able to look back at his unfolding life. How things would change. And, those changes did not come about because of Paul's true soul, who he was, but they came about because of society's prejudices.

But, here, I wanted to highlight the fact, that, at 5 years old, before the toxicity of society's thought systems take hold, every child is happy and prejudice free.

We are not born prejudicial. We are not born to hate.

I continued to write:

"Always smiling. He is never looking for an argument. Paul talks out his feelings and doesn't hold grudges." How amazing I would write this at his being 5 years old. This is exactly how he remained his whole life.

It was a very full year in looking back at that calendar!

Along with the unexpected blips that occurred, fortunately with good endings, we were in full swing at our St. Mary's Church and all our obligations there. The boys were taking Confraternity of Christian Doctrine (CCD) classes and Frank received his First Holy Communion. There was Bible Study, Choir Practices, and den mother responsibilities for Frank's cub scouts. Plus the birthday parties, holidays, play dates, etc.

Paul was always in the midst of so much going on, and yet always remained solid as a rock.

He was never rattled by all the confusion and just stayed as calm as can be.

The summer of 1981 was busy. Paul and Frankie spent a lot of time clearing out our woods, creating trails for the go cart my dad was building for them.

It would be the most exciting "toy" they could ever have and would be the hit at all future birthday parties.

So, that kept Paul busy that summer, along with going to the Lewisboro Town Camp until 2:30 pm each day. We would all meet up at the Town Pool, which was on the same grounds, and we would all spend the rest of the day there. This was their life—swimming, day camp, community, friends. It was also the summer Paul learned to play checkers, which he excelled at. He also started collecting pennies like his brother Frank did. Paul would continue his collection of all kinds of coins and after he passed away, several boxes of these were found, meticulously organized and hand recorded.

As Bobby was getting older, Paul was able to play more with him. They loved listening to Christmas records all year long, doing puzzles and watching Gilligan's Island.

By this time, Bobby, who was the youngest, moved into Paul's room where they each had a twin bed. Bobby's room would then become the nursery for the new baby.

On August 1, 1981, my fourth son, Richard Joseph, was born.

A full house to say the least. It was all good. As a past teacher with plenty of experience, I was used to large groups of children in one room!

One year I taught 52 second graders with no aide assistance—just me. And, that was my Baptism by fire in my very first year of teaching, and, I never had a bad day. Busy—but I loved it. So, four little boys didn't scare me.

The first day out with all four sons would be to go to the Town Pool. The Lewisboro Town Pool was really our lifeline. The boys loved it there. It's where all the day camps met and sports were played.

It was a huge complex with several pools, accommodating all swimming abilities, as well as a food counter.

I arrived at the pool parking lot, parked the car, and started to assemble what was needed to be taken out of the car. I took baby Richie out of his car seat and placed him in his carriage. He was about 2 weeks old, so he slept mostly, except for my "scheduled" feedings. I then removed everything else to bring, such as the diaper bag, towels, folding chair, pool toys for Bobby in a bag, small umbrella, etc. I placed it all on the ground in one bunch by the trunk, expecting all the other boys would pick some of it up, following me while I was pushing the carriage. I know I must have given out that request as I was concentrating on the baby, but I can't remember. I do know I was talking to them out loud to make sure they were close together right behind me because we were in a parking lot area, and I always found them to be potentially dangerous with children darting in and out as cars are pulling out and in.

Well, as I was approaching the gate, my friend Gloria and her family saw us arrive and she was hysterical laughing, pointing behind me. I turned around and saw no one carrying anything but Paul.

He had towels wrapped around his neck, along with the straps of the umbrella and chair, and bags hanging off both shoulders. It's one of those moments when you don't know if you will laugh or cry?

We did laugh about it for years because it was exactly who Paul was, always helping and doing things, oblivious to who isn't helping or doing things.

But, now I want to cry, thinking of what a good soul he was.

And, why in the world did someone like that, my son, have to die?!!

Paul turned six on September 25, 1981, immediately following that summer, in what was a drama-filled many months.

He entered the First Grade with Mrs. Geddes as his teacher.

She writes:

"Paul is a lively and enthusiastic child. He is a pleasure to work with."

This is a time when Paul began to get more physical, playing team soccer. He wasn't too fond of running because he said he got out of breath (I have the same problem) but, later on in life, wouldn't you know, he loved running and hiking!

One of our favorite stories about Paul playing team soccer was how he was made goalie, probably because he didn't like the running part. Well, social Paul would be more interested in waving and greeting the spectators behind and around him through the netting.

Paul would be twisting his fingers in the netting around him. (Don't know why). That became an issue one day when he got tangled in the netting as the ball was being kicked at high speed heading toward the goal, but Paul was totally entwined in the netting and couldn't get loose!

Fortunately, the kick missed the goal area! Needless to say, we were all relieved and had a good laugh. After that, he remained a lot more alert!

It was his claim to fame on the soccer field, but he handled it very well. Dumbo was his favorite movie and he knew the entire dialogue. I need to watch that movie again by myself sometime, but I know it would be very emotional, and I'm crying as I write this. Maybe I'll hold off on watching it for a long while. Maybe never.

Paul stayed at my mom's house a few days at Easter vacation. The boys loved going there by themselves once in a while for all the individual attention they would get from my parents and their Great Aunt Rose.

They would get their favorite foods for meals and their favorite dessert—chocolate pudding, with real whipped cream. My mom and Aunt Rose would "argue" as to who was going to make the chocolate pudding. It was so funny. All they wanted was to please.

Paul started watching Dark Shadows at 4:30 pm while he was there, which I wrote in my notes. My Aunt and Mom loved Soap Operas, so that must have been yet another one of their shows. Paul wanted to keep watching when he came home, but TV was only allowed on Friday afternoons and weekends, so maybe he caught it on a Friday afternoon. It didn't matter with soap operas. Nothing much happened in a week anyway.

I have no memory about this Dark Shadows TV show!

Speaking about memory, Paul's favorite game was *Memory*, and he was excellent at it. No surprises there.

To play one more game with him…

Atari was another pastime he had with his brothers, but at set times.

In August, 1982, I was about to have another frightening experience. I watched over those boys like a mother hen, but, there are times you are just not in control of what unfolds before your very eyes, no matter how vigilant you try to be.

We went to the Rhinebeck Fair with all four of the boys, which would present some stress in and of itself since they were so young — 8, 5, 3, and 1 years old.

We parked the car in the huge parking lot after waiting quite a while to get in. And, then, once parked, and when everyone was safely out of the car, we waited on another long line at the actual entrance to pay our admission. We didn't realize it would be so crowded!

While on that second line, with three of the boys standing beside us, and Richie in the stroller (that could hold 2 children if Bobby got tired) I started to inwardly feel uneasy about the crowds. (Mother's intuition).

So, when we were at the Fairgrounds front gate entrance, I told the boys to stay close together and that if anyone got lost, go to the place we just came in from as our meeting place.

After those instructions, I asked the boys, while we were still standing there, if they had a certain animal they wanted to see. I figured to get some sort of plan in the works. Bobby was the first to say elephants and we would go there first, heading in that direction from the map.

We were like salmon swimming upstream, because there was this sea of people walking against us, making it difficult to maneuver the stroller or even walk together. Not even 30 seconds into this nightmare, I looked to my side where Bobby was walking, and he was gone. It seemed impossible. I turned around and there were throngs of people, seeing only their backs. Bobby was completely gone! We had just entered from the gate! How could this be? I just started screaming, "My son! My son is gone!" In seconds, security and others came to us, along with everyone else. I described him and what he was wearing, through my hysterics. This could not be happening! Frank and Paul were all upset about their brother. I ran to the entrance gate area, which was jammed with people, and he wasn't there. I was convinced someone took him. My then husband was looking all around us and it was the most devastating, hopeless feeling. The security team throughout the Fairgrounds was notified and they told us to stay exactly where we were, off to the side, on a bench, and not move while they searched. That was the hardest part. I wanted to run everywhere looking myself.

My then husband kept saying "someone took him" over and over which didn't help any of us, although I was having those dark thoughts myself.

I was uncontrollably hysterical. I couldn't help it. I felt so helpless. After about 20 minutes, which seemed like forever, I saw a woman coming towards us carrying Bobby in her arms, escorted by a security man. I ran to them and just grabbed him, sobbing. Evidently, Bobby was swept backwards by the crowds (as

I figured) and since we were so close to the entrance, he knew to go there, but he went outside the gate! That's why he wasn't there when we looked. He sat on the ground by the gate outside and was noticed by a woman waiting on line for 15 minutes. She thought it was strange that this little boy was alone just sitting there, so she told the security man who said, "that's the boy who's missing!"

We hugged everyone thanking them and I thanked God that the woman who found Bobby was a good person to do the right thing in reporting it.

Well, we did wind up getting to the elephants, as Bobby had wanted. We had to give this trip some good memories for the children. Myself, I would have preferred to go right home and gone to bed. But, taking deep breaths, I was able to take some cute photos of Paul and Bobby on the elephant (see photo).

All's well that ends well.

We all never forgot that terrifying day. It's probably why I don't like crowds.

It left an impression that's hard to explain, and it haunted me.

I would think "I can't imagine what I would do if I ever lost one of my sons." Little did I know I would find out many years later.

Always had company at the house. Paul loved the swing.

Creating happy memories.
Rhinebeck Fair, 1982.

Bobby in front, Paul behind him on the elephant.

Second Grade

PAUL ENTERED SECOND GRADE with Mrs. Cummings. Again, he was one of the youngest, at 7 years old.

She wrote:

"Paul works and plays well with others and shares ideas."

I write how Paul is smiling all the time and cooperative with all his house chores. Every hand was needed in the day to day life with four young sons.

Each son had several chores that would rotate every week.

I must say they were all so helpful in every way. They knew their mom couldn't do it all! Paul's job was to straighten up the playroom and downstairs closet where the sports equipment was kept. And there was a lot of that! He also needed to make his bed and Bobby's every morning, and he really did it well! And, of course, the never ending filling of the wood on the log hoop so we didn't freeze to death. That was three times a week, along with the help of Frankie. That was a huge job in itself! Not only to get all the wood in, but the clean up after.

I write that Paul had excellent insight and thinking skills. And, it reminded me of the time one day on our way to Jones Beach. We were caught up in a lot of traffic at the Throgs Neck Bridge. There were rows and rows of cars completely stopped. Paul was looking out the back window of the car, observing this whole situation, and, all of a sudden, he said, "You know what they should do? They should have a line where they charge people extra if they want to go through faster. I bet a lot of people would be willing to pay just not to wait on this line for an hour."

Wow! What a thought for a seven year old! And, sure enough, years later, hello to EZ Pass!

Paul kept himself busy constantly coloring, drawing, writing or reading.

Second Grade, Mrs. Cummings

Craig Shurtleff	Tommy Constalatto	Brian Mongillo	Ed Kolowski	Pat Wayland	Pete Eggington	Mrs. Cummings
Sharon Mayor	Leigh Esposito	Abby Pribus	Sanna Smyth		Emily Patek	Kathy Murray
Billy Casey		Paul Giaccio		Mark Lynn	John Ryan	

Paul's 7th Birthday.
Go cart fun, 1982

Loved taking photos of my four sons. This is one of my favorites.

Their TV time was very limited, so they would have time to use their mind skills.

As a treat, I would rent movies from the Cross River Pharmacy for $2.50 a day. Their favorites were *Davy Crockett*, *Poltergeist* and *Rocky I*.

This was all before Netflix!

Paul still really just enjoyed being home with his brothers, playing outside on our property, or just alone in his room, with little projects he was always involved in. He rarely, if ever, asked for friends over and yet, he was always being invited everywhere.

My dad, their Pepa Frank, gave the boys a go cart and when Paul turned seven years old, I had a big birthday party for him which was a blast. I barbecued for all the children along with organized games, but the big thrill for everyone was putting on a helmet and being taken through our trails in the woods by our teenage neighbor Colin. My faithful baby sitter Lenora helped me with baby Richie.

In October, right after Paul turned seven, he started piano lessons with Mrs. Campbell on Thursday afternoons, thanks to my parents who gifted us with a piano.

Paul would ultimately be the only one who wanted to learn, although Richie tried for a while.

Mrs. Campbell, when she would come over, really got to see what the Giaccio household was like in the years she came to us.

Further into these pages, you'll read a very funny story that happened one day with Mrs. Campbell.

I'm asked to tell it over and over to this very day.

From now on, I'll be able to tell people, "just read my book, it's in there!"

1983 was jam-packed with events and memories.

Paul had his first newspaper debut that January when he was interviewed, along with other children, about what they liked to do. It would be the first of many articles in the newspapers for Paul.

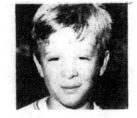

In January 1983, Paul made his debut in our town's newspaper in a survey asking children what they loved to do.

Paul Giaccio

Paul received the Sacrament of Penance at St. Mary's on February 5, and on May 7, he received his First Holy Communion there.

Waccabuc's **Paul Giaccio** is a second grader at Lewisboro Elementary School. In the warm weather, his sport is swimming, but he is also goalie on his soccer team. Paul has fun playing with his three brothers...

Church services for St. Mary's in Katonah were actually held at the Presbyterian Church in South Salem, where Sunday Masses were held and where I sang in the choir.

First Holy Communion, May 7, 1983

February 1983. Paul
receiving Penance.

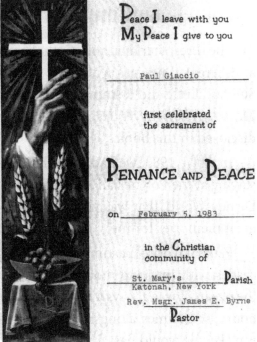

Peace I leave with you
My Peace I give to you

Paul Giaccio

first celebrated
the sacrament of

PENANCE AND PEACE

on   February 5, 1983

in the Christian
community of

St. Mary's   Parish
Katonah, New York

Rev. Msgr. James E. Byrne

Pastor

" My Jesus,give me the grace
to receive You always
with a pure and contrite heart "

Paul Giaccio

received
the **Blessed Eucharist**
for the first time

in *St. Mary's Church*

Katonah. N.Y.

May 7th.1983

The Presbyterians and Catholics both shared the building at different times. It's where the boys and I went to Mass every Sunday. Little did I know what Paul was praying for at those Masses. A certain request. I would find that out many years later, disclosed in this book.

In April, 1983, we had a family trip to Disney World Orlando, staying at the Polynesian Hotel. For the few times we would go to Disney World, that was where we would stay, and it holds many great memories for me.

Paul's favorite pastime was playing on the beach, making castles with intricate moats, adding water back and forth from the ocean. It was always a huge project, seriously working on it for hours, sometimes alongside his brothers, unless they got in his way. People would pass and marvel at all the effort he put into it.

We then had another great beach vacation when we rented a

Paul loved going to Disneyworld

The Polynesian Resort- Disneyworld, Florida, 1983

With my parents living in the Bronx, 10 minutes from the Bronx Zoo, my dad and I would take the boys there whenever we visited. It's where I spent every Sunday morning with my dad after I went to church. My boys were very close to Pepa Frank and Grandma Mary, along with "An Rose". (Aunt Rose)

house on the ocean in Surf City, New Jersey, with another family, the Siscas. It was fun for Paul being steps from the sand and having other children around.

Then there was the usual Town summer day camp and Pool, Frankie's all star baseball games at night and 2 weeks at Vacation Bible School in Armonk that all 4 boys went to, divided up in separate age groups. The moms had their own group. They all actually loved going. It was a very unique program.

Summer was over and it was on to Third Grade.

Third Grade

MRS. CODY, PAUL'S THIRD GRADE teacher writes:

"I'm pleased with Paul's progress in all areas this term. He is a very hard worker."

At this time, Paul had his room to himself as I moved Bobby to the room where baby Richie was. Richie was relocated to a smaller room facing the front of our home.

Now, Paul had lots of space to do his projects in peace.

I would tuck Paul in every night by either reading to him or his reading to me, usually around 7:30 pm. All the boys went to bed early every night their whole lives.

Paul told me he liked "funny stories" that would make him laugh and that reading the books I chose was boring. I would take the boys to the Library all the time to choose their own, but I don't think they really picked up the love of reading.

They had too many other things going on that they had passions for.

This was also Paul's first year in Cub Scouts and I was the Den leader for his Den #4. A total of four boys came over every Wednesday after school. We took two cub scout trips. One was to Camp Siwanoy and one to the Leatherman's Cave. It was a great group and I enjoyed being with them, as I enjoyed being Den mom for Frankie's cub scouts.

The hardest part, though, was sewing on those badges!

They all looked so cute in their cub scout uniforms. Paul was very easy about clothes. He had no interest in fashion. He put on whatever I put out without a peep. He actually never changed about that. He was happy in a tee shirt and cargo shorts all his life.

I write:

"Paul is very observant of my moods and feelings. He's a very sensitive and perceptive child." This would hold true his entire life. He would be the one people would call if they needed advice or a lending ear. He would always come up with a solution or compromise. The peacemaker. Manny has called him "Uncle Spiro" many times. Manny's Uncle Spiro, his dad's brother, was the peacemaker in the family and elsewhere. Everyone relied on him to make things right.

Although TV time was limited in our house, I noted that Paul liked to watch *Ripley's Believe It or Not*, and *Abbott and Costello*. He wasn't into records or songs that much, although later on in life he became obsessed with going to concerts, attending at least hundreds!

His concert attendance is a whole other story. I give a skeletal explanation of his going to concerts with about 30 of his friends somewhere in this book. I say "skeletal" because Paul's arrangement of these concert plans was not exactly "legal."

Lewisboro and Georgian Testimonials is a Chapter that includes stories and testimonials given by his Georgia friends, as well as his childhood friends in Lewisboro, New York.

Paul's life was by and large split in 2 states, New York and Georgia.

The first half was in Waccabuc, New York, and the second

half was in Atlanta, Georgia, from when he started Georgia Tech. After college graduation, he remained living in Atlanta, starting a whole new life there.

So, now his Georgia friends will get to know the young Paul, whereas his childhood friends will read Paul's life after high school.

I found Paul's original letter to Santa that Christmas of 1983 and have included it here. Paul wanted Santa to put him on a treasure hunt! I have no idea where that idea came from, nor do I remember this at all.

But, here it is, exactly as he wrote it.

"Dear Santa,

Give me a present under my bed and then it says look somewhere and I look there and do that a lot of times and it will be like a treasure hunt but you are going to do it and at the end of the treasure hunt I want you to give me 10 dollars and some Christmas lights and some other things like ornaments and make it a big, big, big big box of presents and wrap it up fansy (sp)!!!!!!!!"

Paul's actual letter to Santa.

Christmas, 1983

Third Grade, Mrs. Cody

Kipp Beltramello	Billy Casey	Erica Green	Lisa Lusk	Abby Pribus	Amy Marciano	Anthony Percoco	Dennis Grady
	Winnie Barry	Tammy Donahue	Emily Patek	Sanna Smyth	Kathy Murray	Liz Lefton	
		Paul Giaccio	Jared Green	Brian Mongillo	Craig Shurtleff	Pete Eggington	

Fourth Grade

Mrs. Sonberg Writes:

"Paul is a good student and a friendly, polite little boy."

She awarded Paul with the Citizenship Award that year.

Paul's birthday, which was right after school began for the new year, brought a large crowd of friends and family to the house. I barbecued and the friends watched the movie *Footloose*.

At the time, more responsibilities were put on Paul and Frank to help me out. Chores were alternated with both of them each week, like emptying the garbage and dishwasher, bringing up the folded clean laundry in baskets, clearing the table after dinner, and, of course, bringing in that darn wood!

They were both amazing workers. Bobby and Richie had easier jobs for their age, like letting Ralph in and out. Ralph would bark to go out and bark to come in. Also, they needed to see he had fresh water and food. And, just now I had the memory of Ralph's dog food. My dad had a customer who owned a dog food company and offered my dad a bag of dog food to give Ralph. It was absolutely huge. Dad put it in the garage along the wall that actually was the wall of my pantry closet on the other side.

After a few weeks, I noticed little things flying around in my pantry and I freaked out. I couldn't imagine where they were coming from or what they were!

I immediately called an exterminator, who was actually Paul's friend's father, and he discovered it was coming from the big bag of dog food on the other side of the wall in the garage!

Everything had to be thrown out. Another project and mess.

One of the things Paul loved to do was make eggplant parmigiana. The other boys would join in as things got set up.

I would peel and slice the eggplants and one would dip each slice in beaten eggs, drip it, then pass it to the bread crumb person

Mrs. Sonberg
Left to Right: Emily Rems, Lisa Mandell, Sonya Holcombe, Kathy Murray, Winnie Barry, Sharon Mayor, Penny Chantry, Anne Pessani, Liz Lefton, Sanna Smyth, Amy Marciano.
Front Row: Anthony Percoco, Peter Eggington, Bryan VanVronken, Paul Giaccio, Mark Lynn, Parog Chordia, John Ryan, Billy Casey.

to coat, shake, and put on a pan, ready for me to fry.

I think of them every time I make this dish and wish I had all of them together again to help.

Paul enjoyed sitting down to dinner with me and his brothers.

He needed to talk about everything on his mind. Unfortunately, mealtimes were not as relaxing as we would have liked them to be because of the constant interaction of the two younger brothers (6 and 3) so it would sometimes be frustrating for him to speak. There were always interruptions of one kind or another. It comes with having a large family, which is good. It's good training for interaction in the real world, I guess.

But, Paul had patience even with all that.

He was such a good big brother to Bobby and Richie. He'd play games with them, but, Richie, as with many baby brothers, could be annoying, breaking up puzzles, etc. Paul stayed calm, however. We all spoiled Richie because he was so darned cute

Christmas 1984…Always fun when the Bernasconi family came over.

and extremely comical. He entertained us constantly, having us in stitches with his antics, which Paul would wind up filming. I was the most lenient with Richie, maybe because he was my last, but also because it was so hard to get mad at him. He was extremely mischievous. In nursery school, he was always disappearing, and the teachers had to watch his every move.

The question, "where's Richie?" would be a constant one at home and everywhere. None of the other boys were like this!

Then, there was "that time" that people never would forget (along with others). Paul would talk about it all the time because it was a crazy situation.

Paul's dad took all the boys to a championship basketball game. I was probably at home on the couch getting a much-deserved break.

Several hours later, the boys came flying through the door to find me to tell me what happened. Remember, this was all pre-cellphone days.

Paul couldn't get the story out fast enough. Evidently, escape artist Richie got away from the sights of his father, climbed under the table of the game announcers, and unplugged all the sound and electrical equipment!

Don't ask. I don't know how. The whole gymnasium went dark! The game had been tied and it was a crucial one!

Immediately, Paul and everyone asked "Where's Richie?" as if they knew he had to be involved. There are many Richie stories, but this was Paul's favorite.

Today, Richie is a good son, successful owner of many businesses, and doesn't disappear anymore.

I noted that another movie Paul enjoyed was *The Golden Soul*. I don't remember that movie at all, and it's why I'm so glad I made constant notes.

I wrote that Paul especially liked the part when the boy made a fall that looked really fake. He thought this was extremely funny and would just laugh and laugh.

What I would do to hear that laugh again.

September 1984 brought the death of our Yorkshire Terrier, Ralph, who was 14 years old. Honestly, it was like he was part human. He was so smart, full of personality.

It was very devastating, especially for me. I laid on the couch for days. People came to visit to cheer me up. I was heartbroken.

At the time, Paul was in his second year of piano lessons with Mrs. Campbell and on the Thursday, several days after Ralph died, she came to the house for Paul's usual lesson.

Whenever she rang the bell, or anyone rang the bell, for that matter, all 4 boys would run to the foyer to see who it was and answer the door, along with barking Ralph.

I slowly made my way there as well, looking horrific in my grief, I'm sure, which prompted Mrs. Campbell to ask, "Mrs. Giaccio, what's wrong? Are you okay?"

I burst out crying and said, "Don't you see? Don't you see who's missing?"

I'm sure the woman was so confused because there was always chaos at my house with not only my own group, but with other children and lots of noise (although everyone had to disappear once Paul started his lesson, in peace). She probably didn't know how to answer that question, so she politely asked, "What happened?"

I said "Ralph died! My dear Ralph died!" And I started sobbing so she hugged me for a while as I continued crying.

Little did I realize she immediately thought "Ralph" was one of my sons! Not my dog!

So, the rest of what will follow here will ultimately be hysterically funny. This story has been told a thousand times through the years. Manny always asks me to tell it when we meet someone new.

So, while she's hugging me, she starts crying herself, saying "No! No! How horrible!" "I know! I know!" I'm answering on her shoulder.

"How did this happen? Was he sick?" she asks.

Sobbing, I'm answering in broken sentences. "It happened four days ago. My husband and I went away on a business trip and we had Mr. and Mrs. Bailey (not their real names) watch the children. They noticed Ralph was not acting himself. They didn't want to bother us, so they called my parents since they knew my father was very close to him. They came right over."

Mrs. Campbell asked, "Did they take Ralph to the hospital, then?"

"No," I said, "while they waited for my parents to come, they tried to give him water, but he wouldn't drink and then they thought to give him some air, so they brought him outside, but he ran into the woods and wouldn't come out! He never did that before! He always listened when you called him back in.

"But, when my dad got there, and Ralph heard my dad's voice call for him, he started crawling towards him with no strength. My dad got him and held him and in minutes, he was dead. He died in my dad's arms! Just like that! And I wasn't there for him!"

I was basically rambling and Mrs. Campbell didn't say a word, until she asked, "Did they find out what it was?"

"They think it was kidney failure by the tests they took, but I don't have all the information yet," I answered.

"I can't imagine getting that phone call while you were so far away!" Mrs. Campbell sympathized.

"Well, actually they didn't tell us until we got home the next day since there was nothing we could do at that point," I said.

If I were thinking clearly at the time I would have noticed the blank stare on her face. It was only further along in the conversation, that things would become clear (for both of us). "I wish I had known earlier about this, Mrs. Giaccio. Did you have a service?"

"Well, the children and I decided to bury him in the front yard with some of his little toys. So, Frank dug a hole and we bought a box to put him in. It was a very difficult thing to do. The boys and I were crying so hard. It was just us. So glad he's right there in the front yard, under the trees."

I can't imagine the thoughts in Mrs. Campbell's head at that time! I am sure she was wondering how she could cancel any further piano lessons with Paul, since this was one crazy family!

But, the next part of the conversation would prevent that from happening, and put her mind at ease, unbeknownst to me.

She continued, "I'm so sorry, Mrs. Giaccio, I just don't know what to say."

"Thank you, Mrs. Campbell, There's nothing to say. People told me to go out and get a puppy, but I can't do that! No dog can take the place of our sweet little Yorkie right now. He was with me for 14 years, even before my children. I don't think he can be replaced, at least not now."

We were standing facing each other in the front hallway during this entire exchange and suddenly she looked at me very strangely as though something clicked in her brain. She started to stutter something, but, instead, just pulled me close for another hug.

It wasn't until she was gone (left quickly after the lesson) that it dawned on me that all along she thought "Ralph" was one of my sons that had died, and not my dog!

I always thought I would bring this up with her one day, but never did. I decided to let it be. It might have been embarrassing. Meanwhile, it's one of those family stories that gets brought up to share at parties or dinners.

Yes, Paul grew up with lots of stories in our home. I couldn't possibly include them all.

Synopsis of Paul's 9th year:

I cried a lot in reading my comprehensive entries in his Baby Book for the section of nine years old.

I had a really hard time reading my own words because they were so true to who he was as an adult. I wanted him alive again.

I actually wrote at three different times for the boys—usually around their actual birthday, then again, four months later and then again, giving updates on the same book questions.

These are the sentences I wrote at different times that year:

1. Paul is so nice to have around—always willing to please

2. His hair usually needs to be combed, but he always has a smile.

3. He's never in a bad mood or ruffled—he's controllable, yet has a mind of his own.

4. Always smiling and helpful—a breath of fresh air.

5. Shoelaces always untied and dragging about.

6. Paul is dressing a little better these days—not because others are—he never speaks about what others are doing or wearing—really an individual—a true leader.

7. Paul is very sensitive to other people's needs. He's always seeking out those that are unhappy or alone.

8. Paul has an excellent mind—I really feel he'll go places.

These sentences were exactly as I wrote them, when Paul was nine years old.

Except for the sentence that his hair needed to be combed (because he didn't have any, being bald) every sentence held true his entire life.

It made me so filled with grief, that I had to write a different section of this book for a couple days to give myself a break.

I have to admit that although I've been labeled strong through all this, and I surely have worked on it through my grief and afterlife research, there are times I become inconsolable. I keep asking "Why?" over and over. "Why did he have to die? He loved living!" And, then, I take a deep breath and remember what I now know and learned. There are no answers to these questions here on earth, but there are answers.

It's predetermined and part of what each one of us has to go through in our personal journey.

It's not exactly comforting during the times you just want to see and hug your son, or loved one again, but that's it.

And, acceptance of this is the only relief to give myself.

Avanti 3
Hornets 1

Avanti triumphed in a superb display of coordinated team play. The balanced attack was led by one goal each scored by Alex Albert, Brian Lonergan, and Mark Lynn. Also contributing to the aggressive offense were Megan Coote, Sam Orlofsky, David Rinaldi and Jamie Stumpf. Rock solid defense was played by Jason Blair, Shannon Kearney, Rud Niles, Katie Reynolds, and Stephanie Wirth. David Coote and Paul Giaccio made numerous spectacular saves in the goal, as well as contributing to the midfield defense.

AGES 7 AND 8

Vikings 1, Avanti 1

Behind one goal, made by David Fiestal, the Vikings played the Avantis to a tie. Brian Carr, Philip and Daniel Glasser, Julie Buist and Billy Stevens had an outstanding game.

Showing great effort to overcome the disadvantage of being one player short, the Avanti played their usual aggressive team game. David Rinaldi scored early in the second half to take the lead. However, a late Viking goal foiled another Avanti win. Playing well on both offense and defense were Alex Albert, Shanon Kearney, Brian Lonergan, Mark Lynn, Sam Orlofsky, Katie Reynolds and Jamie Stumpf. Ted Ferrarone and Paul Giaccio made several spectacular saves in the goal.

Cub Scout Carnival Day at our house, June 1984

Lewisboro Swim Team, 1984

Spring 1985.
Paul playing piano for 4th grade recital at Lewisboro School.

April 1985. Disneyworld with the Bernasconi's.

Paul in sand, his favorite place.

10th Birthday party.
Where did I get the energy for these?

Cape Cod 1985

Fifth Grade

BEFORE I GET INTO PAUL'S 5TH GRADE RECORDINGS, I found two papers among Paul's attic storage boxes in Atlanta, Georgia, that contained stories that gave me the chills. They were written for his Language Arts class with Mrs. Creighton. Yes, he saved all his reports from those years!

Evidently, the class was asked to write their own biography! Reading what Paul wrote in his biography as a 10-year-old led me to many tears, especially since it was written in his own handwriting.

Who would think I would be writing HIS biography 33 years later? I don't remember him doing this report, but he obviously obtained all the details from all the baby books that I kept, which, eerily, I would refer to years later myself!

He also wrote about the things he enjoyed doing. This is a segment in his own words.

"My favorite and best subject in school is Math. I have so many friends I can't name them all. I look for kindness, careness, and truthfulness in a friend. They should have most or all of these things or otherwise I usually don't pick them."

You can see why this stopped me in my tracks. What wisdom from a 10-year-old!

It reminded me of a quote from Og Mandino:

"Beginning today, treat everyone you meet as if they were going to be dead by midnight. Extend to them all the care, kindness, and understanding you can muster, and do it with no thought of any reward. Your life will never be the same."

And, in the verse 81, in the Tao Te Ching, Lao Tzu says, "...the heart that gives, gathers. That mysterious Karma returns favors from your actions of kindness, generosity, and compassion. The most successful people elevate themselves by lifting others up with help and advice."

This is what Paul was like...exactly.

And seeing how much he affected those around him, through not only the testimonials included at the end of this book, but through everyone that ever knew him, we know that this works.

Even as a small child, Paul knew the value of a true friendship by his own words above. And, he knew how to be that friend.

Another report I found, in what I call his treasure box, was a description of HEAVEN. I never saw this report as well. Paul was very independent in doing his school assignments. But seeing that composition entitled HEAVEN! What 10-year-old writes about HEAVEN? You can imagine how this got my attention, as well as tears.

Paul gave his character the name of Billy throughout the story, but I know Paul was physically and emotionally describing himself. Here it is, mostly in its entirety:

HEAVEN

The boy named Billy walked through the crowd hearing, "Do I know you?' or "I remember you!" or "Hi, how are you doing?"

He never eats up there and neither does anybody else. He has so much fun up there that he doesn't even think of it. He is a chubby little boy with brown eyes and brown hair. He is kind to every person that is kind to him. When someone is mean to him, he wouldn't even bother with him. Billy doesn't like some things like when smoke rises and it stinks with all the pollution coming up, but otherwise the air smells good. The clouds up there are white as snow and very fluffy. When Billy looks over the cloud, he sees the beautiful Earth like a blue and white marble.

Yes, this is Paul talking about himself.

And I know he is in HEAVEN.

Language Arts
Mrs. Crichton

Paul Lieci...
Sept. 12, 19...

I was born on the night of Sept 25, 1975 at 11:20 Nyack Hospital was the hospital I was born at. My family was living in West Nyack at the time. My parents said they were glad to have me, I weighed 6 pounds, 3 ounces. I also was 20 inches long. I had much brown hair when I was little that my dad called me fuzzy bear. I turned over in the crib on the very first day that I came home. My mom said that I had "piano fingers", when I was a newborn baby. I was brought home to an older brother who was always in the crib with me. My parents tell me that when I was a baby I laughed all the time. My older brother Frank played with me constantly. When I was about 4 months old I sat up and when I was 5 months, I started to crawl. My parents have so many pictures of me growing up. Many pictures show what a messy eater I was. The food would be all over my clothes, highchair, floor and face. Of course I don't remember any of this but I love looking at all my pictures.

I got my first tooth when I was 10 months old. When I was almost 2 years old, we left Rockland County to come to Lewisboro. I was too little to remember my dad and other builders building my house which is in Waccabuc but I like looking at all the pictures. I was in a play group with many other friends when we just moved here. I went in a big boy's bed just before I was three years old and toilet trained just about the same time. My mom needed me to grow up a little because my brother Bobby was born right before my third birthday. Half a year later I started riding a three-wheeler. Just about then I made sentences that made sense. My mom said that I talked late but now I make up for it. When I was four years old, I was going to nursery school for one year with the four year old group at the South Salem White Church.

Fifth Grade

Mr. McCormack

The following comments are from his various subject teachers while in the Fifth Grade, taken from his actual report cards stored in his *School Days* binder.

1. Paul always sees his jobs through in school and even the jobs no one else wants.
2. Test scores outstanding.
3. Excellent skills and attitude.
4. Conscientious and capable student!
5. Works very hard. Shows great deal of interest.
6. Very responsible and helpful around the class.

Going back to his Baby Book records, I found one thing that was less than perfect written down by me:

I write:

"Paul needs to be reminded to brush his teeth. They go from yellow to white when he brushes them."

This statement was made under the Grooming Habits section in the record keeper. I had to find something he needed improvement on, I guess!

Unfortunately, the Baby Book record-keeping ended at ten years old. It had been so helpful to be able to go back and read Paul's life in such detail, thanks to this book. I also have to give myself credit for somehow finding the time and patience to keep all 4 books going, especially now for Paul.

The questions in the book were very detailed, and so the answers needed to be well considered and thought out, including information and tidbits that would have been lost to memory.

Paul's love of work and completion of chores was evident from the beginning. It's said he had unlimited patience in whatever he

Fifth Grade, Mr. McCormick

Mr. McCormick	Mike Gerosa	Billy Casey	Erin Lambert	Amy Marciano	Jen Imperia
Winnie Barry	Bryan VanVranken	Paul Giaccio	Anne Pessoni	Lisa Mandell	Sonya Holcombe
Dan Koh	Dennis Grady	John Ryan	Pat Wayland	Jason Blair	

Lewisboro Rec Basketball League, 1985
Back Row:L-R: Paul Giaccio, Greg Clark, Anthony Percoco, Craig Shurtleff,
Seated, Front L-R: Matt Herman, Brian Mongillo

134

Soccer Club News

Avanti 5
Scorpions 1

Showing superb team play, the Avanti opened its spring season with an impressive win over the Scorpions (previously known as the Kicks). David Rinaldi made a hat trick plus one (four goals!) and Mark Lynn made one goal, assisted by the excellent passing, ball control and defense of Alex Albert, Jason Blair, David Coote, Megan Coote, Shannon Kearney, Brian Lonergan, Rud Niles, Sam Orlofsky, Katie Reynolds, Jamie Stumpf and Stephganie Wirth. Ted Ferrarone and Paul Giaccio played superbly as goaltenders and also contributed to a solid Avanti defense.

2A   The Ledger, Bedford/Lewisbo⑤, N.Y.   May 23, 1984

...made some excellent defensive plays.

Avanti 3
Hornets 1

Avanti triumphed in a superb display of coordinated team play. The balanced attack was led by one goal each scored by Alex Albert, Brian Lonergan, and Mark Lynn. Also contributing to the aggressive offense were Megan Coote, Sam Orlofsky, David Rinaldi and Jamie Stumpf. Rock solid defense was played by Jason Blair, Shannon Kearney, Rud Niles, Katie Reynolds, and Stephanie Wirth. David Coote and Paul Giaccio made numerous spectacular saves in the goal, as well as contributing to the midfield defense.

Christmas 1985

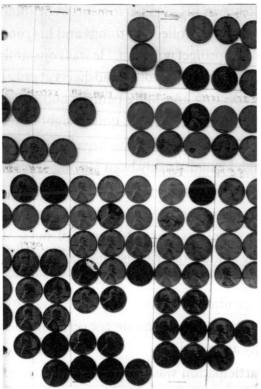

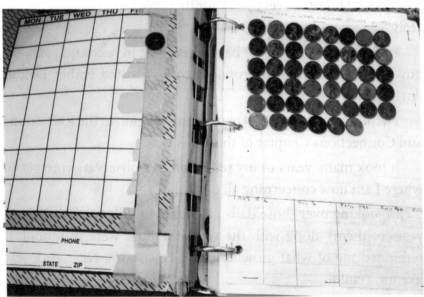

Paul collected coins for many years and kept detailed records.

did. He definitely was his own person and went about his little life with passion. He loved collecting things and his room was always the center of some project going on. He was constantly organizing, making files, his own version of spreadsheets at only ten years old. Also, always collecting and filing pennies and quarters. We have the boxes of all those and they are quite a sight to see.

This was also the first year Paul began to show an interest in sports, although he had already been playing soccer.

He had a great baseball season which ended in June 1986, coached by Ron Herman. Ron Herman, his wife Mary and their three children were close family friends of ours. We were very fortunate in the wonderful friendships that were developed while living in Lewisboro that still exist today.

Again, as mentioned before, Lewisboro was a great place to raise a family. There was a genuine concern for one another, and the community as a whole.

Church participation was a big part of our lives. The boys all went to CCD classes every week for their age groups, receiving the Holy Sacraments accordingly.

Paul was the only one to have an interest in becoming an altar boy and I was always so proud when he assisted Father Dalton during Mass.

I wrote extensively about church and religion in the Reflections and Connections Chapter of this book.

It took many years of my reflection and observation to get to where I am now concerning all of it.

In looking over those daily calendars I told you about (all 43 years of them) along with the years the boys were in school, it reminded me of what growing up in Lewisboro, New York was like for a child.

It was really an idyllic setting in many ways.

There was always something to do with the family, whether at the Town Park, community center, Library, school, sports, etc. My calendar boxes were always filled to capacity with events for the day.

Paul also became involved with after school activities like flag football and floor hockey. Still having a love of singing, he joined the School Chorus.

In his All County Chorus group, five children were selected from each Westchester school to sing at the Mount Vernon High school on April 12, 1986 and Paul was one of them!

He was also involved in the "extra" programs at school where students did thought projects.

That spring of 1986, Paul was invited to go with his friend and family to Myrtle Beach for a week, during Easter break. I remember being very uncomfortable letting him go, and asked that he call me every night. I knew it was important to have a chance to do something fun and experience a new place, but I still worried. With four little boys, we didn't get away that much, so I was happy for him.

Birthday parties at this age no longer had girls, morphing into other activities such as war games in the woods (he went to one of those and that was the end of that) wearing cammies and smudged faces, pizza and pool parties at the Ridgefield, Connecticut YMCA or sleep overs with movies and pizza. He went to these, but by this age, I stopped the parties myself for my boys.

As much as Paul liked getting together with school friends, he really loved the adult company at home, especially, with his grandparents and relatives. He loved to be around them, listening and interacting. He was really an old soul.

In the summer of 1986, Paul went to two weeks of computer camp. He really enjoyed learning whatever he could, especially when it came to numbers!

All County Chorus, April 12, 1986

Emily Rems	Liz Lefton	Jen Imperia	Jennifer Clock	Mrs. Head
Paul Giaccio		Bill Casey		

Great Grandma Pauline. Paul conducted a long interview on video asking his great grandmother about her childhood in Italy. She died at 103 years old.

Sixth Grade

1986-1987 — Mr. Miller

He writes:

"Paul is a cooperative young man and a pleasure to have in class."

This was a very, very exciting year for Paul with all kinds of events and surprises.

It was an extremely busy fall. Paul was in the Lewisboro school play in September, and that experience was so enjoyable, that he went on to participate in productions through Junior and Senior high school, with some major parts.

All three of the older boys were playing soccer that fall, and Frank and Paul were playing football. Paul was on the football team with Mr. McGowan and Mr. Van Vranken. Paul remained extremely close to the Van Vrankens, Bryan's parents, his whole life, and is the Godfather for Bryan's first son, Amici. Bryan has spearheaded many events in Paul's name as well as started a clothing line with *LivelikePaul* on teeshirts, etc. More on that later.

Soccer and football segued to basketball and Paul's coach was Mr. Rinaldi. All of these sports took practices as well as the actual games, so I basically never stopped driving, taking the boys everywhere. I had to have a special calendar for the schedules of practices, etc. in order to get to each one separately and on time.

Life was never dull. Of course, there were all the boys' birthday parties with friends and family, community events and holidays. It was really mounting up as they got older because they were each involved in so much more and needed to be driven everywhere. I actually didn't mind, but it was so tiring! I never stopped. No wonder I was half the size I am now! I would go to bed very late at night doing laundry, mopping floors, etc., and was up early continuing chores or just having my coffee in peace.

Paul was the video man of the house. He carried that heavy video camera everywhere on his shoulder, and, because of him, we have an entire album of family videos, spanning many, many years. They were originally made on VHS tapes, which he took care of completely. He would meticulously label the spines of each tape after he filmed. He was about ten years old when he started this. Then, about eight years ago, he converted all those VHS tapes to DVDs and gifted me and all his brothers a set. It was truly a gift of love and had to be an enormous project watching all those tapes to add music to. It still amazes me to this day. Again, thanks to Paul, we have all those DVDs in a special case.

One day, I have no idea where I was, Paul taped Bobby and Richie in a skit about me. They made up this whole little play imitating me in the house.

It was actually hysterical, and, even though it was kind of making fun of me, I loved it. Richie was wearing my apron and slippers (which was a hoot in itself) while carrying around my coffee cup everywhere. All true. Then he pretended he was talking on the phone with one of my friends telling her I was up from 5 am cleaning house. True stuff.

Then Paul had Richie (being me) laying on the couch relaxing calling out to Bobby to make sure the playroom was neat.

They had Richie (me) asking questions to which the boys would answer, only to ask the same questions again, showing I wasn't listening the first time. Definitely.

Really, it was so funny.

I also took lots of photos and videos or else Paul wouldn't have been in any!

The one very big event that took place this year was the trip to Hong Kong and China that Paul won in February, 1987.

First, I have to tell you how it all started.

This is my all time favorite story about Paul for many reasons.

He was only ten years old when the event evolved. I actually gathered up the strength to tell it at his funeral service.

Coming up, I have given this story its own section within this chapter (*The Beginning*).

Sixth Grade, Mr. Miller

		Jason Cooper	Emily Rems		Mr. Miller
Sonya Holcombe	Parog Chordia	Pete Eggington	Dan Koh	Kipp Beltramello	Anthony Percoco
Winnie Barry	Peter Beaupre	Brian Mongillo	Brian VanVronkon	Paul Giaccio	Rachel Dorgan
Kathy Murray	Emily Patek		Lisa Mandell		Jen Imperia

Sixth Grade, Basketball Team
Winter 1986/1987 - 5th & 6th Grade

Mr. Rinaldi

Mike Gerosa	Pete Eggington	John Ryan	John Alfano
Dan Glasser	Dave Rinaldi	Phil Glasser	Paul Giaccio

Sixth Grade Football Team, Fall 1986

Mr. McGowan	Mr. VanVranken		Mr. Collins		Mr. Alfano
Jim Norton	Jason Blair	Ray Pagnucco	Rud Niles	Kipp Beltramello	Anthony Percoco
Tim McGowan	Neil Baron	Dave Rinaldi	Artie Harrison	Paul Giaccio	Mike Mudge
Dan Ryan	Dan Kehoe	Keith Arnold	Brian Lonergan	John Alfano	Peter Hall

You'll See It When You Believe It

SOMETIME IN THE EARLY 1990's, I became familiar with Dr. Wayne Dyer and his works. Before then, I studied the writings of Dr. Norman Vincent Peale, author of *The Power of Positive Thinking*. I was teaching at Lincoln Hall School in the 1980's having gone back to teaching full time when Richie was in school for the day.

I decided to rewrite *The Power of Positive Thinking* at a lower grade level so I could present it to my students there, to help them with their life skills. I became so engrossed in that endeavor that I went to the *Guideposts Center* in Pawling, New York, where the head office was at the time. I met Ruth Stafford Peale, Dr. Norman Vincent's wife and widow.

Together, back in 1945, they cofounded the global inspirational organization, *Guideposts*, along with the magazine of the same name. It is still a leading publication, and I still receive my copy every month, after almost 40 years.

On that visit, I spent a lovely morning with Ruth Peale and her assistant, Sybil Light. They asked me to return to lead a prayer meeting, which I did, and it was the start of an amazing relationship with the Guidepost family, one I have to this day.

Mrs. Peale passed away in 2008, at the age of 101 and I treasure the books she personally gifted me.

I was always attracted to the concept of "positive thinking" my whole life. I rarely saw obstacles I couldn't handle, but looked at them as opportunities in disguise.

Dr. Wayne Dyer's books resonated with me. He was an American self help author of over 40 books as well as a motivational speaker. He made countless audio tapes and appeared on many PBS specials. He starred in the movie, *The Shift*. *The Shift* was released in 2009 and it explores the spiritual journey from ambition to meaning. Instead of the emphasis on achievement and accumulation, the shift in one's life is to focus on serving and giving back. An amazing concept and one that can change lives.

Paul lived this every day.

Dr. Wayne Dyer, 1940-2015

I could write a book on Dr. Wayne Dyer alone, and how he, in his wisdom, influenced my life. He unfortunately passed away in 2015, and I feel that loss to this day. I would listen (and still do sometimes) to his audio tapes in the car or on my long walks. I miss his soothing voice, humor and wisdom.

My youngest son, Richie, and I would go to see him whenever he came to the Javits Center in New York City. Richie actually took a photo of me with Dr. Dyer which I treasure. I took one of Richie with him too, but it didn't come out and I always felt badly about it.

The reason I bring him into this book, along with Dr. Norman

Vincent Peale, is because, although Paul never read his books (but I would talk about him all the time) Paul was already living the life Dr. Dyer talked about at a very young age.

Giving. Sharing. Serving.

It's uncanny when I think about the similarities in their thinking.

Dr. Dyer encouraged us to tap into the amazing powers that lie within all of us. In doing so, we can direct the course of our destiny.

Despite growing up in foster homes and orphanages, Dr. Dyer overcame his difficulties to make his dreams come true, so he spoke entirely from experience.

In 1986, without ever knowing about such professed concepts, Paul, at ten years old, inwardly knew them and that's how he won the trip to Hong Kong.

The Beginning

IT ALL STARTED SOMETIME IN THE EARLY FALL of 1986 when Paul was ten years old, in the 6th grade. The local radio station, WVIP, stationed in Mt. Kisco, New York, about 20 minutes south of our home in Waccabuc, announced they were having a contest whereby participants would complete a Chinese picture puzzle as an entry. The individual puzzle pieces needed to complete this Chinese picture would be obtained at local merchant stores who advertised on their radio stations, such as gas stations, grocery stores, restaurants, etc. So, when a person would shop, or stop by these establishments, a puzzle piece would be given out. That one puzzle piece would then find a spot on the entry form to eventually complete the picture, one puzzle piece at a time. A completed puzzle made ONE entry.

There would be only ONE winner for a ten day trip for two to Hong Kong, all expenses paid plus $2,000 spending money!

Now, just the logistics and efforts of all this would seem daunting and intimidating to any adult, never mind a ten year old! But, as soon as Paul heard about this on the radio, he was all in. And, I do mean ALL IN. He developed a plan all on his own and set it in motion.

The first step, he realized, was to gather as many entry forms as possible in order to get the puzzles started. More entry forms filled out meant more chances to win! He set his room up like a command center laying out all the blank entry forms in a row on tables around his room's perimeter, ready for the addition of the puzzle pieces as they were gathered from the stores.

Of course, that's where I came in. After school, I would drive him to all the participating locations that were giving out the puzzle pieces. His younger brothers were also in the car.

After all the collections, we would go home, and he would go straight to his room to add in the day's puzzle pieces, slowly filling in the spots, day after day after day. Sometimes the available pieces distributed were duplicates and therefore useless, but then we'd go back and get more. It was a strange looking Chinese picture and not that easy to assemble, even if you did have the right pieces. But, Paul never gave up! For months! Of course, he also had to deal with the ribbing of his three brothers, as brothers will do. They would go in his room to see this entire project in the works, and roll their eyes. Their brother Paul was at it again. But, Paul was completely unfazed by dream stealers. He had a plan and he believed he would win.

The final days were approaching for all entries to be submitted, and after filling out about 40 entries, Paul made the interesting discovery that the same one piece was missing from each puzzle to be completed!

It was obvious that one piece was purposely held out till the very end!

Paul figured that it would be easy to get that last piece in the last days, and, sure enough, it was. All entries were finally completed. Mailing all the entries to the WVIP radio station was not an option for him for fear they might get lost, so I drove him to Mt. Kisco, with a big envelope in hand for a personal delivery. Done.

And, then, it was the anticipation for the announcement date of the actual drawing.

Of course, the date would be on a snowy Saturday in February 1987 and, of course, the venue was about 45 minutes away at a ski resort. Considering I never liked to drive in the snow (and I still don't and won't) this was a huge issue for me.

This was the entry form for the Hong Kong Contest (1986).

I tried suggesting to just stay home and listen on the radio for the winner's announcement, but Paul said he needed to be there in person when they said his name.

It suddenly occurred to me that he really, really was expecting to win this contest and I started to be internally concerned.

What happens if he doesn't win? No mother wants her child disappointed.

I had come this far in my support of his dream, so I knew I had to pull myself together to see it through all the way. I knew we had to go. I said a prayer, and we got into our blue 1974 Ford Torino station wagon, getting there without a hitch.

When we arrived, there were crowds and crowds (not happy with crowds) of people skiing and standing around the area where the entry drum was located. They were getting ready for the winner to be chosen. Paul took a look at the entire set up. He then looked up at the building (lodge) adjacent to the drum, and suggested we go up to the second level to sit by the window which happened to be directly above where they would be turning the drum! We could have the perfect view out the window! There is actually a photo that he took of me out the window.

What 11 year old would have the foresight for such a great idea?! When we entered the lodge on our way to the second level, we were given a raffle ticket which could win a prize in the following hour, separate from the Grand Prize.

So, we sat by the window, drinking hot cocoa, and waited.

I was holding the raffle ticket in my hand when several small prizes were announced but none of my numbers matched. Paul said "mom, don't worry about these little prizes because we're winning the Hong Kong trip."

Now I was getting nervous. I started rehearsing some comforting phrases in my head to use if, in fact, this grand prize didn't materialize. All of a sudden, as I'm trying to think up those useless offerings that I might say, all kinds of horns and drums erupted. It was time for that one entry in the huge drum to be picked out.

We both hung out the window and waited while looking straight down at all the activity below.

I smiled thinking how smart Paul was to suggest this comfortable vantage point instead of standing in snow all this time. We truly had the best warm seats!

The drum was turned several times and then a hand went in to retrieve the lucky entry form, all so visible from our perch two flights up.

The man, holding the entry, started to try to pronounce the name as he held it in his hands. He began G-I-A saying each letter and Paul shouted out the rest—"GIACCIO!! That's us!!"

Every head looked up at us hanging out the window. They all yelled, "Come down!"

So, Paul and I made our way downstairs while everyone was clapping in the lodge and the WVIP announcer met us, with his microphone holding it so both of us could speak. We were live on the WVIP radio station for everyone to hear! All our friends and community members heard the entire event unfold as it happened.

It was absolutely surreal. The only one who wasn't surprised was Paul. He knew he would win. There was never, ever a doubt in his mind. And, the best part of Paul was that he was never about going back to the nay sayers with "I told you so," or "what do you say now?"

He just went about his life.

All he wanted to know from that moment was when we would go to Hong Kong! We found out that the trip had to be taken within a few months, so we went that May 1987 having had to take him out of school, but what better education than to experience Hong Kong?

I decided to use the added $2,000 they gave for educational, private tour groups. That worked out extremely well. Paul became the go-to person for all the tourists in our group who needed to know what items would cost in American dollars as they shopped.

They were amazed at how he would translate the Chinese money into US currency in seconds.

My little travel companion took me on a trip I will never forget.

While in Hong Kong, we went to Canton, China by a very long 3 hour train ride.

I'll never forget getting off that train in China and seeing soldiers with rifles everywhere.

We went to Macau by jetfoil, Pike's Peak, visited the Aberdeen boat people, Stanley Market, 600 year old temples and, of course, Ocean World.

It was nonstop traveling and sightseeing. Never once did Paul whine or complain about anything. He took it all in and enjoyed every minute. (Pretty much how he lived his entire life).

Paul took my photo looking out the window above where the drawing would be.

The Resort

May 1987, on our way to Hong Kong

Pike's Peak Point, Hong Kong 1987

Looking down on Hong Kong, May 1987

Aberdeen

Three hour train ride to Macau

Paul in front of Hong Kong hotel

Our tour guide and Paul

And, all this happened because of his strong inner confidence and convictions.

It's that inner self-confidence, that Dr. Dyer described, that allows us to "see it when you believe it."

That June, in 1987, after we settled back in from our whirlwind trip to Hong Kong and China, Paul went into action selling raffle tickets for the Lewisboro Baseball Association. This would be the beginning of Paul's commitment for several years.

No matter where you went in our town, you would see Paul selling raffles, especially at our local (and only) supermarket, Foodtown, subsequently called D'Agostino's, where the entire community shopped.

He set himself up with a shopping cart, which supported his hand made sign, advertising what the raffle tickets were for. He also provided a lapboard and pens so people could easily fill out the tickets.

All of this was completely thought up and organized by him, and him alone.

He greeted everyone by the entrance door, and, anyone who ever knew Paul saw how he was always happy and smiling, no matter where he was or what he was doing.

He genuinely loved people.

Therefore, he was like a magnet for people to go over to talk to him. He just radiated positive vibrations naturally.

His presence there would be at least 2-3 hours every day after school. I would drive him there and pick him up.

Weekends, he'd be there at least 5 hours a day. Again, I'd bring him and pick him up and would check on him in between, bringing him food and drinks. Thankfully, it was only a 5 minute car ride away from our house.

Remember, those were the days before cell phones! I wonder, looking back, how we did it! But, of course we managed. It would have been so convenient to be able to text or call my boys in those days instead of driving around to reach them to tell them something. They could call home by pay phone, but how was I to reach them? And what if I was outside, or not home, to get their call? Remember those days (for those of you my age) when you would be opening the door to a ringing phone, and you'd almost kill yourself to get to it, and then it stopped ringing?

And, you'd be so frustrated wondering who it was, or, worse yet, waiting for news. Those were the days then. Much easier now.

Well, all the hours he invested that June paid off because he sold a record breaking amount of tickets adding up to 689, which won him recognition at a special ceremony in our Town Park.

The Lewisboro Baseball Association President, Mr. Geoffrey Eggington, gifted him with a bat, a $50 gift certificate at the local sports store, and 4 box seats to a Mets game, while the Lewisboro Ledger's photographer took his photo.

It was to be the beginning of his being recognized in all our local newspapers for his persistent community service. He continued selling raffle tickets for all the town's events and his reputation as "Mr. Raffle" was established. Yes, every one of us can do so much. It reminds me of a quote by the Dalai Lama, "If you think you're too small to make a difference, try sleeping with a mosquito."

That June 1987 marked the end of elementary school at Lewisboro. He was honored with many awards throughout, such as the Award for Outstanding School Service, Citizen of the Month (many times) along with many subject awards.

Upon graduation, he would find out he was the winner of a contest he wasn't even aware of. The New York Mathematics League awarded Paul a Certificate of Merit for his Superior Achievement in the New York Mathematics contest!

It was totally an honor!

AND THE WINNER IS... — Paul Giaccio, a member of the Lewisboro Little League Bulldogs, picks a winning raffle ticket. Paul sold 690 of the 3,000 tickets. — Jennifer Stark photo.

The Entrepeneur

Paul Giaccio, a 12-year-old Lewisboro resident, has been busy for the last month or so. While other kids spent their time hanging out at the mall, or would if there was a mall, Paul didn't have time for such frivolities, he was too busy hanging out at Foodtown.

For the past month and a half, the Lewisboro Little League, of which Paul is a member, has been selling raffle tickets in the hopes of raising money to put towards an electric scoreboard. If they get that scoreboard, it will be due in large part to the work Paul has done for them.

On his own initiative, Paul took it upon himself to spend most of his free time — two to three hours after school and five to seven hours on the weekends — selling raffle tickets in front of the Foodtown Supermarket. All in all, he sold 690 tickets, raising $690.

Setting himself up with a carriage, a big sign explaining what he was selling and a lap-board to make it easy for the purchaser to fill out the ticket, Paul sold about 20% of all the Little League tickets.

"It was fun," said Paul. "I enjoyed it. I got to meet a lot of really nice people."

Though he sold no tickets to his family, Paul did have about 10 raffles in his own name. "People would give me money and say fill it out to whoever you want," said Paul, who naturally always wanted himself. "One guy gave me five dollars and told me to fill it out in whoever's name I wanted, so I made them all out to myself," related Paul.

Because Paul had contributed so much to the fund-raiser, it was

decided that he would be the one to pick the winning ticket. Despite his current run of luck (he had recently won a trip to Hong Kong from a local radio contest), Paul did not select his own ticket, nor was the winning ticket even one that he had sold.

Barbara Carlson, a Katonah resident, was the winner of the raffle and will receive either a TV or a VCR, whichever she chooses.

For his efforts, Paul received a bat, a $50 gift certificate from ARC Sports, and four box seats to a Mets game. Though Paul's goal had been to sell 1,000 tickets, both he and the Little League, were very pleased with his results.

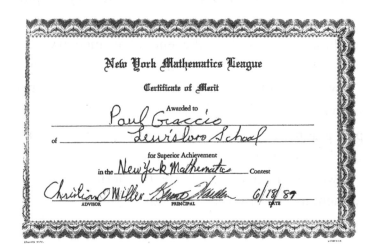

Lewisboro School Graduation, 1987

Town Park, 1987. Paul getting ready to pick the winning raffle ticket.

Football 1987— 4th/5th Grade Team, 6th/7th Grade Team

			Mr. Collins	Mr. Alfano		Mr. VanVranken		
Anthony Percoco	Dennis Grady	Rud Niles	Ray Pagnucco	Pat Wayland	Dan Cunniffe	Mike Gerosa	Matt Tine	Pete Eggington
Dan Kehoe	Bryan VanVranken	Paul Giaccio	John Alfano	Brian Lonergan	Pete Hall	Dave Rinaldi	Jim Kehoe	Tim Hall
	Charkie Gossett		Neil Baron	Sean Cunniffe	Tim McGowan	Robby Collins		

1987 Football

Paul as an Altar Boy, May 1987

7th and 8th Grade

IN SEPTEMBER OF 1987, Paul began 7th grade at John Jay Junior High School. It was literally about one mile from our home and so convenient when the boys went there as well as the Senior High School, which was adjacent to the Junior High School. Not only was it close to our home, but it was within walking distance to the one and only shopping center in the area. There was a grocery store, pizza shop, pharmacy, post office, sports store, Chinese restaurant, cleaners, etc.—all in one place.

It opened up a whole new world for my boys, since we were so far into the woods. Now, after school, they could venture to the shopping area if they wanted.

Paul had a very successful year in 7th grade. He was on the Honor Roll every single semester as well as being a junior counselor.

He started to play football with Mr. Alfano as his coach, and was on the basketball team. Of course, he joined the Math Club, with his love of numbers.

Once again, he took on the Raffle Challenge for the April Go For It event at his school. He sold 740 raffle tickets and was awarded the Mr. Raffle trophy. Once again, in the newspapers.

Sports started to take over more of Paul's time, and he seemed to enjoy it. In the spring, he was on Mr. Bill D'Eletto's major baseball team.

Somehow, Paul found time to work a part time job where he was now getting paid for his time. He started working at the local pizza shop washing dishes.

I actually have a note he wrote about that time he was at the pizza place. He had saved it and put it in his personal scrapbook, which I received after he passed away. I won't include the actual writing of it in this book because people's names are displayed, but I will tell the gist of it.

```
Katonah Lewisboro UFSD              HAPPY VALENTINE'S DAY
John Jay Junior High School         ENJOY YOUR MID-WINTER VACATION!
Route 121                           SPRING IS ON THE WAY!!
Katonah, NY    10536

                                 ABSENCES        0              Tardies
                                 SCHOOL TELEPHONE NO.    COUNSELOR        PHONE 121
        Report Card                              914 763-3194 LUSTIG, R          0000    Home
                                                                                         01
        STUDENT NAME      I.D. NUMBER  GRADE   REPORTING PERIOD  PERIOD ENDING
(ACCIO, Paul  C          S02037  7  Quarter 2         01/27/88
  COURSE TITLE       SECTION          MARKS
  TEACHER                     Q1   Q2 EX1            FNL  CREDITS  ABS.    TEACHER COMMENTS
ENG7ST(2)            0012  89   91                                       SHOWS INTEREST AND ENTH
LEFEVRE, *                                                               PARTICIPATION IS OUTSTA
SOCST 7S (2)         0040  85   92                                       ATTITUDE IS OUTSTANDING
NOAKES, *                                                                WORKS CONSCIENTIOUSLY
                                                                         SHOWS INTEREST AND ENTH
MATH 7S (2)          0108  90   97 95                                    WORKS CONSCIENTIOUSLY
MINEO, *                                                                 SHOWS INTEREST AND ENTH
SCIENCE 7S (2)       0061  90   90 100                                   CONDUCT IS GOOD
KRUCHKOW, *                                                              EFFORT IS GOOD
SPANISH 7           0152  94   95                                       ATTITUDE IS OUTSTANDING
BATES, *                                                                 EFFORT IS OUTSTANDING
                                                                         PARTICIPATION IS OUTSTA
ART 7               0251      A                                         ATTITUDE IS OUTSTANDING
KILGRAN, *                                                               CONDUCT IS OUTSTANDING
                                                                         EFFORT IS OUTSTANDING
HOME EC. 7          0212      96                                        EFFORT IS OUTSTANDING
HUESTER, *                                                               WORKS CONSCIENTIOUSLY
                                                                         SHOWS INTEREST AND ENTH
BAND 7              0277      85
RICHARDSON,
IND. ARTS 7         0191      P
MARSTON, *
PHYS. ED. 7         0289      P                                         ATTITUDE IS GOOD
HORN, *
HEALTH 7            0180      88                                        EFFORT IS OUTSTANDING
HURLEY, *                                                                PARTICIPATION IS OUTSTA

  FAIL
  PASS       (PASSING GRADE IS 65)           Mr/Mrs John  L Giaccio
  INCOMPLETE                                 Par/Guar of Paul  C Giaccio
  MEDICAL                                      Schoolhouse Rd
  WITHDRAWN PASSING                          Waccabuc, NY    10597
  WITHDRAWN FAILING
```

He wrote about his first job as a dishwasher and bus boy at this pizza place, making $5.00 per hour. He started on June 25, 1989. Then he goes on to explain that the restaurant changed hands in January 1990, and his pay dropped to $4.00 an hour! So, he then decided to apply to D'Agostino's grocery store on June 25, 1990 where he was immediately hired at $4.75 per hour.

He was thrilled.

I will talk more about his years at D'Agostinos later on, but, in his scrapbook, he saved the original dollars he was paid at the pizza place. He said "this was my first paycheck, although I actually got paid in cash!" Paul worked at D'Agostino's throughout that summer, but one of his fun activities was to be involved in the production of *Pippin*, the summer camp play. It was a huge success in the community, and was again recognized in the newspaper.

Copy of the original first dollars Paul ever made and saved in his scrapbook.

Eighth Grade

EIGHTH GRADE WAS ANOTHER FULL and successful year for Paul.

Not only did Paul participate in all the Chorus concerts, he had a major role in his school's production of Guys and Dolls (April) playing the role of Lt. Brannigan.

He received a personal letter from Robert Lichtenfeld, Assistant Superintendent of Schools for his performance. Paul loved the camaraderie of all those performing on stage. He also received a letter from Mr. Dwyer on his excellence in the production of Where's Charlie?.

Seventh Grade Basketball Team
Winter 1987/1988 - 7th & 8th Grade

Mr. VanVranken   Corey Cowles   Josh Kewley   Sean Delfause   Adam Connors

Rich Apiscopa   Jim Kehoe   Bryan VanVranken   Paul Giaccio

Somehow, he maintained his honor roll status every semester, and was a member of the National Honor Society throughout. He was also presented with many awards for Math, Health, Computer Science and Perfect Attendance!

I found all these awards in his own personal scrapbooks in his Atlanta, Georgia home. So much of this I didn't remember.

Of course, baseball season means raffle tickets for Paul, and, sure enough, he was at it again, making the newspapers.

He would always be the one to pick the winner on the day of the drawing and he loved that part. This event was always being photographed for the newspaper. He was always wanting the person winning to be the one he sold the ticket to, and that would actually happen a few times.

In another newspaper article, in 1989, the question was, "What was your best or worst experience in school?"

Paul answered, "when I went to the bathroom in my pants in the first grade." Paul actually wrote about the whole incident in one of his essays in junior high school, which I found.

Evidently the rule of his first grade teacher was that if the door to the bathroom was closed, it meant someone was in there and not to enter. Paul had to use

Paul, Eighth Grade Football

the bathroom but kept looking at the closed door and he didn't know what to do. This went on for quite some time. He asked his teacher about the closed door but she said someone must be in there so he had to wait. That was the rule. And then it happened. Nature couldn't wait any longer! And, the sad part is that no one was in the bathroom, as it turned out. It was a very embarrassing experience and he never forgot it.

In June, he received his Confirmation Sacrament at St. Mary's Church in Katonah, New York. Bill D'Eletto was his sponsor.

We were, and are to this day, very close friends with the D'Elettos. Evelyn and Bill actually came to California to visit with us after Paul passed away. Evelyn calls me all the time to see how I'm doing.

We've been so blessed with such faithful friends.

Incredibly, Paul found time to take part in a piano concert in June which took place in North Salem, New York, not far from home.

Margaret McGlinn became his new piano teacher. I actually forget now why Mrs. Campbell was no longer available, but she was a little elderly. Unless it's because of that crazy story when she didn't realize Ralph was my dog that died. I guess I'll never know.

But, we loved Margaret McGlinn. She was young and very talented with lots of energy. Unfortunately, she passed away unexpectedly soon after. It was extremely sad.

She was also Richie's piano teacher and he was also in the concert, playing an easy piece.

My parents and I attended the concert and they were so happy especially since they were the ones to gift us the piano.

Paul loved playing most of all. He would play the music of *Memories* and I would sing the words along with him. Just the two of us.

It brings tears to my eyes every time I hear that song.

Eighth Grade Football, Fall 1988

Mr. VanVranken		Mr. Collins			Mr. Alfano		
Artie Harrison	Paul Giaccio	Peter Hall	John Alfano	Brian Lonergan	Dave Rinaldi	Keith Arnold	
Tim McGowan	Bryan VanVranken	John Wayland	Sean Cunniffe	Scott Vacarro	Dan Kehoe	Robbie Collins	Neil Baron
Peter Weagan	Shane Wilson	Glen Baron		Greg Rinaldi	Tim Hall	Mike Pink	

LIVE LIKE PAUL

(914) 763-5000

JOSEPH P. FLETCHER JR.
Superintendent

ROBERT V. LICHTENFELD
Assistant Superintendent

JOHN E. THIBDEAU
Director of Support Services

RONALD G. BRESNICKY
District Clerk

April 28, 1989

Paul Giaccio
John Jay Junior High School

Dear Paul,

Congratulations for your wonderful performance in "Guys and Dolls."

First, you should realize that you participated in a "history making" event at John Jay. This was the first full-scale musical production in the history of the school.

You will be able to look back with great pride and satisfaction, at your participation in the production that began a tradition at John Jay. That is an experience that few students ever have!

I saw the Friday night performance and was a part of the standing ovation that you and the rest of the cast received from the audience - an ovation that was well deserved.

The production was professional and spirited. You contributed greatly to the success of the play. Your portrayal of Lt. Brannigan was outstanding.

The only problem is....we are going to look forward to seeing you in future productions!!

Again, thank you for sharing your talent with the John Jay community and for helping make "Guys and Dolls" the hit that it was.

Sincerely,

Robert V. Lichtenfeld

Robert V. Lichtenfeld
Assistant Superintendent

170

June 1989. Paul picking the winning raffle ticket at the Town Park.

9th Grade 1990-1991

ANOTHER STELLAR YEAR FOR PAUL. Besides making the honor roll every semester again, he played football and was on the Babe Ruth baseball team.

He continued selling raffle tickets and it was said out of the 8,000 raffle tickets sold in the community, 2,000 were sold by Paul alone.

Again in the newspapers, choosing the winner, he was awarded a color television for his room, an AM/FM cassette player and a calculator to add up all his future receipts.

The perfect gifts for him! He was just ecstatic.

Upon his John Jay Junior High School graduation, Paul made the papers again, only this time for his Math award, Presidential Academic Fitness Award and Honor Roll status.

This particular year was really the start of many difficulties in our household. Although the marital circumstances were not particularly good for several years by this time, things really came to a head for me and the boys, which led to many changes and stress.

How Paul kept it together at that time (at least outwardly that I could see) amazes me to this day. Because, actually, he was also being challenged with his own personal issues which I knew nothing about until many years later.

The other boys, Bobby and Richie, were the youngest and perhaps too young to understand the full impact of what was going on, but, children sense everything no matter what age. Negative energies affect everyone. And there were plenty of negative energies around.

I guess I could say Frank and I felt it the most, while our world was turned upside down for the following two years.

I was completely blindsided and naive since my attentions were always towards my boys, my home, and my new teaching position once Richie was in school full time. With the help of the boys, I was managing pretty well, considering there was so much to do all the time.

I never took care of household finances from the day I was married in 1969. Taking after my Italian grandmothers, aunts and mothers, and therefore, my role models, I felt that the man took care of the finances and the mom, the house and children. I know this sounds insane right now, but this is kind of the way it was many, many years ago.

I still believe a mom (or dad) should be present in the home while children are growing up (that's another conversation) but the difference now is that both mom and dad should have knowledge and responsibility of the finances.

Without getting into the "negativities" and "financial ruins" at that time, and, believe me there were many, I had no idea that the mortgage had not been paid in over a year, as well as electric, phone or medical bills until literally, the electricity was out. There's so much I would love to put down on this paper right now, but I will take the high road. I know I'm not taking the high road in even saying what I just did, but, believe me, even with that, I'm taking the high road.

It was a total disaster until I was finally awarded a divorce.

But, that didn't end my problems because SOMEHOW I was never awarded alimony or child support! You read that right and you can read it again.

SOMEHOW I was not given one penny in alimony or child support. The child support would be "whatever the father could afford to pay at some point."

We lost our home and we all ultimately moved to a condo in Cross River, New York. By that time, Paul was on his way to Georgia Tech as a freshman.

But, before I get ahead of myself (which I already just did) let's get back to Paul's high school days.

LIVE LIKE PAUL

Lewisboro Recreation Basketball Team
John Keene

Paul Giaccio	Carter Sherwood	John Alfano	Craig Shurtleff	Pete Serezze
	Bryan Kiss	Davis Auster	Eric Zamft	

John Jay Junior High School
Katonah, New York 10536
Katonah-Lewisboro U.F.S.D.

Douglas Dwyer
incipal
Albert J. Donaldson
ssistant Principal

(91

June, 1989

Dear Paul,

It is a great pleasure to congratulate you for your placement on the honor roll for the fourth time this year. You are truly among a select group of students to achieve that honor.

To make the honor roll in any marking period of a school as demanding as this one is an accomplishment. To make the honor roll at any time is remarkable, but to make it each marking period is outstanding.

It is very rewarding for educators to be able to work with students as highly capable and motivated as you.

Congratulations and good luck in the future. I hope you have a wonderful summer.

Sincerely,

Douglas Dwyer
Principal

cc: Guidance Counselor

Excellent work, Paul!

Wednesday, Sept. 13, 1989

PEOPLE

Spotlight on: School Days
What Was Your Best or Worst Experience in School?

Steve Nardini
Thornwood

"When I was suspended for blowing up the toilets in the bathroom."

Paul Giaccio
Waccabuc

"When I went to the bathroom in my pants in the first grade."

Cameron Woods
South Salem

"My best experience at John Jay was folding caps and gowns and tassels after my graduation."

Gabrielle McDonough
Lewisboro

"The nicest experience I had as a teacher was the day my class, which was not a particularly good class, decided to surprise me with a birthday party...It set the tone for the rest of the year, and it was uphill from that point on."

Interviews and photos by Eileen Friedman.
Have an idea for a question? Send it to:
The Ledger, P.O. Box 188, Cross River, N.Y. 10518.

Billy Delaney
Cross River

"My best experience was snow days and field trips and art sketching by the little pond."

For a
Special
Young
Man
ON YOUR
CONFIRMATION DAY

Dear Paul,
Remember to always keep your faith as your guide. Let it be your strength. You've been blessed with so many good qualities – nurture them and use them.
You've brought us so much happiness. We're so proud of you. Continue to be the fine young man that you are & know that we will always be there for you and God is always there for you in prayer.
We love you so much.
Mom & Dad

To our Dear Son
June 11
1989

May you always know that God is with you to guide you and protect you– And may God always bless you with all the things that bring you happiness.

Congratulations
All Our Love
Mom
&
Dad

Paul's Confirmation at
St. Mary's, 1989.
Bill D'Eletto, sponsor.

Awards Night at John
Jay Junior High School,
1989. Mr. Hurley
presenting to Paul.

The famous movie camera Paul carried around for years taking hundreds of family videos, which he later converted to CD's for everyone in the family.

Cape Canaveral, Florida Grandma and Pepa's house on the beach.

Cape Canaveral, 1989
At Grandma and Pepa's house
Paul's favorite place—the beach.

Paul loved when his Great Aunt Rose came for dinner..

Hammond Museum, 1990.
Paul's piano recital in North Salem, New York,
arranged by Margaret McGlinn, piano teacher.

Grandma Mary and Pepa Frank were always
there to celebrate special events, 1990.

TO PAUL GIACCIO IN
RECOGNITION OF
HIS OUTSTANDING
EFFORTS AND
CONTRIBUTION IN
THE SALE OF RAFFLE
TICKETS, THE LBA
HEREBY PRESENTS THIS
AWARD 4-23-90

Ron Herman, coach, LBA officials Geoffrey Eggington and Peter Rinaldi,
surprising Paul with thank you gifts.

Ninth Grade (continued)

IN THIS SECTION IS A STORY I FOUND written in the ninth grade, among his other reports from the elementary school.

To see his beautiful handwriting, page after page, warmed my heart, while it also made me sad. Every paper was either graded with an A or A+.

This particular one caught my eye:

His class was exploring and studying several different cultures from different countries, and the one that intrigued me was Paul's story about racism in South Africa.

Paul created this story about a nine year old white boy named Bran, who had never seen a black person before, because of segregation. He didn't know he shouldn't speak to a black person either; however, while shopping with his mom one day at a nearby town he never went to, he ventured off while she shopped. He noticed a black boy about his age and became so curious about seeing him, not only because of his dark skin, but because the boy looked upset and worried. Bran walked over to him to see if he could help, but the boy became frightened and shouted to go away from him but Bran said not to be afraid, that he wanted to be his friend and help him. The boy said no! If anyone sees you talking to me, me and my family will be arrested so please get away! Suddenly, Bran's mom appeared, and sure enough, she started screaming. She tore Bran away from him, saying she was reporting him to the police.

Bran was punished to his room while his mom made her call. Bran cried in frustration, feeling responsible for the boy while angry at his racist mom.

Paul wrote Bran's thoughts:

"That poor black kid! He was nice. We were similar. Now, he probably hates me. I can't blame him. Well, what can I do? I'm only nine years old. I can't make a difference now. But maybe, just maybe, I'll make a difference. That's my goal in life. To end black discrimination. Someday, somehow, I'll make a difference. I promise...someday."

Paul's words, speaking as Bran, in South Africa, were so prophetic as he wrote this in ninth grade. He would spend a lifetime of loving everyone, without judgement of color or anything for that matter. Many of his closest friends were Afro American!

I never read what his classmates wrote in his junior high and high school yearbooks, and it was fun to go through them. It was obvious how respected he was from his peers.

In his junior high school book, one classmate wrote "You are the nicest person in the ninth grade. You have made my life much easier. Thanks a lot. You are a great friend."

Asking around, I found out this young boy was new to the area and school. So much like Paul to reach out and help someone.

It was what made him so special and why people were attracted to him. Couldn't we all be that person to positively affect another's life?

Of course we can.

* * *

High School, Grades 10, 11, 12

As I MENTIONED, LAST YEAR was the beginning of what was to come. There was a lot of unwanted chaos in my home. For someone who loved order, peace and organization, I had to dig deep and get strong. Physical work never bothered me, but this was emotional abuse that tried to wear me down. Truthfully, it was hell. It wasn't what I imagined for my life, nor my children's. Those beautiful sons of mine did not deserve this.

I had recently gone back to teaching since Richie was in school full time, so at least I had a little money to work with. Not much. I was offered an extra job getting involved with a network marketing company where I could work from home, making calls and appointments, so I took it. Frank and Paul, seeing what I was doing, also became involved and joined the company. Paul helped me in the paperwork or whatever he could do, and even came to some meetings. Frank also enjoyed working with the company, and, if nothing else, we met some really nice positive people.

And, as if I had any time left over, I sold jeans from my house in a back spare room. My cousin owned a clothing store and would supply me with jeans and some blouses. Once in a while, I would pack all this heavy merchandise into my station wagon, take it to someone's house for a house party, unload it all, set it all up on my portable clothing rack in their house, only to reverse all that to go home. It was backbreaking work, but I did whatever I could to add to our own finances.

It was like 2 full time jobs, total, and I never stopped moving. My heart broke for my boys. It could not have been easy for them. Suddenly their mom was all over the place. They were so understanding and never complained. And, always, always, so supportive. All of them.

Paul would especially say "mom, you are so strong. You, and all of us will be fine."

I think back to those days and I don't know how I survived, but, quite frankly, all of that made me and my boys who we are today.

Paul was right.

Certificate of Award

This Certifies that

PAUL GIACCIO

of

John Jay High School

has been awarded this certificate for

CITIZENSHIP — 11th GRADE

Date   June 3, 1992

Laura E. French

Certificate of   **Membership**

National Honor Society

of

Secondary Schools

This Certifies that

PAUL GIACCIO

was selected a member

of the   JOHN JAY   **Chapter**

of the

National Honor Society of Secondary Schools,

membership is based on

Scholarship, Leadership, Service, and Character.

Given at   JOHN JAY HIGH SCHOOL
this FIFTH   **day of** JUNE   19 92

Dale S. Hawley

SECRETARY, NHS NATIONAL COUNCIL
DIRECTOR, NASSP DIVISION OF
STUDENT ACTIVITIES

Finit J. Dyer

EXECUTIVE DIRECTOR
THE NATIONAL ASSOCIATION OF
SECONDARY SCHOOL PRINCIPALS

ADVISER

PRINCIPAL

Laura E. French

PAUL'S JUNIOR YEAR WAS MAINLY filled with his schoolwork, (still always on the honor roll) work at D'Agostino's supermarket, football on the High School Team, and the John Jay Varsity Lacrosse Team which he was manager for (have no idea how he managed all of it). And, as class officer, he had those responsibilities as well.

He also received the Citizenship Award.

It was another year filled with awards and surprises and, we needed all the good news we could get during this time.

This award was totally exciting and unexpected.

Paul, by this time, had been working at D'Agostino's for a few years as cashier. Although a part timer, he was very well known throughout the community and customers would only want to check out on his line. He was the fastest and most efficient and, of course, the friendliest. He never, ever made a mistake at the register. He was incredibly smart in the handling of money. He certainly didn't take after me. I never enjoyed figuring out anything financial I guess because I never did. I just liked my words and writing, rather than numbers.

But, Paul was a genius at the register and he seriously was rated the fastest cashier ever. Funny thing is that he would be ringing up and talking at the same time, asking customers if they realized the coffee or Tide was on sale or asking about their children. Still talking, he gave their change, never with a mistake.

The reason I know all this is because of all the people who would come up to me and ask if I was Paul's mother, and then they would get into their stories.

So, all of this kept getting him the coveted Associate of the Month award where your photo is displayed in the store. This happened many, many times and he was only a part timer at 16 years old!

The full timers that also worked there loved him even though he was the one getting all the attention. He became good friends with all the employees in every department and always extended himself to anyone who needed help. When I would go in there to shop, I was "Paul's mother" and all the employees wanted to talk to me to tell me how much they enjoyed Paul, or how he helped them.

Paul became especially close to Julian, an older Afro-American woman, who had been working at D'Agostino's (formerly Foodtown) for many years. Her register was next to Paul's and she became like a grandmother to Paul. He absolutely adored her and even visited her in the city when she retired. He became part of her family. When I would go in the store, she would be beaming talking about "her" Paul. She knew Paul and his brothers were collecting the bicentennial quarters so she would keep an eye out for them if any came through the register to give to Paul.

Paul's extended family was at D'Agostino's and he was very happy there. He would continue to work there in his summers home from college.

It's so interesting to see the things that I'm remembering writing this book. I know I get off on tangents sometimes. Now, back to the totally exciting and unexpected award I started talking about!

Paul was voted Associate of the YEAR at D'Agostino's in January 1992 and it happened to be the same year that D'Agostino's was voted Store of the Year!

Paul was treated to an awards ceremony in New York City where he was taken to by private limousine. He spent a full day with a beautiful lunch and dinner.

His Junior Year was winding down and the next two events would be his National Honor Society Awards Night Presentation that June 1992, along with his Junior Prom.

That summer of 1992, he worked a lot of hours at D'Agostino's. He was going into his senior year.

He saved every penny he made. He never spent money on anything. He never seemed to need or want anything (except maybe when he was little, at Christmas), I never remember Paul or any of his brothers asking for certain clothes, sneakers, or anything! And, they were all so supportive and helpful around the house. They really worked hard when I think back at it now. I don't know why but I just thought of one of the chores that the youngest son would always have because it wasn't strenuous and yet it was an important one to keep up with. So, all dirty laundry would originate from upstairs, where the bedrooms and bathrooms were. That means sheets, pillowcases, towels, washcloths, pajamas, all clothes and underwear would need to get downstairs to the washer and dryer. Sports uniforms (muddy at best) and accessories, would never go upstairs but would be removed by the laundry area.

Anyway, we had a laundry chute in one of the bathrooms that led to a huge basket, once thrown down this hole, and that was a big job, although not hard. But, somehow there would be a lot of laughing going on when this was happening because one of them would put themselves under the hole instead of the basket. I don't know but I was just thinking about that laundry chute and all the noise going on.

I'd like a whole day of all of them in that house one more time.

Getting back to Paul's years at D'Agostino's, I had heard about some "spreadsheet" that Paul had, or was making, from working at D'Agostino's but I never saw it nor knew anything about it until after Paul passed and I found it in his stored boxes. I was shocked. I don't think anyone has even done anything like this to my knowledge. My husband, Manny, also shook his head in disbelief, smiling, as if to say "only Paul."

It was a 40 page document of every day Paul worked at D'Agostino's. Across each page were columns with the words: date, wage per hour, week's gross pay, actual payment, hours worked that week, average wage for the week, etc.

This was kept up for 6 years!

From July 4, 1990 to his last day October 9, 1996. He shows he went from $4.75 / hour to $7.75 / hour. Who does this?

Paul, of course.

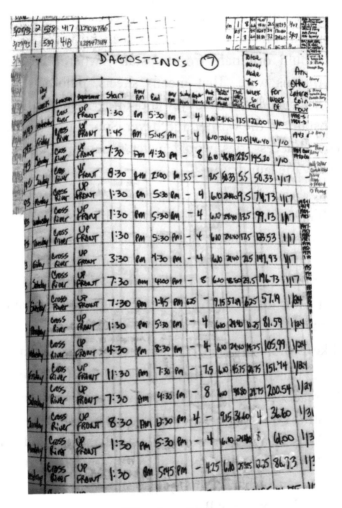

Who does this?
I found many notebooks filled-in just like this.
18 years old. Columns and columns of information. Average value of a bicentennial each day. Coins found, etc.

January 10, 1992

Paul Giaccio
D'Agostino Store #17-CR
Routes 121 & 35
Cross River, NY 10518

Dear Paul:

It is with great pleasure that I present to you
this framed picture of you taken at the "Associate of
the Year" Awards Ceremony. I congratulate you on your
achievements in the area of customer service. You are a
credit to our company and well deserving of the title of
"Associate of the Year" from your store.

Congratulations and keep up the good work!

Sincerely yours,

Roi R. Tucker
Vice President, Human Resources

Junior Prom, 1992
John Jay Junior High School

Senior Year

SENIOR YEAR CAME AND FOOTBALL became his passion.

It was his second year on the John Jay Football team and at the close of the Senior year, he was given the Most Improved Player award. This was an extremely important award for Paul and he was very touched by it. It meant a lot to him to be recognized as one of the valuable players and "one of the guys" in general.

He was very serious about that team and he cut out every single article that was written about every single game for those two years.

I now have the binder that holds all those articles in plastic sleeves, neatly cut and organized. I recently was told that he made a similar binder for each football player on the team at the end of Senior Year. Paul didn't look for recognition. He just loved making people happy.

The school year ended with the Senior Prom and the Senior Trip to Mexico. I don't know how I finally agreed to that because I do remember some push back, but I guess I let him go because he just wanted to, and he rarely did anything fun and he rarely (if ever) asked for anything.

The Baccalaureate Mass for graduating Seniors was at St. Mary's that June. Then, finally, Graduation Day. My parents came for the ceremony and a new chapter was to begin for Paul.

In looking through his personal scrapbook, I saw that he actually saved the Graduation card that I sent him with all that I wished for him written inside. He also saved his brother Frank's card.

But, he also actually saved certain other greeting cards from me, my parents (his beloved grandparents) Aunt Rose, his brothers, etc.

Yes, I guess he was a lot like me.

League Champs, Bowl Champs
Most Improved - Paul Giaccio. This trophy meant the world to him.

John Jay Indians, 1991-1992

Baccalaureate Mass, June 11, 1993

Paul's High School Graduation

Paul's High School Graduation
June 1993 - John Jay High School

Grandma Mary, Bobby, Richie, Paul and Pepa Frank

College Years

P AUL STARTED GEORGIA TECH in September, 1993.
He had left in August to get situated. Everything is a blur around those last four years. The divorce was final in 1992, but there was no end to the existing fires I had to put out, with no alimony, no child support and a house in foreclosure. That was only the tip of the iceberg. I don't want this to be so depressing. There was no financing for Paul to go to college (nor for any of the other boys for that matter) so he had to be creative and figure out a way. And he did. He applied to be the equipment manager of the Georgia Tech basketball team. It was practically a full time job. He had to take care of all the players' equipment, attend all the home and away games, etc. which made it a huge commitment, but his college education would be almost paid for, and, along with some grants, he would be able to go.

Bobby Cremins was the head coach at the time and Kevin Cantrell was the assistant coach and, thankfully, Paul secured that position. It was a gift from God!

Both of these gentlemen reached out to me when Paul passed away. They always had a wonderful relationship with Paul all the years Paul was manager.

Paul was used to hard work and keeping a lot of balls in the air (literally) but this was really hard, along with going to his college classes.

He never, ever, ever complained, but I knew how hard he had it. I am crying as I write this part because he didn't deserve such hardship. He deserved to go to college, with a free spirit, enjoying what college life had to offer, without worrying about anything. He did everything right his whole life and now he was faced with this. I was frustrated and angry that my boys and I were put into this awful predicament. But, I didn't want us ever to feel like victims and so I just kept validating we were in a tough spot, but it would work out. Somehow, it would work out. We would be stronger in the long run. But, it was so darn hard keeping it together. Our house was in foreclosure (I still can't believe it) and I was trying to save it all myself, going to court.

I knew it wasn't long before we would be out of it, so I had to start clearing out rooms, getting rid of almost everything since I figured there wouldn't be much room in whatever condo we would wind up in. It was a monumental job that I did on my own, with help from the boys.

I came up with the idea to donate everything to a Church, as long as they could come and get it. Twelve men from the Church came with two big trucks and loaded them up—done.

Paul would call from time to time and came home for his last holiday at Christmas in our home in 1993, but between his work with the team and his classes, it was very hard. My parents kept in constant contact with him. They lived in Florida and a couple of times drove to Georgia to see the games, or else, they watched the Georgia Tech games on TV, because Paul was always on.

That's how I got to see him as well. Paul sent me a Georgia Tech mom sweatshirt which I have to this day. Even with all he was going through, he had time to think of me.

That September, Paul joined the Phi Sigma Kappa fraternity, which gave him a sense of family, along with the Athletic Department.

On the home-front, that August, when Paul left for Georgia Tech along with my *"things will get better; this will make us stronger; the best is yet to be"* goodbye comments. Frank was working in his landscaping business he started, along with other work, and the boys were in summer camp. I was home from teaching duties, getting ready to go back in a couple weeks.

At that point, we were still in the house, waiting for the final letter to leave (which would ultimately happen several months later).

I was home alone that morning trying to figure my life out when my friend Joyce called to see if I would meet her for a walk. I told her that I was in no mood to go for a walk, but she encouraged me, so I went. After the walk she suggested that we go have some coffee at our usual coffee shop. It was about 10:30 am at that time, on August 26, 1993.

So, we entered the coffee shop and it appeared to be empty but I thought I saw someone sitting at a table at the far end, but didn't look again.

Joyce and I sat down, with me facing her, and ultimately facing the one person on the other side (who I didn't look at or notice). We talked a while, as I was catching her up on my drama filled life, and then she got up to go to the counter to order us coffee. She turned to me and said, "Adrienne, do you want to share a bagel?" I said fine. She sat back down, and we continued talking. I thought I heard the door open with someone leaving at some point, but again didn't look back or pay attention. I just kept talking to Joyce.

About 10 minutes after that, the owner of the coffee shop, who knew us both well as regulars, came over and said, "Adrienne, you have a phone call."

I panicked. I thought maybe someone was trying to track me down because one of the boys got hurt! Who would be calling me? I ran to the phone and this wonderful voice said, "Is this Adrienne?"

I said "Yes! Who is this? What's wrong?"

And, this wonderful voice continued, "Well, this is very difficult to explain, but I was just having breakfast in the coffee shop when you and your friend walked in, and then while you were talking to her, facing me, I just felt like I had to know you. I heard your friend say your name, so I knew that much and wanted to come over to introduce myself, but it was all so awkward, so I left, on my way to visit my mom on Long Island. But, on 684 I couldn't get you out of my mind, so I pulled over to use the phone at the rest stop, hoping you were still there."

Now, you all have to imagine what is going through my mind. And none of it is good. I now am thinking, on top of my already crazy life, that I have a stalker to deal with! Up to that point, I did nothing but listen to this long story (he did and still does, have this calming, wonderful voice).

But I finally asked, "WHO is this?" He told me his name and that he lived in Waccabuc. I told him I knew everyone in Waccabuc, but never heard of him at which he responded that he had recently moved there.

So, I said, "Well, I'm checking you out!" and hung up the phone.

My friend asked, "NOW what?!"

"You won't believe this!" I answered. "I think now I have a stalker. I think we should go to the police because I have his name. But, first, let's go to the post office to see if Dot knows him."

Our Waccabuc post office was (and probably still is) the size of a small living room and we knew Dot, the Postmaster, for years. So we rode over there and asked her if she ever heard of him, and, she said, "You met HIM?"

"What do you mean HIM? Like he's somebody?" She then explained that he just moved to Waccabuc and he was a wonderfully good-looking man and such a gentleman. It's the gentleman part that got my attention.

I told her what had just happened, and, she looked at me, saying, "You know, you two would be perfect together!"

You can imagine the shock and craziness of all this happening, but, believing in serendipity, and things happening for a reason, I told her she could give him my number in his mail box because I checked him out with her.

I had no intention of dating anyone. I was divorced for almost two years, and my EX husband was my only boyfriend from 15 years old. That did not end well at all. No, I wasn't interested, but something told me to follow through, like my divine intervention that always seems to show up when I need it.

Well, the next morning, when he went to get his mail at the post office, he got the note, called me immediately and asked to go to dinner that night!

This was getting crazier by the minute. The girls came over and went in my closet with me to pick out my "date dress." I still have that dress, in the hopes I will fit into it again one day. So far it hasn't happened.

Manny, my date, picked me up at my foreclosed house (smile) and my son Bobby was home and the first to meet him. He didn't want me to go out with a stranger without checking him out. It was my first time meeting him as well, although Dot gave me a perfect description. He definitely was handsome and definitely a gentleman!

Our first date was amazing. It was dinner at La Camelia in Mt. Kisco, New York on August 27, 1993, the day after he saw me in the coffee shop on August 26.

That was 26 years ago, and every year, at my dear husband

Manny's insistence, who is such a romantic, we celebrate both days. On the day we "met" on August 26, we have our photo taken in front of a coffee shop. I have a whole wall in my Southampton, New York office with photos from every year.

Then, on August 27, we have dinner at La Camelia at the same table.

One time La Camelia was closed for repair and Manny was frantic that we might have to break our tradition, so he called the owners to say he would do whatever it took to have them serve a meal there. So, the owner and his wife prepared a meal and brought it to us to eat on the outside patio.

That's the man I married. He has been a devoted stepdad to all my children as well as a grandfather to my grandchildren Olivia and Frankie, as well as an amazing role model in being moral and ethical. Of course, seeing how Manny is so devoted to me and my happiness has given them peace as well. Paul would always tell me how happy he was that Manny found me.

I reminded Paul that I always told them that everything would somehow work out for the best, and that there's a reason for everything. We just needed the faith to believe it. I did have the faith of a mustard seed and wanted the boys to have the same. It was the only way. Worrying would get us nowhere. We had to keep doing the right thing, work hard, and let it go.

I'm so grateful for my life now. Manny always tells me he's the luckiest man in the world to have found me. It's so nice to hear, believe me.

I would have been remiss if I didn't tell that full story because it's another example of how life can turn around and work out for the best if only we believe it can.

Everyone enjoys that (our) love story and I've been asked many times to repeat it, but, once again, now I'll just tell them to read this book!

Christmas 1993
Traditional Christmas
dessert at the Gumbel's

Fraternity
Brothers

Paul had many photo albums of his fraternity.

Phi Sigma Kappa
Fraternity House

So, Paul was at Georgia Tech, settling into his courses, his job with the Athletic Department there, and "running" the fraternity, from, what I heard. It wouldn't be long before he was getting involved in projects there!

Knowing how much those two areas at Georgia Tech meant to him, as well as all the relationships he formed, I decided to set up a Foundation at both the Phi Sigma Kappa fraternity and the Athletic Department, giving scholarships each year to deserving recipients, demonstrating healthy work ethics and kind, generous attributes.

PHI SIGMA KAPPA
On behalf of the men
of
Phi Sigma Kappa
We would like to offer you this formal invitation
to continue your rush affiliation
with our brotherhood
Your immediate consideration and reply
will be greatly appreciated

Sept 19, 1993　　　　　_Richard C. Rover II_
　　Date　　　　　　　　　　President

Paul had a great rapport with all the team players.

USILA DISTRICT IV LACROSSE
NORTH CAROLINA, VIRGINIA, MARYLAND, DELAWARE, PART OF PENNSYLVANIA
BOB SANDELL, DISTRICT APPOINTING AUTHORITY

POST OFFICE BOX 5107 · CHARLOTTESVILLE, VIRGINIA 22905
TELEPHONE (804) 296-8042

5/26/95

Dear Paulie,

I can't tell you how much it meant to our family that the support that your Fraternity showed during the past few days. It really was great of so many of you to come to Charlottesville.

You know where we live so please visit us whenever you can.

Sincerely,
Bob Sandell

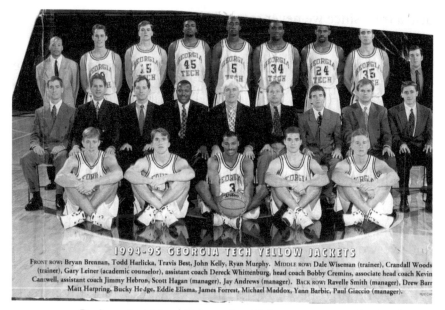

1994-95 GEORGIA TECH YELLOW JACKETS

Front row: Bryan Brennan, Todd Harlicka, Travis Best, John Kelly, Ryan Murphy. Middle row: Dale Wiseman (trainer), Crandall Woods (trainer), Gary Leiner (academic counselor), assistant coach Dereck Whittenburg, head coach Bobby Cremins, associate head coach Kevin Cantwell, assistant coach Jimmy Hebron, Scott Hagan (manager), Jay Andrews (manager), Back row: Ravelle Smith (manager), Drew Barr, Matt Harpring, Bucky Hodge, Eddie Elisma, James Forrest, Michael Maddox, Yann Barbic, Paul Giaccio (manager).

Paul worked himself through college as manager of
the Georgia Tech basketball team.

DURING PAUL'S COLLEGE YEARS IN GEORGIA, he would visit from time to time, but his commitments there were extremely time consuming, and I was still dealing with the aftermath of a disastrous divorce, and all that went with it.

Sometime after he left for college, I eventually moved from our family home in Waccabuc with Richie and Bobby. We had been living there for 16 years, and despite that, all the boys adjusted extremely well, which I was so grateful for. They looked at it as a new chapter and they loved the new location of the condo I rented. It was walking distance to their schools and the shopping area; it was small, compared to our large home and property, but it was more than adequate. I set up an area for Paul in the finished basement for when he did come home for holidays, or summer work at D'Agostinos.

Frank lived nearby and started his own landscape mowing business. At least we were all together in a happy, safe environment with no stress. Actually, it was wonderful. Having neighbors was also a treat since we never saw anyone around us before.

Things were falling into place little by little.

Manny and I saw each other constantly, going out with the boys, taking trips to see my parents in Florida, or just hanging out getting to know one another.

We got engaged at one point, but still didn't take the next step of marriage until 1997. In the meantime, we all enjoyed each other's company and the boys respected him immensely, especially since he was so good to me, as well as to them.

Manny adored my parents (and they adored him obviously) and we would sometimes fly to Georgia and meet my parents there to see Paul at his basketball games.

And, on one special Easter, in 1996, Manny took my parents and Paul to Amelia Island where we had a mini vacation just so we could see Paul on the little time he had off.

*   *   *

Paul was starting to think about what he would do when he finally graduated Georgia Tech, and, as always, appreciated Manny's wisdom and guidance. Because Paul basically had a full time job as an equipment manager for the basketball team, he would need to spend an extra year in college to get all his college credits.

But, as usual, Paul was always planning. Paul initially thought he might want to work at Merrill Lynch, where Manny had been President of Money Markets before he retired, so Manny gladly helped to set that up in December, 1997. As thoughtful and generous as Manny always is, he bought Paul a beautiful dress suit for his interview and Paul was so grateful. Paul then got to also wear that suit for our wedding on December 14. I treasure the photo of us with our blended family of seven sons, Paul and his handsome suit.

Manny and I had a small intimate wedding with our seven

sons, Manny's mom and sister, her husband, my parents and Joyce, who encouraged me to go for a walk that day.

Manny and I, both Catholics, and both divorced, asked to be married in the Catholic Church I went to for many, many years for services with my children, as well as being a choir member. But, it was not to be. Not unless we both got an annulment. It was the most ridiculous thing we had ever heard. We were told we couldn't receive Holy Communion either from now on.

Now, knowing that we weren't able to have a Catholic service wedding, we went to Plan B, which was actually ironic and comical. Our Catholic Mass was held in a Presbyterian Church building every Sunday. The Presbyterians would have the early service times, and we would have the 11:30 AM slot each week. This location was to accommodate all the Catholics in our area, rather than the 20 minute ride to Katonah. So, Manny and I asked the Presbyterian minister if she would marry us, and there was absolutely no problem. Shame on the Catholic Church!

The best part is that my Choir Group, who I sang with for years, agreed to sing at our wedding, so it all looked the same!

Same building. Same choir. Only a Presbyterian pastor.

*　　*　　*

THAT FEBRUARY, 1998, Manny and I took a trip to Atlanta to see Paul receive his award given by Bobby Cremins and Kevin Cantwell for his service as manager of the Georgia Tech basketball team for the total of five seasons. My parents came from Florida as well, and it was very exciting. I was asked to go on the basketball court with Paul when he received his recognition while photos were taken of us. Paul was very respected and liked by the coaches and players.

Paul graduated Georgia Tech during the weekend of June 12, 1998. We all went to celebrate with him, my parents driving from

Florida. I love the photo of Paul and I in front of the Georgia Tech antique car.

Paul would soon be making some big, important decisions as to what he wanted to do for a job.

In the meantime he was to be best man at Frank and Erin's wedding! My oldest son was getting married and I was so happy for him. The Church service was at St. Mary's in Katonah and then we all went to our friend June Gumbel's estate for the reception. June's family and ours were extremely close. They also lived in Waccabuc, and my boys felt like their home was their other home and vice versa. We spent holidays together back and forth, as well as days in between.

It was idyllic to have the celebration on June Gumbel's grounds, which is like a resort. It was probably one of the best weddings I've ever been to, with the venue and endless supply of lobsters, corn, etc. A true clambake with music and dancing.

Paul gave a very funny speech talking about some "brother" stuff but it was also heartfelt. Frank and Paul were incredibly close. We actually have a video of that speech and someday I will look at it if I ever get strong enough to do so. I'm actually crying right now writing this.

Again, we were so grateful to be at June's for the wedding. The Gumbels were a huge part of Paul's life, as well as my other sons.

We actually got to see Paul again that November 1998 when he came in for Thanksgiving. Manny and I planned a beautiful dinner at our home. Despite my protest, Manny would not let me cook! He wanted me to relax and enjoy the day with all my sons and Erin, so he had the entire Thanksgiving meal prepared and served by a team of chefs!

This was a huge readjustment for me since I did everything myself for years, but I eventually got used to being treated like a queen. To this day, Manny treats me with utmost love and respect which has been so healthy for my sons to witness.

That December, Manny planned a huge family Christmas celebration at Black Diamond Country Club, where we had recently bought property. It was in Florida, but not near the ocean, so we sold it soon after. In the meantime, we would have everyone stay there with us at the resort to play golf, eat, go to spas, etc. We used it as a great "get together" location as it wasn't far from Paul and my parents.

As it turned out, Paul decided that working for a financial institution was not a good fit for him. He realized he'd like to be on the move, ultimately owning his own business.

But, that was not to be just yet.

---　✳︎　---

After Georgia Tech
Graduation

~~~~~~~~~~~~

As it happened, the Atlantic Hawks recruited him to be their manager after graduation and so he was back on the road with a basketball team.

Paul stayed with the Hawks for 2 years from 1998-2000, giving my parents, and all of us, more times to watch him on ESPN during games!

Although Paul was living in Georgia full time and established permanent residence there, I continued his biography here as related to our times when we would get together as a family in New York, when he would visit, or when we would all go away together for family vacations.

This is part of Paul's life was different for me now. I was no longer writing in his "development" books or adding his report cards in his school binder.

He was away from me all the time, so I only had treasured moments a few times a year, at best, to write about it according to my own personal accounts written in the first person.

As I mentioned in the Introduction, I have a chapter at the

end of this book entitled Lewisboro and Georgian Testimonials and Tales. There, I have shared comments and stories sent to me by many of his widespread circle of friends from Lewisboro, New York, where he spent the first part of his life, nursery school through high school.

From there he would go on to Georgia Tech for college, remaining in Georgia for the rest of his life.

I didn't know many of his Georgian friends personally, only through Paul's conversations about them. From what many of them wrote, I can see that Paul continued his life of compassion, love, and generosity.

On April 27, 2000, the Patent Trader newspaper in Lewisboro New York, wrote a huge article about Paul being manager with the Atlanta Hawks.

As it turned out, it would be the last time Paul would be recognized in our town community papers, after so many years. I have included that article here. My youngest son Richie was so thoughtful in having that article recreated and put into a framed poster which is in my Southampton office.

Not long after that article came out, Paul decided to leave the Atlanta Hawks as much as he loved his job, since he was still wanting to start his own financial business.

It wasn't easy at first, trying to build up a clientele. While doing that, he needed to augment his salary to pay bills, so he started working at Twisted Taco's bar in Atlanta as a barback.

It should have been termed backbreaker because he had to bring up very heavy cases of alcohol from the basement as part of his job. I would get so concerned when he told me what he was doing. I know that was the start of his back issues. He said the money was really good and he enjoyed it. But, I knew he was literally working day and night. He worked at that frantic pace for a few years.

In the meantime, he was having conversations with a college friend of his, Jose, about another business venture to consider. Jose suggested that he and Paul start an ATM business. Twisted Tacos became their first ATM, and big changes were about to happen.

Also, in 2000, Paul's first and only niece, Olivia Mary, Frank and Erin's daughter, was born. Of course, Paul came to New York and was just beaming. She was the apple of Paul's eye, and he loved spending time with her through the years.

Bobby graduated University at Delaware in 2001 and Paul joined all of us there for Bobby's celebration. I must say that even with all that Paul had going on, he would come to all family events. He made the time and effort to be there. No excuses. And, he really had plenty of them.

In 2001, Manny and I moved to Vero Beach, Florida, an hour south from my parents.

We custom built our home at the Orchid Island Beach Club and it would open up a whole new chapter with the boys coming there for visits and the holidays, while being with their grandparents at the same time.

Everyone would stay with us at our new home and there was so much to do. All the boys would play golf with Manny and my dad at our club, have lunch at the restaurant there on the ocean, sit by the pool, play tennis, etc. And, we'd all go to our private beach in between.

Paul loved to come, and it was only a few hours drive from Georgia, although most of the time, he'd take the shuttle.

That December, 2001, Olivia's brother Frankie, was born. Paul had his first, and only nephew.

Whenever Paul could, he made sure he spent quality time with both Olivia and Frankie, as many photos show. He loved those two babies so much (they were 16 months apart).

His dedication and love for them would continue throughout

all the years as they both grew up. Paul took a sincere interest in each of their passions.

Olivia became a member (and still is) of the U.S. Ski Team, and Paul attended many of her competitions from when they lived in Vermont, Vail, Colorado and finally in Park City, Utah.

He would call me after watching her on TV and in some country in the world during a World Cup event, and say "Mom, Olivia is amazing, right? She's just unbelievable!"

I knew Paul was calling right after an event every time.

After Paul passed away, Olivia had a World Cup event in Ruka, Finland. It was a very difficult time. She put LLP (LiveLikePaul) on her ski helmet so Paul was right with her then, and now.

And, with Frankie, Paul loved talking math and numbers. Like his Uncle Paul, Frankie is a math whiz. And, as Frankie got older, Paul would have Frankie go to Atlanta to stay with him during Paul's famous polka tournaments!

What an experience for Frankie!

Amelia Island, Florida
Easter - 1996

Mom & Dad's 50th Wedding Anniversary - June 1996
Manny held a huge party at his home at Waccabuc for my
parents. We were engaged at the time. June Gumbel, Me,
Richie, Frank, Mom, Paul, Dad, and Bobby.

Yankee Game - Summer 1996
Manny reserved a suite at Yankee Stadium for Paul and his friends.

Paul worked at D'Agostino's for many years.

December 14, 1997 - Our Wedding Day
Photo from our Waccabuc home
Richie, Paul, me, Frank, Bobby

Our 7 sons

February 1998 - Paul received an award for his service with the Georgia Tech basketball team Coach Bobby Cremins.

I was asked to join him while getting his award.

Paul and Bobby Cremins, Head Coach, Georgia Tech Basketball.

Paul's Graduation Day from Georgia Tech.

Frank and Erin's Wedding
It was an amazing day, held on the grounds of
June Gumbel, our friend like family.

September 12, 1998
Best man at his brother
Frank's wedding.

Pepa Frank, Frank and Paul

Degree from Georgia Institute of
Technology
Dupree College of Management,
Marketing - June 1998

Georgia Institute of Technology
Bachelor of Science in
Management
June 1998

Georgia Institute of Technology
Industrial and Organizational
Psychology - 1998

Paul Giaccio, Manager
Thank you for your outstanding
contribution to the Georgia Tech
basketball team that posted a 19-14
record in 1997-1998

Thanksgiving at our home in Waccabuc, 1988.
It was all catered with my whole family and Manny's three sons.

1998 - Christmas celebration at Black Diamond
Country Club, Florida

B12 — THE PATENT TRADER Thursday, April 27, 2000

Sports

IN THE NBA: Paul Giaccio, who was the center on John Jay's 1992 Section One football championship team, has taken an unlikely journey into the NBA, where he works as the equipment manager for the Atlanta Hawks.

"Traveling is awesome," says Giaccio, shown here in the shadow of Hawks star center Dikeme Mutombo. "Everything is first class. They have their own plane. When we go to the airport we go right on the runway and walk on the plane. There are no terminals."

THE PATENT TRADER Thursday, April 27, 2000 — B9

TRADER

Sports

Dawn DiMicco
Stars at Albany

See Page B-11

sen
ces

B-10

Adventures in Atlanta

Former John Jay Football Standout Enjoying Life in the NBA

By AMY KIRSCHBAUM

You're a 24-year-old former high school football player going up against a 6-foot-5, 215 pound, seven-year NBA veteran who is five years your senior.

And you're going to tell him what to do? And you believe he'll listen?

If you're Paul Giaccio, hallucinations like this are part of the job description.

Giaccio, who was the center on John Jay's 1992 Section One football championship team, often finds himself facing this exact type of situation.

As equipment manager for the Atlanta Hawks, Giaccio does a little bit of everything.

He needs to make sure that the laundry is done, the uniforms, equipment, sneakers, socks and jocks are ordered and that the locker room is organized.

He is in charge of the ballboys and seeing that Dikembe Mutumbo gets his lemon/lime Gatorade in a bottle because he doesn't like it from the jug.

He also meets visiting teams at the bus and gets their bags. Going to a player's car if he forgot something or getting them food after practice isn't unheard of for Giaccio either.

Cross River's Paul Giaccio, the Atlanta Hawks' equipment manager, stands behind a seated Jimmy Jackson while Lenny Wilkens address his team during a contest in March. Wilkens, the winningest coach in NBA history, resigned from his position earlier this week.

Life in the NBA

Continued from Page B-9

And in addition to all this, he needs to deal with the attitude of a NBA veteran who doesn't want to change his shorts.

About two months ago on a road trip to Sacramento, the Hawks were fined because rookie Jason Terry's shorts were longer than the regulated one-inch above the knee length.

Knowing that the team could be fined again if any other player's shorts went past his knees, Giaccio switched the shorts of former Hawk J.R. Rider to regulation length.

When Rider realized his uniform had been changed, he demanded to have his old shorts back. Though Giaccio tried to talk him out of it, Rider gave him an ultimatum.

"He said 'I've worn these shorts all year and I haven't gotten fined,'" Giaccio recalls. "He wasn't listening to anything I had to say. He said that he wouldn't play unless he got his shorts.

"Now, I'm not in the official position to say, 'Well then, you're not going to play.'"

So Giaccio talked to his boss, head coach Lenny Wilkens, and even Atlanta's general manager who said Rider had to change his shorts or would be fined $50,000. [Editor's Note: In a related development, Wilkens, the winningest coach in NBA history, resigned from his post earlier this week.]

"So, it's back on me and I have to go tell this to Rider," Giaccio continues. "I'm not looking forward to it at all. I went back and said, 'Please wear the new shorts.' He said 'No.' I said I will get fired if you don't.'

"It would all come down on me. Rider laughed for a minute and then said 'OK. Get me the new shorts.'"

Though Giaccio has to deal with instances such as this, he realizes the perks outweigh the abuse.

"My favorite thing about this job is that it's not a nine-to-five job," he says. "It's different every day. No two days are the same. Even if they play two days in a row there are two differ-

"You get on the plane and there are 25 people and four stewardesses that cater to your every need. We get off the plane and walk five feet and get on the bus."

Besides the ease of traveling, visiting the 29 different NBA cities is also exciting for Giaccio.

"I love going to the different cities," he says. "There are 29 NBA cities and I know people in about 15 of them.

"It's great because I can keep in touch with friends of mine from college that have moved away. There's always something to do in each city."

So how does a Cross River resident such as Giaccio go from the amateur football field to the pro arena?

"I got into this in 10th grade because I didn't get on the baseball team," he says. "I decided to do stats for lacrosse. I figured if the baseball team didn't want me I'll do this. So I did it for lacrosse and then I did it for basketball.

"By the time I was a senior, I was helping the varsity basketball team and playing football as well. Then when I went to Georgia Tech [for college], I figured I could get involved with basketball and do stats there."

Following one year as statistician for the Yellow Jackets, Giaccio became a team manager for his remaining four years at the school.

His duties were similar to his current job. The 1998 graduate had to order equipment, get uniforms together and do laundry.

"Each year, I got more and more responsibility," he says. "In my final

cut teams.

"I love that I'm not at a desk. There's a new challenge everyday and new things to do. I meet new people every day. I love every part of this job."

Giaccio raved about some other benefits to being part of a profession-

year. I got to travel with the team."

But don't let be said that hard work will get you everywhere. It's definitely a lot about who you know. Luckily for Giaccio, he knew the right people.

When the Hawks were having a new arena built, they played 10 games on Georgia Tech's campus where Giaccio would help Atlanta's trainer with anything he needed.

"When it came time that they were looking for an equipment manager, they were looking for someone from Georgia Tech that they knew," Giaccio explains.

That was connection No. 1. The second connection came from Giaccio's old neighbor in Cross River.

"They asked [Knicks coach] Jeff Van Gundy [who now resides in Chappaqua] about me and he gave me a good recommendation," Giaccio says. "I think that's what put me over the top."

Of course, hearsay isn't everything, though it helps when it comes from the mouth of a NBA coach.

"My work ethic is why they hired me and [the Hawks] really took a chance on me," Giaccio insists. "I didn't have to fill out any application. He kind of said, 'Would you like to give this a shot?' I was just at the right time in the right situation."

So this must have been a dream come true for a young sports fan, right?

Not according to Giaccio, who has dreams of dollar signs dancing in his head while in college.

"People asked me in college if this is what I wanted to do and I said not

really," he admits. "I was a finance and marketing major. I was going to go back to New York and work on Wall Street. But I thought this would be fun to do.

"I'm never going to get a chance to do it again. I can always change if I want. This is great while I'm young and single. I can travel and not have to worry about a family.

"I feel bad because there are people that would die to have this position and here I am. It was never my dream and it just sort of fell into my lap."

Giaccio has taken it all in stride, though he deals everyday with the idea that the players could probably buy everything he owns of of him and not even have to go to the bank for change.

"They treat me with a lot of respect," he says. "There's a level of respect they have for what I do. They treat me very well. The interesting thing is these are multi-million dollar guys.

"We have friendly relationships. They treat me well and with a lot of respect. They know I would do anything for them and they always say thank you."

The second-year equipment manager is serious about the friendly relationships.

Just ask the players, especially rookie and ex-Yellow Jacket Dion Glover.

After knowing each other at Georgia Tech the two are friends off the court and hang out with other players their age in their free time.

al sports organization.

"Traveling is awesome," he says. "Everything is first class. They have their own plane. When we go to the airport we go right on the runway and walk on the plane. There are no terminals.

Continued on Page B-12

fantasy, there is the reality that the NBA is a business and that brings him back to earth every once in a while.

"It's hard sometimes," he says about players and friends being traded. "When I got here this was the Atlanta Hawks that I knew. These 12 guys. This year, only five players came back.

"It's the way of the business though. It's a constantly changing team."

But Giaccio is able to find the positive even in this situation.

"The good thing is that when players are traded they appear somewhere else," he says. "Do now when we go to other cities I know players on the other team. I can say hello and it's cool."

Giaccio is enjoying his time as part of the Hawks' organization for now but doesn't see himself as a permanent fixture.

"Right now it's great," he says. "In the long term, I don't know. I'm meeting lots of people and making connections. This could lead to something else.

"Maybe something else in the sports industry. I'm not going to be the equipment manager for 30 years."

With all the exciting aspects of the job, there is one problem Giaccio faces almost nightly.

"It's a lot of fun," he says. "But I'm always asked to get tickets and gear for people. I always get hit up for that. I guess that's the worst part of the job. All my friends have now become Hawks fans, though.

"I just love every part of my job."

Atlanta Hawks Team 1998 - 2000
Paul, Equipment Manager

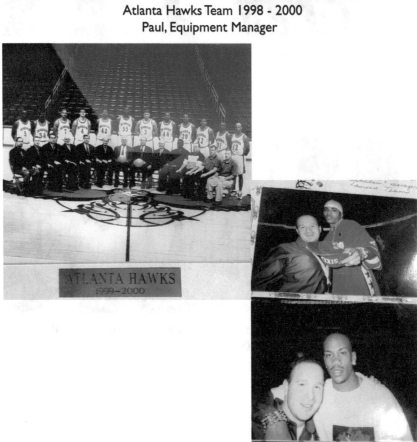

Olivia's first Christmas, 2000

Great times at our home at Orchid Island Beach Club in Vero Beach,
Florida—2001. Close to my parents.

Paul's first and only niece, Olivia Mary.

Olivia's first birthday with 3 uncles.

Fun get togethers in Vero Beach when everyone visited us there.
Frank and Paul with nephew Frankie.

You can see the joy in Paul's face being around Frankie and Olivia.

MOST HOLIDAYS WERE SPENT with us in Vero Beach, Florida, since it was close to Georgia and Paul would take a shuttle plane for a quick visit.

My dad started to become ill in 2002 and I eventually had to get both parents in a residential care facility near our home in Vero Beach, Florida. My mom was not able to stay home alone so I arranged for both of them to be together.

The next few years were extremely occupied with their medical care, with me motoring everything, but at least they were close by, safe, and together.

Paul visited them and me as often as possible. Of course, this was also during the time he was working two jobs: financial planning in the day and Twisted Taco at night. He certainly didn't have too much time left over. Besides living in Vero Beach, Florida for most of the year, we decided to purchase a residence in Carlsbad, California at the Four Seasons Residence Club. The summers were way too hot in Florida and decided California would be a nice break for a couple of months.

We also decided to spend time in New York so we would have an apartment there as well for a few months, enabling us to be with our East Coast children. We were then back to Florida in November. That scenario existed for almost six years, until we moved from Vero Beach altogether, after both my parents passed away.

It was difficult for me to be away for any length of time from my parents, because, as an only child, there was no one else. I therefore would make several trips back there while I was gone and hired private help to be with them every day in my absence.

In the summer, while in California, Paul and Richie would visit us. Even then, Paul had friends nearby and we'd all get together.

That summer, in late August 2002, Frank and Erin planned the first Giaccio-Bernasconi Reunion at their home in West Redding,

Connecticut. My friends, Marie and Bruce, had three children, Brian, Mark and Kristen and my sons grew up with them from birth. They would all stay with us or just visit us in Waccabuc, New York and we also enjoyed Disneyworld vacations with them. Lots of memories.

The Giaccio-Bernasconi reunion would be an annual summer tradition until Frank and Erin moved permanently to Vermont.

Manny was all about planning family get togethers whether it be dinners or vacations. Starting in 2003 Manny and I took all seven sons and their families to Disneyworld in Florida for several days. It took a lot of organization, but Manny was so good at that. Paul just loved these times, as we all did.

December 2002. Paul would always find time to visit his grandparents in the nursing home in Florida, as did the other boys.

December 2003
Another visit with Grandma and Pepa in Florida.

August 2003
One of Paul's visits to New York. He loved spending
time with Olivia and Frankie.

Christmas in New York City, 2003 with Brother Richie.

Paul and his Dad, 2003.

2004 - Manny surprised Paul and I with tickets to go together to San Antonio, Texas for the Georgia Tech NCAA Men's Basketball finals. Here with Paul's very close friends Matt and Mandy Harpring.

Paul and Governor Sonny Perdue of Georgia, 2003-2011.

I found so many little treasures stored away in Paul's boxes.

Thanksgiving 2004. We all went to Frank and Erin's home in
Vermont. Paul would always ski with them in the morning
before dinner. It was a tradition held for many years.

Christmas 2004 at Frank and Erin's.
West Redding, Connecticut

Seaport Village
San Diego,
California
2005

Paul visiting Grandma Mary,
August 2005 at Frank &
Erin's. West Redding, CT.

Disney, 2004
One of our family reunion vacations Manny would
plan, usually at Disneyworld.

THE YEAR 2004 IS KIND OF A BLUR. My parents were not doing well at all. We were in Florida, fortunately, as things were heating up. Dad had lost most of his memory and was going downhill very quickly. It was so hard watching this intelligent man become a vegetable before my own eyes. He was so medicated, which upset me, but his eyes would light up whenever we went. He didn't speak much, or not at all, but whenever Paul or any of the boys went, he said their names.

Mom was having her own issues with memory and depression. She wanted to just stay in bed most of the time, which was really sad because she was usually so friendly, loving to be around people to talk. Not anymore.

I employed a private aide to keep her company and to encourage her to move around, especially when I wasn't there.

With everything going on, and my mind totally distracted, I took a bad fall at home and had to be taken by ambulance to the hospital with; a severely broken ankle. I ultimately had surgery and wound up in a wheel chair for months. There was no way for me to manage the crutches. So, we were a fine lot. The three of us were down and out, but at least I still had my mind to monitor their medical care.

Then, my dad, Pepa Frank, passed away on March 19, 2005. Arrangements were made to bring my dad to New York for burial. As having served in World War II in the army, he was given the rendering of Military Funeral Honors and I was presented with our flag.

Manny and I flew to New York with my mom and her nurse and met our family there. All four grandsons were pallbearers. It was a very beautiful and touching ceremony.

My dad played a huge part in my sons' lives, as well as mine. We all took it very hard.

We all then went back to Frank and Erin's where our family

and friends gathered after the funeral. Manny and I then flew back to Florida with mom and her nurse.

In a few months, we were back in California for the summer and Paul was to visit us there once again, going to Padres vs. Mets games, seeing his friends and just relaxing by the pool.

By this time, Paul sold his financial planning business, left Twisted Taco and was in full gear with his ATM business. This was at the very beginning of what would be a huge success, although he didn't realize it at the time. He was always "working" even when he was vacationing. His mind never stopped.

It would, therefore, be almost a year before I saw Paul in person again. There was so much going on everywhere it seemed.

But, Mother's Day, 2006 would wind up to be one of my top remembrances.

Paul was always wanting his brothers, Erin, Olivia and Frankie to stay with him in Atlanta, Georgia, especially now since he just purchased his first home.

We all decided to make it happen. Paul rented a huge van so we could drive together as a group. I don't remember the last time it was all just us, and so it was really special. Paul, of course, planned all the events which included hiking, museums and local parks. We ate at child friendly restaurants having little Olivia and Frankie, who were always so good.

It made Paul so happy that we finally did it.

It would wind up to be the first and last time we would all be together there like that, although he was always trying to make it happen.

He would even try to get me to go, even myself alone, but it always seemed easier for him to come to me.

However, after twelve long years, in September of 2018, two months before he would pass away, I know I was divinely inspired to go. And, it was the last time I would see him alive.

More on that in this book.

The summer of 2006 brought us back to California with Paul's visiting us there. And, then it was the Giaccio-Bernasconi Reunion.

Paul was busy with being in about 12 wedding parties, either as best man or as an usher. He would call me and say, "I'm in another wedding!" And, many of these weddings were "destination weddings"—in other countries or islands!

And, we were busy with moving again!

In 2006, Manny and I had sold our Vero Beach home and bought an apartment in New York City, by Central Park and The Plaza. It was a great location and Manny was thrilled. Me, not so much.

Although living in the city is convenient and exciting (maybe too exciting) and we lived in a beautiful building with white gloved service, I loved having a backyard with my car in the garage at my disposal. So, we then purchased a brand new custom townhouse in Southampton, New York, where we could all go to on weekends and all summer. It was a good plan at the time.

Not wanting to leave mom alone in Florida, I brought her to a beautiful senior citizen assisted living facility in Westchester so that I could be close to her from New York City. She didn't last long there, even after the craziness with moving her there and fixing up her apartment. So, it was back to Florida where she was originally. I still don't know why. I don't think she did either. Paul and the boys were always being filled in with "Grandma stories" and how my life was filled with drama.

Honestly, those stories could fill another book. And, looking back at what happened, we would get hysterical laughing, but it wasn't funny at the time.

One drama just came to mind when I moved her to a Westchester County assisted living apartment which I completely decorated. Once settled, I thought it would be fun for her if I took her to a lovely water-view restaurant with her cousins and sister in laws. I met all the relatives at mom's place and everyone piled in my car to drive to the restaurant. It was really a lovely afternoon. We then returned to mom's apartment.

If you know Italian women, (myself included because I think that's in the genes) Italian women go no where without their "pocket books" nor do they ever put them down. Meaning, they will carry that "pocketbook" and keep it by their side even at someone's house. You never have it out of your sight. Even if there's nothing in it. So, that's the background.

Everyone was raving about mom's new digs, but she was not interested in hearing anything. They all were walking around to see the amenities, etc. and went back to her apartment as we all sat around. All of a sudden, my mom screamed "my pocketbook is gone!" I calmly told her it was probably in her closet or somewhere in her room from when we got back from the restaurant. She screamed, "No! Someone here stole it! I told you I didn't like this place." I'm trying to quiet her down because I didn't want any staff to hear these accusations since we were only there a few days! By now, I'm totally exhausted but trying to stay calm. We were all trying to figure out when we saw her pocketbook last. Did you hold it? Did you see her carrying it out of the restaurant? So, I ran to my car to go back to where we ate (15 minutes) but no pocketbook could be found there either. I went back to where everyone was waiting at the apartment trying to calm my mother.

Now we were all sitting in her room and I glanced over at her bed and noticed a lump under her covers, which looked weird. So, I went over to the bed and pulled the comforter back, and there was her "pocketbook". At some point when we all got back, she hid it there.

Need I say more?

Well, obviously, she didn't last long there. She wouldn't go out of her room or do anything. It was two weeks of hell. So, back to Florida she went, after I investigated the new place I thought she might like.

But that would be the next disaster.

You can only imagine the reaction of Paul and his brothers as all of this is unfolding.

So, the new place in Florida seemed nice in that it was in a private home with just a few residents. There seemed to be enough staff who were friendly and caring.

I didn't want her in Florida because I was in New York. It didn't make any sense, but I was trying to please her.

I settled her in, and she seemed okay. Fortunately, I still had mom's house in Cape Canaveral (with all this going on) and was able to stay there while I made sure she was fine before I flew back to New York.

I also hired an aide to visit her everyday while she was in her new place to make sure things were going smoothly and that she was eating properly.

Well, they weren't.

Mom would not get out of her bed. Her aide, Carol, who we knew for a couple of years, could not convince her to move around or get out of her room.

This was very concerning for me, since I was back in New York. I called mom every day and spoke to the staff and they said the same thing.

In the meantime, Carol got sick herself and had to go to the hospital, so now I didn't have those extra eyes on my mom.

Several days after that, the hospital called me to say that mom was rushed there by ambulance. And, then, a policeman gets on the phone! What is happening now? Well, it seems she was rushed to the hospital because of severe bed sores. And, I mean severe. It was so bad that the hospital called in the police to report negligence and abuse. Because she was not moving around, bed sores formed and evidently, no one looked! Carol was devastated because she admitted she never thought to check her bottom.

Well, she was transported to a wound care facility with specialized wound care physicians.

It was a total nightmare. The nursing home where it happened was cited and they were sued.

If there was anything to be grateful for, mom, in her dementia, was not even aware any of this was going on. She was happy as can be, and actually happier than she was at the nursing home. I, however, was so devastated and would have to make an excuse to leave her room so I could cry my eyes out, then go back in.

It was the beginning of the end for her.

Sadly, my mom, Grandma Mary, passed away November 19, 2006. What are the chances Paul would also pass away on the same date? November 19, twelve years later.

Once again, all fours sons were pallbearers. They took it extremely hard.

They had now lost both of their maternal grandparents, who were the world to them. They were there for each of those boys individually from the day they were born. Always there to listen or help in any way possible.

One of the many memories the boys had of their grandmother was how she would bring boxes of cereal that I refused to buy because of the sugar content. They would plow through those boxes, ready for the next batch to arrive the following Sunday, when mom and dad drove up for their traditional Sunday macaroni and meatballs.

And, the boys got a kick out of how little grandma actually paid for the cereal using her coupons! Especially Paul! It was such a game with them that lasted for years.

And, then, there was their grandfather, a huge, positive influence on all their lives. He was the one they went to for advice. When he came each week, he would be found outside in the backyard either playing baseball with all four of them, tinkering with the go cart he made for them, or walking the trails of our property.

Giaccio-Bernasconi Reunion Day
At Frank and Erin's, West Redding, Connecticut

Loved his niece and nephew so much.

Paul at the office.

"The Partners"
Paul, Jose, Ryan (Incognito)

Paul's calling card.

243

Ralph, our little Yorkshire terrier, joined right behind my father, although he was a very independent pooch. At the mere saying of the name Pepa out loud, Ralph would tear across the rooms to the front window, shaking his whole body, anticipating my dad's arrival. Even better, we noticed that Ralph would actually hear my dad's car as he turned into our 1000-foot driveway because he'd start barking and shaking by the same windows, long before my dad's car would appear.

Dad loved projects and I always had plenty of them on a list. The boys would be right by his side no matter what he was doing. He was a kind, gentle, brilliant man in every way and I'm so grateful to have had him in our lives. My mom too. I know they were a huge, positive, loving influence on my boys' lives. They loved unconditionally and, as we know, so did Paul.

Sometime in December each year, Manny and I would host a special Christmas dinner at the Four Seasons, New York City for our seven sons, their families and some extended family. Paul always made his plans to New York around that, and we always counted on Paul being there even though he lived the farthest away. Of course, now that he was self-employed with his ATM business, he could adjust his schedules, but he always had his computer to check on things.

Then, Christmas Day was spent at Frank and Erin's home in West Redding, Connecticut. Olivia and Frankie were surrounded by all three uncles, giving them lots of well-deserved attention. Paul, of course, would be found on the floor or couch playing with both of them. He loved them so much. He took a genuine interest in children. All children. Giving them quality time. It came so naturally to him and all children knew it.

At Christmas, he would send me photos of all the gifts he wrapped for his friends' children. Seriously, the gifts would be all around the perimeter of his living room floor! He was so thrilled to give them these surprises. And, when one of my children's books was released, he would ask me to individually sign each of about 50 books that he would then distribute. He couldn't wait for each of my books to be published in order to give them away. He had a spreadsheet of the names of his friends, along with the names and ages of each child, along with their birthdate.

Who does that? I honestly don't know of any single man caring so much for the happiness of the children.

Paul kept asking me when my fourth book, *It's Not Fair!* was coming out, I had a delay because of the illustrations and so the book was not to be ready for Christmas 2017. It was to be done by Christmas 2018 and he was so looking forward to that. He had his list ready and the plan was to bring the list that Thanksgiving so I could sign all the books, and then he would take them back in his suitcase, ready for Christmas gifts. Well, that was not to be. He passed away days before he was to arrive for Thanksgiving.

I wanted to fulfill his wishes, so I gathered the children's names by asking his friends, and sent them out individually in his honor. From Uncle Paul.

Great memories spending quality time.

Paul rented this van so we could all drive around together.
Mother's Day, 2006. Atlanta, Georgia.

We all said we should do this again.

Beautiful hikes together

I always wished he had children of his own.

I'm not that old to know that a gay man can still have a child by surrogate.

I actually approached Paul about doing that about two years ago (crazy mom that I am).

Paul smiled and said "Mom, I love being Uncle Paul to Olivia and Frankie as well as to my friends' children. Raising a child while running several businesses, going to concerts and traveling would be impossible. It wouldn't be fair to my child."

His answer made sense, but, nonetheless, I was disappointed in knowing I would never have a grandchild from him. A little Paul or Pauline.

But, as I have discovered in my 71 years, some things are just not meant to be. For reasons unknown.

Interestingly, about a month after Paul's passing, I received a phone call from one of Paul's female friends, and, without going into details, she told me that, because she so loved and admired him as a person, she offered to be his surrogate mother many years ago. He was very moved by that, but for the same reasons, she told me, he declined.

* * *

IN THE SUMMER OF 2007, Paul came to California as usual for a few days and that segued into our meeting up at Frank and Erin's for the Giaccio–Bernasconi reunion when we returned to the East Coast.

We got to see Paul again at Thanksgiving when we all went to Frank and Erin's in Vermont, their beautiful weekend getaway log cabin home. It became a tradition, especially for Paul, to spend that day with them skiing in the morning and dinner late afternoon with the rest of us non skiers. There would be a crowd of family and friends invited and was so picturesque. Manny and I would stay at the nearby mountain resort.

This Thanksgiving time with Frank and Erin was something Paul looked forward to and would continue until he passed away, spanning two more states.

Because of Olivia's upcoming skiing opportunities, they moved from Vermont to Vail, Colorado when Olivia was invited to join the Vail Ski Team. And, then, it was to go to Park City, Utah when Olivia joined the U.S. Ski Team, where they reside today.

Paul would spend every Thanksgiving with them no matter where they were.

Manny and I spent a Vail Christmas with all of them as well.

With all being told, I would get to see Paul three to four times a year. Of course, we would talk on the phone, but life was really busy for Paul.

Paul's ATM business was growing rapidly. He would call me to give me the current numbers of owned ATM machines throughout Georgia and other states.

He loved his work. It was his total passion.

It had everything he was good at. Organizing, planning, recording and money. It was, however, somewhat of a dangerous job because of the enormous amounts of cash being moved around to fill the machines everywhere. Anyone could be waiting for a delivery of cash for a robbery. So, they tried, as he explained to me, to go all different times. I would tell him to make sure he was filling them in daylight, with people around and to be alert for suspicious characters.

He gave me that Paul look that said "Mom, you're always worrying".

But, on one frightful day, it happened. August 2, 2011.

I will never forget that phone call from Paul telling me that Jose, his business partner, was shot in the face during a robbery. Paul was hysterical and at the hospital waiting for news. He was completely devastated for his friend.

Many surgeries and many years later, Jose has recovered, but who can truly recover from such an experience? Fortunately, the thief and attempted murderer was found and sentenced, but it doesn't change the horror of what happened.

From that time on, they decided to hire armored vehicles and security men to do most of the cash deliveries. And, then, only to find out that Paul was now licensed to carry a gun!

That's all I needed to hear!

I remember the day he told me about getting a gun license. Silence on my end of the phone.

"But, Mom! At least I can protect myself!"

I tried not to think too much about it, but it was always in the back of my mind.

As many people knew, Paul loved to travel and be with people.

It was so sad going through Paul's personal belongings, such

Manny reserved a suite at Mets Stadium for our whole family. Not easy getting all 7 sons in one place at the same time.

Topstone Park with Olivia and Frankie, Redding, CT.
Paul loved the outdoors.

Christmas 2009

Christmas 2010

Four Seasons, NYC
Annual Christmas Dinner for the family.
Manny and I hosted this for many years.

as his passports and seeing all the countries he had been to.

Iceland, Amsterdam, Scotland, Dominican Republic, Mexico to name a few.

In May 2012, all four sons came to Southampton with Erin, Olivia and Frankie. It was supposed to be a Mother's Day celebration although it wasn't on Mother's Day, but it didn't matter at all to me, as long as they were all here. Paul always had festivals to go to where he would supply his ATMs. He would travel everywhere transporting his machines, along with his employees to set up the tents etc. Many of these festivals were on Mother's Day weekend but Paul always managed to work around it to make sure he saw me somehow.

I don't know how he did it.

That time in Southampton in 2012 would be the last time they were altogether at our home there. We went to the beach mostly and Paul played all kinds of games with Olivia and Frankie there on the sand. I don't know where he got all of his energy. He was nonstop moving. It was time for another family reunion with both my sons and Manny's. Manny came up with the idea to go to Sagamore Resort on Lake George in June 2012. It seemed everyone needed a change from going to Disneyworld in Orlando.

It was a huge success. Sagamore is a beautiful resort on Lake George, with lots of things to do. Paul, Manny and I took a boat ride joined by some of our family. We actually invited some extended family, including my cousins from Canada, to join us on the trip.

This would wind up to be the last family vacation Paul would take with us.

I have a whole album from that time and a professionally photographer took a photo of our entire group during our special clambake.

In 2013, it was time for Manny and I to move once again.

I was tired of living in New York City and needed sunshine during the winter months. Manny did not like Florida living but we both loved California having spent many summers there, so we decided to make California our permanent home, while still keeping Southampton for summers so Manny could go to his Yankee games as much as possible when they played at home.

There was a lot to do obviously in this decision. We sold our New York City apartment, my parent's home in Florida, and our condo at the Four Seasons. There were moving trucks coming and going all over the place.

We settled in our home in Rancho Santa Fe, California by the fall of 2013. Paul was thrilled because two of his best friends, Ballard and Scott, along with their family, lived 15 minutes from our home.

These are friends he spoke to almost every day from Georgia, so they were extremely close. Now, he could see all of us in one trip!

And, on these visits, we all got together for hiking expeditions, dinners and walks on the beach.

Mother's Day 2012
Cooper's Beach, Southampton, NY

Southampton 2012, Mother's day

Family vacation at Sagamore Resort, Lake George, June 2012

Paul would usually choose the hiking trails we would take and, in 2014, when Frank, Erin, Olivia and Frankie were in for Easter, we all went as a big group to Devil's Punch Bowl, known as Cedar Creek Falls.

It was a grueling hike of almost 8 miles total! What did I get myself into? Going down to the bottom was not as bad as climbing back up especially after what happened at the bottom.

We had hiked down to a point where I knew I would break my ankle (again). It was very risky and there was too much to be concerned about, so I decided to hang back as they continued on to the waterfalls.

I found some nice flat rocks to sit on, while I could see them. Other people were around me, also sitting on rocks, just hanging out and relaxing. All of a sudden, I see Paul and Olivia and Frankie climbing up the waterfall rocks and it looked like they were planning on jumping down off the cliff's edge! I was too far away to yell at them to get down as this disaster is happening before my eyes! Little did I know that a photo journalist happened to be filming some people jumping off the cliff and those people happened to be my family!

As that is going on, all of a sudden, someone near me yells "rattlesnake!"

This huge snake was literally 2 feet away from me and I froze.

The young man next to me pulled out a knife and somehow killed it. I wasn't watching since I had already jumped into the arms of a perfect stranger next to me with my face buried in her shoulders. Everyone was screaming and others were coming over to see the dead snake. I profusely apologized to the woman for throwing myself at her but she was just amused at the whole ordeal.

The snake killer then proceeded to cut off the rattlers, tied it on a string and put it around his neck. You can't make this up. Then, he went into his backpack and took out this tiny, portable, throw away barbecue and started cooking the snake, handing out pieces (looked like chicken) with the tip of a huge knife.

All of this commotion got the attention of Paul and everyone by the waterfalls and they started waving and laughing, because they know there's usually drama when I'm around.

I don't know why, but it happens.

Paul came running to see if I was okay, with all of them following, and they couldn't believe the whole event going on around me. I was right smack in the middle of everything. The journalist even came over, and that's when I found that he videotaped my family jumping off the cliff.

Going back up that trail was almost impossible for me. The switch backs were endless, it was brutally hot, I couldn't breathe and couldn't talk. I had to keep stopping to rest. I later heard that some people had to rescued by helicopter doing what I was doing. I'm glad I didn't know that then or I would have definitely just given up and waited for one to throw down the ropes.

Paul kept encouraging me, "Mom, you can do this." He kept walking back to me saying the same thing. They were all laughing because I couldn't talk since I was always trying to catch my breath. They made me laugh, though, because they said they never heard me be so quiet.

It took nearly 2 hours, but I made it! Very slowly, but I made it. I was never so happy to see that parking lot. It was like water in a desert.

You can be sure that I did not go on the next hike when Paul, Frank, Erin were in sometime later on. It's called Potato Chip Rock, and everyone gets on line to have their photo taken on the edge of this sharp cliff. Of course, Paul had his photo there to show me.

He just loved hiking and all that went with it and he especially loved waterfalls. On a trip to Oregon, he sent me so many waterfall photos while hiking. Just magnificent.

Family hike at Devil's Punch Bowl

One of his friends has four young sons and Paul took them hiking many times. They never went before and loved it.

Any chance he got, he was hiking, and had a goal to hike at all the National Parks in the United States. He had done some, but never got to finish.

We had a full itinerary on the 2014 visit with everyone.

Besides that memorable hiking trip, Manny arranged for a suite at Petco Park, where we ate dinner, watched the game and even had the San Diego Padres mascot come to visit all the children. Paul's friends' families also joined us. Manny's son Jason, his wife Noelle, and their children joined all of us in California for that 2014 Easter celebration at our Santaluz Club. It was a very busy time together.

Paul was always torn as to where he should stay. I wanted him at our house, and both his friends and their families wanted him with them. It was always so funny how he tried to please everyone.

Ballard and Fallon's little girls wouldn't go to bed unless he read and played with them and slept there, and Scott and Anna's son needed him there too.

They loved their Uncle Paul. I would usually give in to let him stay with them as long as we had time in the day.

Many times we would all be together, walking the beach, going to lunch and just enjoying each other's company.

His friends have been amazing to me.

We always stay in touch. They are hurting so much, like me.

Our next family time with Paul would be during Christmas in Vail, Colorado at Frank and Erin's.

Paul would ski as often as possible during winter months there, leaving his skis and equipment at their new house. Erin mentioned it was so sad seeing all of it there after he passed, knowing he wouldn't come back to use it all. Erin recently told me, while reminiscing their skiing days together, how Paul would actually purchase a season ski pass, (even though he lived in Georgia) for where they were living, first in Colorado, and later in Park City, Utah.

Paul would ski with Frank, Erin, Olivia, and Frankie from when the lifts opened, to when they closed every day he was there. The funny part is how Paul put this app on his phone that would measure his vertical feet that he skied that day. He would then try to increase that reading the following ski day.

At the end of one of these days, as Paul was checking his final "vertical feet", his nephew Frankie, turned to him, and asked, "Uncle Paul, so like what are you getting from all this? It's not like you're getting a prize or anything!"

It was an observation that had deeper meaning for Paul.

No, he wasn't getting a prize, or medal, in the way we would expect, but it was an inner drive of Paul's to always be better than he was the day before.

That was his life in a nutshell.

Not to be perfect, but better than he was.

Besides skiing with them, for many years, Paul would organize ski trips with all his friends and their families, renting a huge home to accommodate everyone.

The ultimate planner and organizer, it came natural to him.

Nothing was impossible or complicated. He just made it happen with ease and competency.

At the end of the day, it was all about making people happy, no matter what it took. Which leads me to another story that I went back and forth about as to whether I should include it.

After careful consideration, I realized I had to, for many reasons. First of all, this story was a huge part of Paul's life on a continual basis.

Second, because this story WAS Paul.

And, third, it would bring a smile to the literally thousands of people who already knew it.

I did not know anything about Paul's "activity" until his funeral service, attended by hundreds of people, the day before Thanksgiving. Many of them still had their suitcases, having arrived straight from the airport. Many of Paul's friends spoke at the microphone, recounting their memories, and then one of them raised his arm, displaying a wristband.

The place erupted and other arms were raised.

I had no idea what was going on, but I later found out the significance.

I will not go into it, but I will disclose the bottom line.

Paul, for many years was an avid concert attendee. He created a huge spreadsheet (he was known for his spreadsheets) of every concert throughout the country.

He would buy his ticket and go. Then he became aware of many friends who couldn't go, because of the cost.

He did not like to see anyone left out, for whatever reason. So, he devised a plan so people could get in free.

Many times, these concerts were sold out so the venue couldn't sell tickets anyway, he reasoned.

This actually became a "hobby" in that people would sign up for it. Friends. Friends of friends. Complete strangers.

He did not make a penny doing this.

When asked why he went through so much trouble, he said he liked to make miracles for people who would otherwise never get to go. His friends shared that answer with me.

He also answered that with all these people he got in, with the food and drink they purchased, everyone was a winner.

Now, I am not condoning this! This was certainly not legal!

And, its why I struggled with adding this in the book, but from

Great idea having a photographer on top of the mountain.

Vail, Colorado

2014 - Easter at Santaluz Club

what I heard, in all the years he was orchestrating this activity, he probably admitted at least 8,000 people!

Yes, this disclosure was quite a shock to me, but, then again, knowing how unselfish he was, and how much he loved seeing people enjoy themselves, I could.

I will leave it there.

*   *   *

I have another great story that has to do with a Grateful Dead concert, a completely different situation from above, but I added it in The Georgia Memories.

His friend, Jack Lansky, generously spent about a hour and a half on the phone with me, recounting it.

Hope you get to read it.

2015

I DIDN'T SEE MUCH OF PAUL IN 2015—only once in August. He came to Southampton along with Frank, Erin, Olivia and Frankie as well as Bobby.

We did the usual when they came. We went to the beach, as well as ate great meals at the local fish restaurants on the water.

It was getting harder for him to get away. He had so many businesses he was taking care of. However, he went to Cuba to celebrate his friend Jose's 35th birthday. I remember Paul saying there were no ATMs in Cuba and they were running out of cash to stay there, since everything had to be paid in cash!

2016

ON THE FEBRUARY FOURTH weekend, Paul, Manny and I went to Deer Valley, Utah to watch Olivia in the FIS Freestyle International Ski World Cup at the Deer Valley Resort.

Thanksgiving was spent at our own home in Rancho Santa Fe, California with Paul, Frank, Erin, Olivia, Frankie and Bobby.

It was the first time that they would not be skiing, as was their

tradition, and Manny and I were so honored. I know how much they love those ski slopes!

It was a great time together again since it was really impossible with everyone's schedule, work and Olivia's traveling all over the world for her world cup competitions.

Always about making children happy (or anyone, actually).

Warrior Dash - 2015
Paul and his partners would provide ATM machines for these events and Paul would always run in them as well. One year all the partners ran. A bit muddy.

July 2015
Trip to Cuba for Jose's
35th Birthday.

Thanksgiving 2016
Rancho Santa Fe, California
Bobby, Paul, Me, Frank, Frankie

Deer Valley, Utah. - World Cup 2016

2017

ONCE AGAIN, PAUL, MANNY AND I would meet up with Frank and Erin in Deer Valley, Utah to see Olivia in the International World Cup in February.

Olivia's Uncle Paul was one of her biggest fans.

He was so proud of her, seeing her on TV in her competitions.

He would always call me after, and say, "Mom, can you believe her? Isn't she amazing?"

That April, Easter time brought Paul, Frank, Erin, Olivia and Frankie to Rancho Santa Fe, California, at our home for the holiday.

We had an amazing brunch at Rancho Valencia, which is probably the best place on the planet to have it.

We met up with Paul's friends Ballard and Scott, with their families, and took lots of photos.

I would not see Paul that summer, Thanksgiving, or Christmas, after that Easter. Knowing what I know now, that our days were so numbered, I wish I had gone to Atlanta that summer, while on the East Coast—woulda, coulda, shoulda.

Frankie, Frank, Erin, Olivia, Paul, Matt Harpring, Manny.

Deer Valley, Utah - 2017 Olivia in World Cup

Easter, 2017- Rancho Santa Fe, California

Easter 2017 at Rancho Valencia, California. We were all together for brunch with Paul's close friends Scott, Anna, Carter, Ballard, Fallyn, Blakely, and Kinsley.

Paul's Birthday - 2017
Go cart racing with his
friends/partners Jose & Ryan

Solano Beach, California -
2017

Paul's Godson Amici, Bryan Van Vranken's son.

The Final Year

Who knows when our "final year" will be?

If we did, would we live that last year differently?

Paul lived everyday as if it were his last. Yes, he lived a very full, happy, busy life. Every single day.

By this year, 2018, Paul's final year on earth, he was the successful owner of several large businesses and properties.

But his greatest success, he would tell you, was in the relationships he had with his friends and whatever good he did for others.

Many of these will be included in the last chapter, Lewisboro and Georgian Tales and Testimonies, but there were so many more!

As you will read, Paul was all about giving and making people happy. In the end, it's all that really matters, and for that, I'm so proud of him.

So, this is what Paul's final year looked like.

In March 2018, Paul came to California and, as always, spent a wonderful few days walking the beach, going out to breakfast and talking. We also met up with his friends and their children.

The photo taken on Solana Beach of Paul and I during that

visit, would ultimately be on a cake that he had made for me the coming September. More on that following.

I didn't know it at the time, but, after that March visit, I would be seeing Paul again. Very soon.

Manny planned a huge surprise 70th birthday celebration at the Angel's Stadium in Anaheim, California on April 28.

I thought I was going to see a game, invited by some friends who reserved a suite.

I almost wanted to refuse the invite because that afternoon I was the Chairperson for a large charity event benefitting Breast Cancer Angels.

My son Richie and his girlfriend, Dawn, came to celebrate my birthday and attend this event, which ended at 3 pm.

I was totally exhausted, but we all got in the car to drive north to Anaheim.

March 2018
Paul's visit to California, Solana Beach. This photo would ultimately be on a cake he made for me when I visited him in Atlanta, Georgia—the last time I would see him.

When we finally got to the stadium suite and entered the door, everyone was screaming "surprise!"

Only the photos taken can do my shock justice.

I just stood there looking around when all of a sudden, from the side, each son appeared, one by one.

The three of them flew in from 3 different states just for my party. They left that night.

Yes, it would be my last birthday, my 70th, that Paul was alive.

Claire's for breakfast, Solana Beach.

Angel Stadium, April 28, 2018. Huge 70th birthday surprise party. Sons surprised me by flying in just for the party. This would be the last photo I would ever take with all four sons.

Paul and Manny had a strong mutual respect for one another..

I have that shirt Paul had on.

September 27-29

FOR TWELVE YEARS SINCE our Mother's Day 2006 visit, Paul had been asking me to spend framily time with him in Atlanta, and to meet all his friends—his framily, actually.

He also wanted me to see his office and all that he does. But there was always something that kept me from making it happen, I am so sorry to admit.

But, by some miracle, or divine intervention, I have to believe, I decided to go on my way back home to San Diego from Southampton, New York, where we spend our summers.

The plan was to fly to North Carolina first to visit Bobby, son number three, in his new condo (that he wanted me to see) and, then, I would drive from North Carolina to Atlanta, Georgia, about a four hour drive. It was a bit daunting as I thought about driving on unknown roads by myself, but I was committed to do it. On my drive, Paul called to see my progress, giving me updates on how much farther I needed to go. He was always so calm and reassuring as I white knuckled the whole trip.

I arrived at the car rental place where he was waiting for me. He then transferred all my luggage into his car and we went straight to his house.

Paul had lots of plans for the next two days. That night we had a "framily" pizza dinner at Antico, in Sun Trust Stadium, which is close to his home.

Manny, ironically, had gone to see Paul at that stadium just two weeks before me to see a game and spent a great night with Paul.

Paul gave me the total tour of Sun Trust Stadium, all the restaurants, amenities, etc. It was just as fabulous as Paul described it.

It was a fun night meeting some of his close friends and their families.

Trip to Atlanta, September 2018. The last time I would see Paul.

From there Paul and I stopped at the store to get last minute items for the party at Paul's house the next evening. I had no idea what he had planned, but it seemed as though it was going to be a big deal from the way they were talking.

I was so exhausted from my travels and excitement; I went right to bed.

The next morning Paul and I went for breakfast and spent some time at his ATM office where everything took place. Monitoring 600 plus ATM machines was overwhelming to me, but Paul was as calm as can be. I watched him in action, literally taking care of several things at once, looking at monitors, talking and directing employees around, texting, answering calls (lots of them) all without blinking an eye.

I sat there taking it all in. It's what he always wanted—my seeing what his day is like.

We had a quick bite for lunch, and then he had to do some bank pickups for the business. All the bank tellers knew him well and he introduced me to everyone.

Back in the car, he said he had to "pick up the cake" so we drove to the bakery.

I waited in the car and when he came out, he was carrying an enormous box. As he was opening the back door, and putting the box on the back seat, I saw what was on the cake.

That special cake.

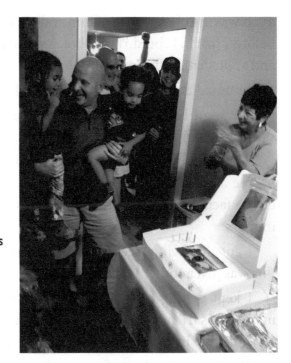

Big party at Paul's for me to meet everyone in Atlanta, 2018—and yes, I have that shirt he's wearing.

"Framily" night at Antico's.

It was the photo taken of him and me by Solana Beach, months before. I lost it. I couldn't help but cry to see his genuine sensitivity and appreciation for my visit.

I immediately took a photo and so glad I did.

We went back to Paul's place where the party caterers were starting to arrive to set up.

I lost count, but, by the end of the night, there had to be 75 people and lots of kids everywhere on the outside wrap around decks, facing the lake, and throughout the first and lower levels, indoors.

I got the feeling seeing how comfortable everyone was, that this was just another night at Paul's.

I kept getting introduced all evening and got to chat with many of his friends who obviously all loved him. I really got a feel for Paul's life in Atlanta in his over 20 years of living there.

There were no signs of anyone leaving at 11 PM and I was so tired, so I said good night, having to leave early the next morning for the airport.

Cheery as ever, Paul was up early and took me to Atlanta airport for my trip back to California.

I told him I was so happy that I went, loved all his friends, and so thankful for the welcoming reception and special cake with our photo. And, I told him how much I was looking forward to Thanksgiving when he would be coming to California, along with Frank, Erin, the Grandchildren, Bobby and hopefully his friends who were also invited.

It was only 2 months away.

Little did I know it would be the last time I would ever see him again. And, little did I realize, as I do now, that the trip to Atlanta, at that time, was meant to be.

All those friends that I met that night would ultimately be with me again in a consoling way.

Since I had already met them, and got to know them, their comfort was that much more meaningful.

There definitely seems to be a predetermined order in life. There are no coincidences. It's synchronicity. All my life, even before reading Carl Jung's work back from the 1960's while in graduate school, I was totally immersed in this idea. Then, in 1993, reading James Redfield's The Celestine Prophecy, further strengthened my beliefs.

The main thought is that coincidences are not instances of mere chance, but carry meaning. Synchronicity.

If we are vigilant, the universe will become more meaningful as we connect the dots. So not only am I ready for these experiences on a daily basis, I expect them to happen.

After 12 years of trying or wanting to get to Georgia but not making it happen, why did I do it THAT September? Because it would be right before Paul would die and it made him so happy to have me there, meeting everyone.

*　　*　　*

Paul's Final Days

A MONTH BEFORE THANKSGIVING, I always start preparing, if we are hosting the dinner.

I have done that my whole life. It was my favorite holiday, so I went all out. When the boys were little, I would take them to a farm near our Waccabuc home and get bushels of apples in October.

I'd set them up on the back deck, and the boys would help me peel and cut them for apple pies and applesauce.

I had a machine that would filter the seeds of the apples once they were cut up.

This was a yearly tradition. I then made about 13 apple pies and several containers of applesauce out of all that which I stored in our stand up freezer in the garage.

The freezer would be full by the time Thanksgiving came with the homemade food prepared, ready to heat up and serve.

The other food preparations the boys helped me with were meatballs and eggplant parmigiana, which also got frozen.

It was quality time with them, and they actually enjoyed it.

So, back to Thanksgiving 2018. Thanksgiving was not like the old days with the boys helping out in the making of so much food. I have simplified through the years, but still make pies (only 4) stuffing, meatball gravy and a potato dish to freeze.

Paul was to arrive on the Monday before Thanksgiving. Two days before, on a Saturday, I received a call from him that he was too sick to come for Thanksgiving. I was shocked! Paul never got sick, ever. He, along with his brothers, were rarely if ever sick as children, or adults, other than the occasional cold. They rarely took antibiotics.

I panicked immediately.

"Sick? What's wrong?"

He explained that he went for an annual checkup on Tuesday and, as he was leaving, was asked if he wanted a flu shot. He only got a flu shot once before in his life, years earlier, because he didn't believe in them, but, he continued, since he was going to be traveling a lot over the holidays, he thought he would get one.

He said he started to not feel well that Tuesday night and went to bed early. He woke up very sick on Wednesday with fever, vomiting, and pain. He figured it was a reaction to the flu shot, since he heard that could happen.

Thursday he was still sick, bedridden, and actually worse.

He had severe pain in his arms and back. One arm was totally unusable.

Someone at the house called the doctor on speaker phone.

(Actually, it wasn't a doctor he spoke to—not sure who it was). He told the female on the other end what was going on and the person said, "You have the worst reaction to a flu shot I ever heard of."

Someone drove Paul back to the medical group the following morning, Friday, and all they gave him was a pain pill and muscle relaxer.

As Paul filled me in on all this, sounding terribly weak, I started crying. Mothers know these things, I said "Paul, you MUST go to the hospital NOW!"

I told him something was very wrong because of that flu shot, and he needed to get right to the hospital. I was sobbing at this point and told him I would fly there right away. He said, "Mom, you're having everyone there for Thanksgiving, how can you leave?" I told him he should know how I always had everything done except the turkey and that I should go, but he said no.

I hung up and immediately called Frank. I was crying, telling Frank everything and how he had to call Paul to convince him to go to the hospital. He did, but Paul said he was not going to the hospital because they said it was a reaction to the flu shot and he just had to rest. I texted both Paul and someone staying at Paul's house right away, asking to keep me updated.

I was worried all that Saturday, so much so that I cancelled our plans that evening. I had a bad feeling I couldn't get rid of. I felt so helpless.

The next morning, Sunday, I texted again to see how Paul was doing.

"A little better" is what I got back.

I was relieved, yet cautious. I still wanted him to get medical care.

That Sunday we were home all day. And at the last minute, we decided to go for a little dinner.

I had not heard anything all day, and I was feeling uneasy.

At about 9:45 PM Sunday night, California time, my cell phone rang. It was late for anyone to call even on the West Coast, but, when I looked at the caller and saw it was the person living in Paul's house. I screamed. It would be almost 1:00 AM in Georgia.

I screamed Manny's name while answering because I knew it would be bad news in some way.

All I heard was sobbing and I kept screaming, "WHAT?! What?! Tell me!"

There was just this crying and no answer. Finally, I asked the question no mother ever wants to ask, "Is Paul alive?!!"

And, he screamed "NO!"

It's a moment in time I played over and over in my head for many months, until I couldn't do it anymore. It was so painful to hear because right then and there, you know it's over.

It's really, really over.

You can't go back.

You can't get a do over.

There's nothing to do.

He's gone for good.

And, I, his mother who would give my life in one second for any one of my sons, does not get the chance to do that.

There are no trades.

There's no bargaining.

Why couldn't it have been me?

Why my sweet Paul?

I am crying right now writing this because that question stills haunts and frustrates me.

Why do I have to live with this unimaginable grief and pain when it would have been easier to just take me instead?

Why am I here, and he's not? Over and over and over.

That same question.

For months.

And, even now, after 8 months, as I write this.

But, somehow, I'm starting to entertain some answers.

Answers that I struggled to fit like puzzle pieces that aren't quite the right ones but can be forced in anyway.

That's what I did.

I forced the answers into my psyche to keep my sanity.

To make this tragedy have a higher purpose. Hopefully.

Because, really, why do these things happen?

Not only to me, this mother, on this page.

But to all the mothers who have lost a child?

I will talk about those puzzle pieces in another section, under Grief.

Paul was gone as of that Sunday phone call.

And, in 2 days, we would be in Atlanta Georgia to be greeted by all of Paul's friends that I got to know in happier times just two months before.

GRIEF

*"Often it's the deepest pain which empowers you
to grow into your highest self."*
—Karen Salmansohn

I HOPE, IN THIS CHAPTER ON GRIEF, anyone who is either in grief now, or will be, will find some encouragement and comfort.

Martin Prechtel, a Mayan Shamon, living in New Mexico, teaches that the words for grief and praise are the same in the Tz'tujl language because you can only grieve for what you have dearly loved.

Grief is the soul's acknowledgement of what we value, and the honor we pay to what's dearest to us.

Grief is experienced not only with the loss of a child, which prompted me to research and share what you are about to read after the sudden, unexpected death of my son Paul, but grief can also enter our soul after a loss of any loved one, home, job, relationship, pet, etc. Grief is an unwanted, unexpected guest that arrives and does not leave.

Sorrow can do one of two things—destroy us completely from the inside out, or increase our capacity to love, live, and be joyful while still being in the midst of it. I'm here to tell you that such grief will never be "over." But I can, and will, share that it's possible to get relief from that gut wrenching heartache we wake up with that follows us throughout the day to bedtime. If we learn how, we can move forward through life when we thought it was not possible. Loss is a universal experience, but it's also a very personal one. We have no idea what a person is going through after, let's say, the loss of a child. It's totally unique. In reading hundreds of accounts of parents losing a child, I became heartbroken, and realized at the same time, that I was not alone. It's a club no one wants or should belong to. Most mental health professionals argue that child loss is probably the most difficult anyone has to bear. Dozens of articles support this understanding of a parent's heartache and lifelong struggle to embrace the pain of losing a child. Out-of-order death is devastating. And, here I am.

When asked about his son years after he died, Gregory Peck replied: "I don't think of him every day; I think of him every hour of every day."

That's true for me, too.

Paul's death plummeted me into an abyss from which I am still trying to emerge, but not as the same person. I know part of me died with him, whereby other parts were born. Life, as I knew it, will never be the same.

But, that doesn't have to be all bad. As I started to come back to the land of the living, I found I had a purpose.

I have drawn inspiration from the huge community of suffering people, past and present, who has endured, prevailed, and became committed to helping others.

It's truly about turning our pain into a motivation to save others. We have the power to choose how we respond.

Victor Frankl, in *Man's Search for Meaning*, suggests we have the power of choice in the face of terrible loss. Frankl concluded that the World War II prisoners in the Nazi death camps transcended their circumstances because they found meaning in their suffering.

"If there is meaning in life at all, then there must be meaning in suffering. Suffering is an ineradicable part of life, even as fate and death. Without suffering and death, human life cannot be complete. The soul grows larger through suffering and can experience both sorrow and joy at the same time."

In *Lament for a Son*, Nicholas Wolterstorff agrees.

"The Valley of suffering is the vale of soul making." Loss requires we integrate sorrow and joy as we go through life.

We are promised, "Blessed are they who mourn for they will be comforted." (Rom 8:26-27)

The loss of a child is like a terminal illness that one cannot get relief from. But, in transcending that illness, I began to heal my decimated soul. Nothing can actually mitigate my sadness in the loss of my son Paul. The suffering I have gone through, along with my family, and all his friends, is an ongoing story that is still being written. Although we all have lost someone so dear in our lives, we also need to see the good that has morphed because of the loss.

His passing suddenly gave me the need and desire to write. I just needed to write. It was all I could think about. Not only to write about my son Paul, and what he meant to so many people who knew him, along with all he accomplished from childhood, but to intermingle all of that with observations I wanted to express for years, but never did.

What I found, as I got into the process, is that the insurmountable grief I was feeling became lighter. Not gone. But lighter. And I then came to the realization it was because I found a purpose. By acting upon something positive, hopefully with positive results, I could turn a devastating event into one with beneficial outcomes.

Death is uncontrollable. We have no say in the time or place. You don't get a do-over, either. It's done. Over.

But, what we do have control over is what we can do to

ultimately honor who or what we are grieving. That's the part to figure out, and it's an individual quest. No one can tell you what that "thing" is, but I can tell you it involves action. Personal, thought provoking action once you discover, define or recover one's life purpose.

It's an opportunity that's been given as opposed to what's been taken away. And, it's all about giving.

Find a person, animal, or cause who needs love, time and attention. Dedicating ourselves to the necessities of others, or volunteering, can be such a healthy tool, providing purpose and direction.

The swift current of grief can swallow us up if we let it, but, then, what was learned? There is always a "takeaway" in everything that happens to us.

Yes, it takes time to move through the shock, sadness, anger, bitterness and confusion after a death, and no one should be rushed into some time frame. But, then, there comes a time when we know enough is enough.

Countless books have been written on the process of mourning. There's the well-known Kubler-Ross five stages of grief: denial, bargaining, anger, depression and acceptance as part of the healing process. Although these are normal and understandable phases to go through, one huge stage that few people talk about is the stage of giving or philanthropy as part of the healing process.

In taking small steps at a time, we can still love with the loss, while living a more productive life, all at the same time. And, there's no greater gift to oneself and others than the act of giving when in grief.

Yes, that loss will always be with us, without a doubt, and it will always be part of who we become, because of its presence.

But living with pure grief is not productive for anyone. For sure, my son Paul would not approve. He always believed in rising above adversity, and always said I was strong. I can't let him or myself down.

Paul, in 2 Corinthians 12:7-10 says "there is always a purpose for our suffering. Instead we are promised grace."

It's not what happens to us that matters as much as what happens IN us.

Grace can transform us in a new life marked by joy, compassion and gratitude in simple blessings even in the midst of darkness.

We can and must get to the other side of tragedy.

And, the only way to do that is ACT. It means to get out of one's body and mind to figure out how and what to do in keeping your loved one's memory alive, while helping others. That's the key. While helping others.

For us, it started with the notion of being kind and generous like Paul was, hence LIVELIKEPAUL became the mantra on a clothing line. Of course, people are always curious as to the meaning of those words on sweatshirts, bracelets, etc. which then leads to the referral back to Paul and his goodwill to others, with the hope of spreading the same.

A foundation was also set up at Georgia Tech, providing scholarships for students who are known to participate in outreach and charities alike.

This book is being written to encourage people to become aware of the value of love and respect for all. All of these things keep Paul's name present in my life, kicking grief out the door as I cleaned house from my unwanted guest. I had to make lemonade out of lemons, as my book *It's Not Fair!* suggested. I could not go around saying It's Not Fair!

Any project where you can be of service to someone or something can alleviate the pain. Find that project. Of course I am sad. His death has rewritten the script of my life, and it's now on a different path, one that will continue the love Paul was known for.

Tragedy into triumph, amidst very difficult circumstances. It's how we respond to loss that ultimately affects the substance of our lives. How I proceed with this new reality in my soul is what will save me. That and that alone.

Coping with death leads to questions about the purpose of life while trying to justify the realities of death.

Yes, it can feel overwhelming. Learning how to cope with loss (grief) has been a common dilemma.

C.S. Lewis, in *A Grief Observed*, writes about what is required of us in living this life in which we have to expect the pain and sorrow of the loss of those whom we love. In the loss of his beloved wife, C.S. Lewis recounts his attempts to come to grips with, and, in the end, defeat, the emotional paralysis of losing the love of his life.

"No one ever told me that grief felt so like fear." (C.S. Lewis)

It's that fear of having to go on without our loved one that is so paralyzing, but, we can find our courage in the act of giving.

Giving. There's that word again.

I'd like to take this even a little step further: Considering Grief as a blessing.

Really?

Rumi, the 13th Century Sufi theologian and poet, wrote that "grief can be the garden of compassion. If you keep your heart open through everything, your pain can become your greatest ally in your life's search for love and wisdom."

Rumi included everyone in his teachings, providing true testimony and proof that people of all religions and backgrounds can live together in peace and harmony. His visions, words and life teach us how to reach inner peace and happiness so we can finally stop the continued stream of hostility and hatred, achieving true global peace and harmony. Even today, Rumi's poems can be heard in churches, synagogues, zen monasteries and stage performances.

This wisdom from Rumi in the Middle Ages, suggests to shift ourselves right in the middle of the grieving process, turning our sorrow into something sweet tasting.

But, what does this really mean?

If we can accept that we are all part of an intelligent universe and system, and there are no accidents, there is always something to learn in the middle of sorrow. Somehow, if we could know, in the midst of our dark times of despair, that it was all in the "plan" urging us to rise to a place for the good, perhaps there would be more of an acceptance. Perhaps it could be comforting to see that it's all part of the perfection of our universe, which has an invisible organizing intelligence flowing through every cell of creation, including the many painful, gut-wrenching experiences we encounter.

And, instead of endlessly suffering in grief over these circumstances, we can be open to the gift of sweetness (hope) in these sorrows.

Rather than be immobilized with anguish, we can know that this despair has within it some sweet blessing.

It's what Rumi taught and it's what I now personally understand. While grieving the loss of Paul, the most devastating event of my life, I can also see the sweetness of the loss as well in writing this book along with all the other higher purposes that have emerged.

Charles Stanley, Baptist pastor and founder of Touch Ministries, makes this all very clear in his chapter on adversity and how many assume that when illness, loss or trouble emerge, it's because of some punishment.

When Jesus passed a blind man going through Jerusalem with His disciples, the disciples asked, "Who sinned, this man or his parents, that he should be born blind?" (John 9:2)

It's the question we still ask today in our grief. "Why did this happen to Paul?"

"Why did this happen to me?"

I frustratingly remember going through that same blaming game, searching for answers. It's a fruitless journey.

There's much wisdom obtained in the Bible. Jesus' response and its implications were both enlightening and staggering.

"It was neither that this man sinned, nor his parents, but it was in order that the works of God might be displayed in him." (John 9:3)

So, it was a purpose FOR, and not a result OF. I know that's a hard concept to take in.

Sometimes the explanations we desperately seek become clear when we respond to adversity, or loss, with an open mind.

What am I supposed to learn from this? There's a blessing in here somewhere. The fact that the Son of God allows those He loves to suffer and die for the sake of a higher purpose may be a difficult idea to fit into one's theology, but I think I actually get it now, by what I am witnessing since Paul passed.

I will admit I'd rather have him here, but I have made the choice to accept this as an explanation, since I have nothing else.

We all look for the compelling claim of fairness—we have this vision of righteousness if we do it all correctly.

It's a "deserving" that we should get when we put out what's needed. Fair would mean that life rewarded the good and punished the bad. No, it doesn't always work out that way.

And, it's why I wrote the book *It's NOT FAIR!*

How ironic is it that my book *It's NOT FAIR!* would be released days before Paul's passing? It was my fourth published children's book, and the messages that I presented in that book were meant entirely for me as it would turn out. I would need to reread my own book over and over to help myself. It's the book Paul was waiting for to give to all his friends' children at Christmas.

Paul was scheduled to arrive days before Thanksgiving 2018 with the list of names that I would personally sign in each book And, he was to take a whole suitcase of signed books back with him. Of course, that never happened.

He died on the day he was to leave for San Diego.

It's NOT FAIR! that Paul died and never made it for Thanksgiving.

It's NOT FAIR! that I would never see him again.

It's NOT FAIR! that he would never attend another concert with all his friends!

It's NOT FAIR! that getting a flu shot would end his life.

My book admonishes, once we've established all the reasons "it's not fair," and once we know we have no control to change them, we need to take the next step. And, that's to concentrate on what we have, rather than what we don't (or lost).

In other words, concentrate on what IS going on in our lives that IS fair, appreciating and being grateful for all of it, rather than what's unfair.

If not, we will lose it all—the UNFAIR and the FAIR.

(I actually have a chapter on the power of Gratitude included in this book.)

"I will not cause pain without allowing something new to be born, says the Lord." (Isaiah 66:9)

Even through the greatest adversity, He is working to develop our character and life for the good.

The circumstances and events that we see as setbacks are oftentimes the very things that launch us into periods of intense growth. Adversity and grief become easier to bear.

Paul, in Romans 8:28, emphasizes this principle:

"All things work together for good to those who love God, to those who are called according to His purpose."

In researching as much as I could about adversity, and grief as a result, I found that unless we accepted adversity as a tool in the hand of God (Universe) for the advancement of our spiritual lives, there really weren't any other options available.

It's letting go of what we thought could have or should have been, and pursuing what can be done for the greater good.

There is no other satisfactory explanation or comfort for the randomness of a loss, but indulging in destructive emotions of cynicism, bitterness, despair and anger won't give me any for sure.

I may not see all God's mysterious purposes come to fruition, but I already see enough to know I'm on the right path.

And, although I'm the author of this book, God is the author of life itself. And I like to think that each random tragedy can set off a whole other chain of events benefitting generations to come.

New beginnings are often disguised as painful endings. Yes, we all want life to be "fair."

Sometimes it is, sometimes it isn't.

I've heard it so wisely stated that "if you are depressed you are living in the past. If you are anxious, you are living in the future. If you are at peace, you are living in the present."

And, that brings us back to acceptance of what is now (the present).

Does everything really and actually happen for a reason?

And, can we ever learn to let go if we can accept that what happened was supposed to be and could not be changed?

The American Buddhist psychologist Tara Brach says to embrace suffering with the silent inner mantra:

I CONSENT.

She says that everything that has happened and will happen is life's perfection flowing through us.

We have to remain centered regardless of the circumstances because "life" will reveal itself in its own way, without our permission (consent). There it is again.

Acceptance. Consent. (Lao Tzu, 601 BC)

Deepak Chopra, another one of my favorite authors who I have had the pleasure of meeting and speaking to many times, reminds us to "be comfortable with and embrace paradox, condition and ambiguity. It is the womb of creativity."

Peace of mind won't come, he explains, if we need to have life explained. When synchronicity happens, trust that the complete picture of events will unfold. A greater plan is being shaped.

Yes. It is. I see it evolving every day.

The effects and purposes of adversity (grief) were discussed by even Aristotle, the Greek philosopher (384-322 BC):

"It is during our darkest moments that we must focus to see the light."

He believed that we each have our own "entelechy," our highest unique potential. Everything happens for a reason to help your "entelechy." Your experiences are designed to shape, define, and grow you into the "mightiest you" possible. He suggests we tap into our "conscious insight" which is the ability to analyze and see life from many perspectives—all the whys and hows to stay strong and be your mightiest self in stormy times, instead of giving up. He acknowledges that life is a fusion of free will and destiny.

It's the free will that gives you the choice to turn pain into gain, seeking out the insights that are meant to be learned.

It's starting to all take shape in my brain. It's coming together, little by little. From the ancient philosophers to the present ones. I needed answers, explanations and validations. I needed help.

Why do bad things happen to good people?

That age old query. Yes, bad things do happen to good people, and it's how I respond that defines my character and quality of my life.

People come into our lives for a reason, season or lifetime, always teaching us something. Paul Coelho, the famous contemporary Brazilian novelist, says:

"There are moments when troubles enter our lives and we can do something to avoid them. But they are there for a reason. Only when we have overcome them will we understand why they were there."

Yes, he agrees, pain and suffering are unavoidable, but remaining a victim after tragedy is a choice.

Besides, he goes on, someday it will make sense. There very well might be a greater plan taking place behind the scenes.

Although this grief will look different over time, it is part of me.

There's this unspoken explanation that eventually you'll be who you were before. But, the truth is, after the loss of a child, especially, you are never the same. I know that losing my Paul has shaped me in a different way forever. My grief will be forever, whereby, my healing, in the ways I've discovered to assist me, will allow that pain to become lighter every day. It's finding how both grief and healing can work together productively.

Yes, Paul's death has rewritten the script of my life. My new normal.

I know I'll have many good days filled with gratitude and times of respite from sadness, but I will never get over the loss.

Nor should anyone feel they have to "get over" their loss.

I'd like to suggest it's about "moving forward" with such loss in achieving a higher purpose for myself and others along the way.

Becoming a better version of myself, while assisting others to do the same. Living with love and loss side by side.

This says it best:

"The reality is that you will grieve forever. You will not 'get over' the loss of a loved one; you will learn to live with it. You will heal and you will rebuild yourself around the loss you have suffered. You will be whole again, but you will never be the same. Nor should you be the same nor would you want to." (Elizabeth Kubler-Ross, David Kessler)

I realized my new beginnings in life came from the end of other beginnings. It's only in looking back that I was able to connect the dots, that I found a reason to start over. My new beginning was precipitated by the beginning of Paul's life, to the end of his life. The end of a beginning. "They" say, (whoever "they" may be) that we gain something from every loss. I had to find that "something," get it in motion, and it started with this book. I had to push myself forward, gaining strength along the way, knowing my new beginnings were waiting.

I had to find a way to live with love and loss, simultaneously, not only for my benefit, but, hopefully, as an example for all those who have suffered loss in one way or another.

And, finally, as I stated in my very first children's book, entitled *What is An Angel?*, we are never alone.

Walking silently next to us are our angels, encouraging us to take the next step, pushing us forward no matter what.

And, of course, I know Paul is always with me. Knowing him, he's been organizing all the angels in heaven. Perhaps even getting them into some concerts.

— ✳ —

GRATITUDE

"Gratitude is not only the greatest of virtues,
but the parent of all others."
—*Marcus Julius Cicero*

THE MONTH OF NOVEMBER, specifically Thanksgiving Day, is a time we think about gratitude, "thanksgiving." It's a time when families all over the United States gather for a huge, special meal while reconnecting, and sharing memories and blessings.

This national holiday of gratitude was born out of hard times. The first Thanksgiving took place after half the Pilgrims died from a rough month and year, in 1623, in Plymouth, Massachusetts. On this occasion, the colonists gave thanks to God for rain after a two-month drought.

However, President Abraham Lincoln declared Thanksgiving a federal holiday in 1863, during the American Civil War. "Together," Lincoln said, "citizens would implore the interposition of the Almighty Hand to heal the wound of the nation."

And for "peace, harmony, tranquility and Union," Americans could be thankful.

When times are good, people take prosperity for granted and believe they are invulnerable.

Once you realize everything or everyone can be taken away, it becomes harder to take for granted.

So, yes, crisis can make us more grateful, and gratitude helps us cope with crisis. Thanksgiving Day is especially set aside each year to express our gratitude.

It's also the time Paul passed away, days before Thanksgiving. He died on the day he was to arrive at our home in San Diego, California, along with my other sons, their families and friends. The dining room table was opened to its fullest capacity, and set.

Various pies were prepared, along with side dishes and the stuffing. That was me, always prepared. Never waited for the last minute with anything.

Always prepared.

What I wasn't prepared for was Paul dying. Who's prepared to get that phone call? That your son is dead? Who prepares for that?

* * *

This chapter on Gratitude is being written on Cooper's Beach, Southampton. The same beach where Paul would play Kadima (beach paddle) with Olivia, Frankie, Erin and Frank just about where I'm sitting. It's where we would all congregate each summer. I have lots of videos taken right here in this spot.

As I breathe in this salty air today, I'm having to take deeper breaths because I'm feeling a crying episode coming on. Usually when I take deep breaths, I can ward off the tears that are usually always "right there." I can't start crying now. It's hard to write and cry at the same time.

Back to Thanksgiving. Everyone seems to think about being grateful this time of year. Blessings in the form of health, family, friends, opportunities, peace, etc.

Thanksgiving was always traditionally my favorite holiday. For me, Thanksgiving was real. It wasn't marred by materialism like Christmas, with shopping out of control, for things people probably don't even need.

Thanksgiving, for me, meant family and friends coming together, and being thankful for having them in your life.

And then, Thanksgiving 2018 happened. When my family would be coming, but didn't. There would be no turkey in my oven, filling my home with that unmistakable aroma.

Instead, a few days before Thanksgiving, we'd be flying to Atlanta, Georgia, for Paul's funeral.

Deep breaths again.

And, on Thanksgiving Day itself, we would arrive back to San Diego, with Paul's wooden box of ashes.

I guess you can say Paul technically did come on that Thanksgiving, but not the way I would have ever imagined.

How were we ever going to deal with Thanksgiving Day again? My favorite holiday? And, be thankful on top of it all?

I had to really dig deep. Deeper than I ever had to before. I'm not one to give up. I knew there were answers out there. But where?

And, then, I remembered "the book."

About three years ago, Manny and I attended a service at Horizon Christian Fellowship Church. Having "left" the Catholic Church, for reasons already disclosed in this book, we have enjoyed the sermons and music at Horizon in Rancho Santa Fe, California, from time to time.

On our way out that particular day, I wandered into the bookstore there, as usual, and impulsively picked up a book entitled *1000 Gifts* by Ann Voscamp, not knowing anything about it or about its author. To be honest, the cover attracted me, which supports my opinion that the cover of a book IS so important, and why I always made sure the covers of my children's books were bright and colorful. I guess it goes against the idea that people claim "you can't judge a book by it's cover." Well, maybe not always, as proven many times for me, as in this case.

Several days later, I began reading *1000 Gifts*, along with all the other books I had going, but suddenly it was the only book I kept reading until it was finished.

And, then, I read it again.

It is a riveting memoir where Ann strives to find the meaning of life, after her horrific childhood and adult experiences. She battles to believe and understand how there could be joy in the sorrows of life along with the moments of celebration.

She goes to the Bible for answers and finds them in the term Eucharisteo.

Her mentioning and explanation of Eucharisteo fascinated me so I studied it further at the time. Keep in mind, my learning the meaning of this word Eucharisteo occurred years ago, long before Paul died. It would eventually put me on a path of healing.

It just confirms what I strongly believe—that everything on this earth is connected and on purpose. Why did I choose that book? Why did I study the concept of Eucharisteo at that time, as almost a preparation of what was to come? I even remember sharing what I learned with many friends in those days, and that book would always be on my bedside table.

Put simply, but I will discuss in more detail, Eucharisteo encompasses the idea that gratefulness, expressed during difficult times, will ultimately bring joy. And, I certainly needed some of that joy, however I could get it!

Even after 17 years of Catholic education, this term, Eucharisteo, was foreign to me. Catholics unfortunately never really studied the Bible in its entirety. As an adult, I attended neighborhood Bible study groups for many, many years, but still never came across this word.

The Eucharist is the central symbol of Christianity which places the whole of our lives into the context of thanksgiving (gratitude).

Christians have received Holy Communion for centuries,

hearing the words "...took bread, and when he had given thanks, he broke it and gave it to them, saying, 'This is my body, which is given for you. Do this in remembrance of me.' " (Luke 22:19)

I probably heard these words thousands of times at Communion, but never dissected the meaning.

Eucharisteo is the Greek word for "thanks." The root word of Eucharisteo is charis, meaning "grace." Jesus took the bread, saw it as grace, and gave thanks. He took the bread, knew it to be a gift, and gave thanks. So, Eucharisteo, which means thanksgiving, also envelopes the Greek word for grace, charis. But, there is also the Greek word for joy in it's derivative, chara.

When Jesus said these words of thankfulness, He knew He was about to be crucified, but saw joy in knowing He would be a part of millions of people made righteous through this sacrifice.

He felt thankful to the Father for the grace and glory that was coming because of the Cross, and this gave him joy.

That is Eucharisteo—thanks, grace, joy.

Eucharisteo is taking pain that is given, and giving thanks for it since it has joy in there somewhere, sometime.

Is that saying I have to be thankful even in the death of my son Paul because if I have faith in it, there is promised joy that I am being thankful for? I am to accept and know there is joy coming, and it's why I am thankful?

This is the secret of giving thanks in all circumstances! Expect future joy because it is promised. Therefore, there is no circumstance that can steal your thanksgiving believing this. But, of course, sight unseen, this would take the faith of a mustard seed.

So, if we are to experience grace and joy, we must begin to produce thankfulness (gratitude) especially during times of brokenness. This is what I had to wrap my head around. It wasn't easy.

"Give thanks in all circumstances, for this is God's will." (Ironically written by Paul the apostle, Thessalonians 5:18)

Gratitude, in the hardest of times, will open the mind and soul for healing. There's no antidote for grief other than gratitude. And, that's why I've included this chapter on Gratitude in this book. As a part of my healing.

In Philippines 4:6-7, Paul the Apostle writes, "Do not be anxious about anything, but in every situation, by prayer and petition, with thanksgiving, present your requests to God. And the peace of God, which transcends all understanding, will guard your hearts and minds in Jesus Christ."

These messages were all over the place in the Bible.

One of Paul's friends, Roger, told me someone asked him if the *LiveLikePaul* shirt he was wearing was for Paul the Apostle. Ironically, many of Paul the apostle's writings could have been written by our Paul or about what he thought. Such as in the following:

In Philippines 4:11-12, Paul the Apostle writes, "I have learned to be content with whatever I have. I know how to live on almost nothing or with everything. I have learned the secret of living in every situation, whether it is with a full stomach, or empty, with plenty or little."

Anyone who knew Paul, the verse above (written by Paul the Apostle) could have been written by Paul, my son.

He never needed or demanded anything from when he was a child. He was happy with whatever he had. Happy when he had little; happy when he had a lot. His happiness didn't depend upon what he "had."

He wasn't one to buy fancy clothes, or any clothes, for that matter! He wore tee shirts and shorts all the time. On special occasions, he wore the same blue plaid short sleeve cotton shirt as depicted in so many photos. I now have that shirt, and treasure it.

He could have well afforded anything and everything, but he was not into materialism. He was simple. His life was not about things and possessions.

His life was about people and how he could connect to make their lives better.

Those exact sentiments are expressed in the verse below, also written by Paul the Apostle!

"Brothers and sisters, we urge you to warn those who are lazy. Encourage those who are timid. Take tender care of those who are weak. Be patient with everyone. See that no one pays back evil for evil, but always try to do good to each other and to all people. Always be joyful." (Thessalonians 5:14-16)

I smiled reading these, because I felt Paul's presence. And, for that, I'm grateful.

So, by now, the message is clear. We need to be grateful in all things. All things mean just that: good things and difficult things, not just some things. We are commanded to be grateful because being grateful makes us happy.

"One act of thanksgiving, when things go wrong with us, is worth a 1000 thanks when things are agreeable to our inclinations." (St. John of Avila)

Processing a life experience through a grateful lens does not mean denying negativity or giving it a form of superficial happiology. It just means that we can transform an obstacle into an opportunity. It's re framing a loss into a potential gain.

This was a lot to take in. Being grateful for the good, bad, and ugly? Being grateful in Paul's passing?

But, then again, what is my alternative? The only one I can think of is a life of depression, totally useless to myself and others.

Would that bring Paul back? Or would being thankful for the joy in carrying on his legacy of kindness and love offer better results all around? To myself and others?

Lao Tzu, author of *Tao Te Ching*, ancient philosopher (604 BC-531 BC) says "Life is a series of natural and spontaneous changes. Don't resist them—that only creates sorrow. Let reality be reality. Let things flow naturally forward in whatever they are like."

"Be content with what you have; rejoice in the way things are. When you realize there is nothing lacking, the whole world belongs to you."

Many times we fail to see the abundant blessings in our everyday lives.

Unfortunately gratitude is a virtue that is becoming lost in our world of "gimme, gimme" or "I should have this."

We will always lack something because abundance and lack of abundance exist simultaneously in our lives. When we choose to focus on the abundance present—love, health, family, friends, work, nature, our strengths, etc., we experience peace.

It was sometime in the first couple of weeks, in my deepest despair, that I was on the phone with my daughter-in-law Erin, crying as usual. It was Erin who reminded me about keeping a gratitude journal. Up to then, I had forgotten all about the study on gratitude that I had done years before, and how imperative it is. Gratefulness was the last thing on my mind! My world was shattered.

However, her reminder brought it all back. I knew she was right. The next thing I knew, I received a gratitude journal from her and I was on my way. I have to admit it was hard at first, but my blessings eventually filled up page after page.

There was so much to be grateful for! I have been surrounded by the most loving family and friends, sons that I love so dearly and who love me back. A husband that adores me and dedicates his every waking hour to making me happy. And there is my joy in writing, and my present good health.

And, then, the most amazing gratitude appeared in my brain. One that I almost took for granted. Although my Paul was taken from me (all of us) at 43 years of age, it could have been far more devastating if he died at 20 years old, at his own hand, if not for the loving intervention of his friends.

God gave him, and all of us, 23 bonus years.

How would I have dealt with that at the time?

Yes, I'm grateful it was resolved when it was.

It makes you realize, in writing your gratitudes, that anything can happen at anytime and with anyone.

There is nothing, absolutely nothing, we can take for granted. It's why we need to stay grateful in the present, no matter what.

In following what I learned about Eucharisteo, and gratitude in his passing, I began to see the grace and joy. Why? Because I now see the plan. Paul's time was done here on earth, but his passing created a firestorm of love and kindness, spreading across the world. His examples of what it means to reach out and help others has influenced and affected people everywhere, with those people wanting to do the same. From what I've read and heard in countless testimonies through phone calls, texts, emails, etc. he has changed many lives and those lives have been committed to change other lives. I have included many of these in the Testimonials Chapter. So, there's my joy and grace in my thanksgiving.

It's what God promised if we give thanks (gratitude) in ALL things.

Now I get it. I am living what I learned years ago. Had I not picked up that book, had I not wanted to dig deeper into that concept, I never would be where I am today.

Is there a divine plan at work for us as we go through life?

Do our choices create our destiny? I think so.

I see connections everywhere I turn as I look back.

It's all "meant to be" and, our journey is to accept and follow our course, and not to ask,

"Why me? Why this? Why now?"

It's to accept what is and find the higher good in it.

"Those with a grateful mindset are able to see the message in the chaos, and even though life may knock them down, they find reason, if only small ones, to get up and keep moving." (Dr. Steve Maraboli)

Even Ralph Waldo Emerson weighed in on gratitude in all things:

"Cultivate the habit of being grateful for every good thing that comes to you, and to give thanks continuously. And because all things have contributed to your advancement, you should include all things in your gratitude."

Acceptance. Gratitude.

Without them, I can see I (as well as anyone) would lead a life of bitterness. Basically, the life of a victim. There's no way I could go down that road.

My sons would always tell me I was strong.

Most people say it's the hard times that have crafted who they are. I know my biggest challenges thus far, with losing Paul my most biggest one of all at the present time, have unearthed a resilience that I never knew I possessed. And, as I navigate other unforeseen disappointments, which I'm sure will occur, this resilience will grow as I let it.

Maintaining a sense of hope or resilience in these setbacks will cultivate my Grit. Grit is the ability to persevere when you face obstacles.

Actually, it's a trait one needs to possess through life more importantly than so many other traits. It's a life skill people rarely talk about. No one is transparent about the need for Grit, nor is it mentioned in the educational systems, although now some schools are beginning to introduce its necessity.

And yet, who goes through life without it?

I see a much greater need for learning about Grit than learning about parallelograms. When was the last time you came across the need to use a parallelogram?

That's what I thought.

Children need to hear about the successful people who never gave up amongst their frustrating disappointments and heartaches. They need to learn how to develop perseverance, and how to develop a *growth* mind-set in re-framing such times.

We all need this!

It's why people are depressed and have low self-esteem. They never learned how to develop their Grit! Or how to be grateful!

Maybe I am strong because I developed this Grit, therefore encouraging me to *LiveLikePaul*, moving forward. To be happy, moving forward through challenges.

No, good things do not always happen to good people. Cancer, death of loved ones, natural disasters—all the unfortunate parts of life. Yes, life can be unfair—without a doubt. As I wrote in my most recent children's book, It's NOT FAIR!, released a week before Paul died, you can basically count on life not being fair sometimes. But, if we concentrate on those times, we'll take away from all that's good in our lives. Gratefulness.

We need to move on in spite of it. Or, maybe, because of it.

Happiness is not from the outside, with all we have no control over, but happiness lies within. We have control over our response to adjusting to what is.

For that we can be grateful.

Navigating hard times brings peace while you choose to stay calm, centered and balanced. You can't have the rainbow without the rain, while hope is never lost as the sun sets and rises each day.

We all have lots to be thankful for. We can all make those lists if we can somehow get out of our own way of self-pity, and thoughts of life not being fair.

We cannot let ourselves be consumed with things we cannot control.

The world has a funny way of testing us to see if we can get to our "potential success."

As Paulo Coelho said, "Before a dream is realized, the soul of the world tests everything that was learned along the way."

And, being grateful for all of it, because "all of it" is there.

Another interesting consequence of being grateful and counting one's blessings is that it changes one's focus, no longer looking inward. Suddenly, the focus shifts outward, seeing the needs of others, realizing how much we really have. And, so, in giving thanks, the need to give arises.

Giving is what life is all about. It's what Paul was known for, by everyone, everywhere.

In the *Tao Te Ching*, verse 79, Lao Tzu says, "one with true virtue always seeks a way to give. One who lacks true virtue always seeks a way to get. To the giver comes the fullness of life; to the taker, just an empty hand."

It seems everything is connected to gratitude! Gratitude has been researched by psychologists as to its value. It's been found that there are neurological reasons why so many people can benefit from this practice, even in times of challenge. Scientists have actually measured the effects of showing gratitude, producing long-lasting positivity.

Robert Emmons is the world's leading scientific expert on gratitude. He shows that being more grateful can lead to increased levels of well-being. He found that grateful people are more agreeable, more open, less neurotic, have better interpersonal relationships and are more optimistic.

Gratitude also offers a long-lasting effect in the way of a positive feedback loop, where the more gratitude we have in experiences, the more situations arise to be grateful for!

He lists many physical, psychological and social benefits.

Emmons encourages having children learn the importance of gratitude for all the above reasons, as well as to "pay it forward," to give to others as they themselves acknowledge their good fortune.

Reaching out to others, as it happens after being grateful, helps to further one's reasons to be grateful. It's a positive cycle.

And, the profound impact of being grateful even extends to the sports world, as acknowledged by coaches for their athletes and teams.

Teri McKeever is regarded as one of the best swimming mentors in the United States. In 2015, she not only led the University of California's swimming and diving teams to the NCAA Championship, she was Coach of the Year.

At the *Greater Good Gratitude Summit* in 2014, she explained why gratitude is good for athletes and how she tried to foster it as an Olympic swimmer and coach. She believes gratitude transforms the energy of her athletes. Before some practices, she asks her swimmers to write ten things they are grateful for and has them share with the team. She feels this helps to build invaluable relationships critical to the team and overall sports environment.

Also, studies from researcher Lung Hung Chen found that an athlete's level of gratitude for their success can influence their levels of well-being. Adolescent athletes who are more grateful in life are also more satisfied and tend to have higher levels of self-esteem.

Even neuroscience is beginning to explore what gratitude does to the mysterious human brain. One study measuring the brain's response to feelings of gratitude with MRIs found that gratitude increased activity in areas of the brain that deal with morality. If so, that makes sense that philosophers and religious thinkers used gratitude as part of their base teachings.

Christianity, Islam, Judaism and Buddhism stress gratitude as an integral step on the path to a good life.

I already referred to Eucharisteo, which is at the center of Christianity, reminding us to "give thanks."

In Judaism, followers of Yahweh are encouraged to start every day by being thankful for waking up again.

In Islam, daily gratitude prayers are sent to Allah.

In Buddhism, gratitude and the concept of Karma make up the driving force in China.

Hearing positive reinforcing statements about gratitude, even about others, can have an impact on anyone around.

Parents on the sidelines of sporting events can be examples to their children by not being critical of referees or coaches by being thankful for their time spent as volunteers, instead of their decisions on the field.

I loved the suggestion that, instead of seeing opponents as adversaries, see them as training partners helping your athlete improve their sport. And, that even in a loss, be grateful for the experience that teaches a child that in sport, as in life, we will all face setbacks. And, in those setbacks, all you can do is accept the outcome, learn from it, and move on.

Great advice all around.

Researchers from the Greater Good Science Center, at the University of California Berkeley, even suggest the possibility that gratitude promotes better cardiovascular health, as a result of its reducing stress.

Studies go on to say gratitude helps mitigate depression symptoms through the positive reframing of depressive thoughts, which generate positive emotions.

Happiness experts are in abundance these days and they all list gratitude is the key to being happy.

They all agree that happiness does not lead to gratitude, but gratitude leads to happiness.

Fred Luskin, director of the Stanford University Forgiveness Projects, teaches about forgiveness. He says that with increased gratitude, comes the increased ability to truly forgive.

I better step up my gratitude journal to improve the deficiency in my forgiveness status!

We always say "patience is a virtue." Well, David DeSteno, professor of psychology at Northeastern University, designed a study to see what emotions had an effect on patience and, you guessed it, gratitude was at the top. Gratitude increases one's self-control, increasing one's ability to wait.

Oh, only to be more patient when stuck in California traffic! More gratitude for me!

Science has also found that being grateful for what you have, makes you less materialistic, a negative pursuit. The desire for material possessions diminishes.

And, at a study at the Wharton School, there was improved productivity in the work place for those who practiced gratitude, as well as being the recipients of gratitude.

It has a contagious effect.

The studies go on and on, too many to go into here.

It's without a doubt an important emotion benefitting the lives of both religious and non-religious people, linked to a desire to be at peace, since it compels a desire to reciprocate.

A positive chain reaction benefitting all. And that is certainly something to be grateful for!

I'm sure there are many authors who write primarily for themselves trying to uncover answers desperately needed.

Along with celebrating Paul's life, and telling his story, the sentence above was also true for me. Paul's death left me with so much uncertainty, fears and hopelessness. I not only needed to pull myself together in healing what was so broken, but I had to share what I learned, in the hope of helping others. Therefore, this book emerged. If I can help one person through all of this, it will be so worth it.

I needed to stay open to the possibility that someday, in some way, a higher understanding of life's purpose, in the midst of this devastating loss, would emerge. I needed to take a fresh, redemptive perspective through gratitude. I found that gratitude is a choice. It's an attitude relatively immune to the highs and lows of our lives, and it has been shown that it certainly helps in temporary, permanent, devastating circumstances.

"Gratitude turns what we have into enough, and more. It turns denial into acceptance, chaos into order, confusion into clarity... it makes sense of our past, brings peace for today, and creates a vision for tomorrow." (Melody Beattie)

Even Laura Garnett, author of *The Genius Habit*, agrees.

"In those moments of being thankful for our misfortunes we find true wisdom."

I needed to learn how to give up resentment for gratitude and anger for joy.

Dietrich Bonhoeffer (1906-1945) the German theological author, also wrote about gratitude in troubled times. He was imprisoned for being anti-Nazi and was eventually executed in 1945. "Gratitude changes the pangs of memory into tranquil joy."

It's precisely under crisis conditions when we have the most to gain by a grateful perspective on life. It has the power to energize, heal and bring hope. Remember, we have been promised that there is joy through gratefulness in all things.

Finding ways that our "misfortune" will have a better ending, bringing joy to others, making us want to give in seeing our blessings, while making us stronger, enlarging our Grit factor for what's to come, are all the results of gratitude.

Life is uncertain.

We can begin to think of these difficult moments as opportunities to connect with others, learn what we are truly capable of, gaining valuable experiences, while giving us the peace we all want in the end.

And, for that peace, I am grateful.

—— ✳ ——

Forgiveness

"When a deep injury is done to us, we never heal until we forgive"
—Nelson Mandela

I JUST ENDED MY WEEKLY PHONE VISIT with Anna, my best friend of 65 years, who grew up with me in the Bronx, attending elementary and high school together. My faithful, wise friend who I can turn to at any given moment for advice or just to vent.

I told her I was in the midst of writing this Chapter on Forgiveness, and how I had a hard time wearing my LIVELIKEPAUL sweatshirt, bracelet, teeshirt, etc. because of some guilt. Especially now after my research on Forgiveness.

Patient Anna...let me continue.

"Well," I openly admitted, "it's because when it comes to this 'forgiveness thing,' I'm not in a good place. I have no intention of forgiving a few people in my life right now. And, actually, I'm enjoying this grudge thing because I truly feel it's deserved."

"Okay, okay," she replied. "What's going on?" She was getting ready for one of our discussions on life.

"Well," I started, "call me 'mother-loses-son-crazy,' but there are several people who totally disappointed me when Paul died. I mean, totally. And, these are people who I felt very close to. They didn't make any effort to attend Paul's funeral in Georgia, while others I barely knew arrived with their suitcases straight from the airport! And there was more.

I reminded Anna how three weeks after Paul passed away, I was scheduled for a book tour in Vero Beach, Florida, planned many months in advance. I was to fly from San Diego, California, to Vero Beach, Florida, and then to New York City for the Christmas holiday. I was originally going on my own to the Florida book tour, and I didn't think I'd have the strength to keep up with a full week of signings and traveling, but, of course, my sweet husband Manny jumped in to save the day and came with me. As usual, he took care of every detail, and all I needed to do was "show up." I was still in shock, although I actually think I still am, nine months later as I write this.

Manny and I used to live in Vero Beach and developed many friendships there. Two of them, Bridget and Hildegarde, were not to be around that week but they changed all their plans to make sure they came to visit us at our hotel for a "sympathy call" for a whole day and night.

However, another very close relationship (at least I thought so) decided a Christmas party at night was more important than a lunch in the day. I'm still trying to figure that out. We are rarely in Florida to begin with! So, we never got to see "this person" during our stay.

In another case, there has never been a phone call, email or text to reach out in all the nine months! Only a sympathy card the week he died. What is that? This was my son that died!

Of course I'm not saying names here, but I told Anna who they were on the phone, and she was blown away. It was just the validation I needed. Not that I really needed it, but I did. I knew how I felt and I felt justified in my disappointment. Disappointment isn't really the word I want to use. I felt much stronger than disappointment. I was angry.

Okay, now that I got Anna's validation, where do I go from here?

She agreed it would be extremely difficult to ever have a relationship again.

Especially with the current status. But there was still more I had to learn. At least on paper, if not in my heart.

I think when a mom (speaking for myself here) goes through so much grief as in losing a child, she is super sensitive. It's a time of utter despair and I found myself to be very vigilant as to who was there and who wasn't in my sorrow.

Believe me when I tell you, the outpouring of love and support I have received in all this was amazing. Manny is constantly commenting that I have the best friends on the planet, and that I should concentrate on them. And, yes, I am so grateful for them. Yet, I can't ignore these few friends I've known for many, many years who made those first few token phone calls or texts in the very beginning and then dropped off out of communication.

Interesting. Not even "when can I see you to give you a hug?" Nothing.

Thankfully, there's just a handful of these people. Sorry, but, moving forward, it's hard for me to even consider them as friends anymore.

Yet, I have many, many old and even new friends that constantly reach out. And, I mean constantly which really helps. It also tells me something about who they are and what lies in their soul.

Manny reminds me of Benjamin Franklin's quote, "Blessed is he who has no expectations, for he will never be disappointed."

That's where we differ. He doesn't "expect" but I do. Sorry, but I think there's a time and place for expectations. And, when people fall short (in my eyes) of those expectations, that's when I'm more than disappointed. Round and round we go.

Now, you may be wondering, what if any of these people came

to me and acknowledged they could have done better? And they were sorry they hurt me? And if they could do it over, they would have acted differently? What would I do? How would I react? I could absolutely accept their apology and hopefully start anew. I do believe we all make mistakes and everyone deserves a second chance and forgiveness.

But, what if those apologies and validations never came? As in my case here and in many cases for others?

Do we, or should we, forgive?

The ultimate answer is yes.

But I myself am not there yet. Keep reading.

My dilemma is that I know I'm supposed to "let go" but I can't right now, and, I don't want to right now. I can't picture these people ever in my life again, especially since there's no contact (or apology).

But forgiveness doesn't have to mean you still have a relationship with the person. You can forgive or forget but you need to choose one.

I'm beginning this section on forgiveness with this disclosure for a reason. Eventually, I'll get there.

I am sympathetic enough to be aware that these examples of my "hurts" are nothing compared to other more devastating circumstances requiring forgiveness, such as being a victim of any kind of abuse, or the loved one of a murdered victim. Or maybe the victim of a financial scam? Or a marital betrayal of trust? Or Holocaust survivor? There are thousands of reasons for the need to forgive.

And, in many of the above conditions, forgiveness took place—even in prisons, facing the murderer. How does one do that?

I have come to the conclusion, as you will see, that it's the only answer for peace.

What would Paul do?

I know what Paul would do in a heartbeat. He'd have that cute little smirk and say "Mom, it's not that big of a deal." This was a statement he was so known for. He wouldn't allow anything to take away his peace. He wouldn't say that statement for a really serious offense. He would just somehow make peace with it.

And, I personally know of two instances that Paul, even at a young age, knew the power of forgiveness. I know there were plenty more in his lifetime because he just didn't focus on negativity. He would just "move on" and do his thing.

I can say with most certainty that Paul never gave these two instances another thought, but, as his mother, I never forgot, all these years later.

You see, I needed to do this Chapter on Forgiveness for myself, as well as possibly helping someone else through my research findings. There's a lot of research on the importance and necessity of forgiveness in one's life. I understand it intellectually, but not ready to embrace it. Not yet.

Following, I will talk about these two situations referred to above, but will be as vague as I can, not mentioning any names. Actually at this stage of my life, let the truth prevail! This all unfortunately happened.

Anyone who knew Paul knew he saved money from when he was a child. It was one of his first words, actually. At ten years old, he opened up his own checking account in Cross River, New York, by our home. He took full responsibility with this account depositing every penny (literally) he received from Christmas, holidays, Confirmations, graduations, etc. as gifts. He was also known to collect plastic bottles under the bleachers after football games, turning these into cash, and, ultimately, into bank deposits. Then, at 13, he had his dish washing job at the local pizza shop, followed by being the fastest, most efficient cashier at D'Agostino's, working after school and on weekends, winning him the title of Employee of the Year as a 17 year old!

Paul would make his constant appearance at the bank, depositing all of his earnings. I mean all. He never kept anything for himself because actually he never wanted or needed anything. He never asked me for anything either. Now the tears are coming, but I'll keep writing. In his room, in special notebooks, he kept intricate details of his bank statements and how much interest he was making each day on the balance. You can't make that up!

He also kept spreadsheets on his earnings at D'Agostino's for each day he worked during the seven years. I have those spreadsheets if anyone ever wants to see them.

Did I mention that he kept the first three dollars he ever made at 13 years old at the Pizza Shop? He labeled everything all neatly in files and I have it all.

He enjoyed doing all this. He was happy to see the fruits of his labor. His brothers were quite in awe at his "money obsession" but that was Paul being Paul.

As for me, I never had an interest in money. I was brought up by an Italian-American mom who left financial responsibilities to the father, while household and child-rearing went to the mom. I followed that lead. Any personal money I ever received for birthdays, holidays, etc. was immediately given over to my then-husband to be "put in the pot," never keeping any for myself. So, you must be wondering where all this is going and what it has to do with forgiveness concerning Paul, (and actually myself).

Well, one day when Paul went to the bank to deposit his week's earnings, his account was wiped out. So was mine.

I'll leave it there.

Years later, Paul would get it back. (I never did) At least that's what Paul told me. Maybe he just said that so I wouldn't ask anymore. And, now I'll never know for sure. More tears.

Following that blow, around the same time, there was the incident in his senior year in high school. As you read through his academic records, he was always receiving medals and recognitions, and was very respected for his leadership abilities.

Thought of highly by his classmates, he was nominated to be Senior Class President. There was no doubt he would win. However, it was discovered that there were votes administered improperly for another candidate, and resulted in his winning instead. (IT'S NOT FAIR!)

Paul was called to the guidance office to discuss what to do. Why, I don't know. It should never have been up to a senior in high school to decide what was to be done. It should have been the school's decision. Knowing this meeting was taking place (I should have gone) I was anxious to hear how the school was going to handle it.

When Paul came home he said he decided to leave it all the way it was! He did not want to bring the issue out into the open, causing hard feelings and embarrassment.

"What?! Are you kidding me?! That's not fair!" I practically screamed. Actually, I did scream.

I was so upset and frustrated. He also did not want to discuss it anymore. He basically said, "It's not that big of a deal" and wanted to move on. But, it was a big deal to me! My son was cheated of a position he earned! Look at this, I'm still talking about this 26 years later!

Why haven't I been able to let it go like Paul did?

He never held a grudge. He never said a word about it again. He just moved on. Oh, how I wish I could talk to him about this now!

I mean, how great is it that to just "move on" and not look back?

Even after writing the book *It's NOT FAIR!* I'm still saying, *"It's NOT FAIR!"* What's wrong with this picture?

What a gift that is to not obsess over people who have done

you wrong! Other than getting a lobotomy, I don't know how I can get to that level. For Paul's sake, I won't get a lobotomy and will and must try.

Paul earned the mantra LIVELIKEPAUL for a reason.

And, you haven't even heard about all the people who would "borrow" money from Paul and never pay back, which never prevented him from giving again when they asked! He just didn't keep accounts of who paid and who didn't. Just the act of giving was what was important to him.

In one way, I'm so proud of his being so generous and forgiving, but, in another, as his mom, I'm sad that anyone would take advantage of him. But, I know in my heart of hearts, he would never think of himself as being taken advantage of. He had an "enlightened" way of thinking, whereas I am at the struggling human level.

As a result of the way he thought and lived his life, he never thought himself as a victim. And that's huge. Thinking of oneself as a victim is so destructive. It, without a doubt, stifles one's entire energy flow.

Getting into a victim's role gives one permission to look for all the ways they are being taken advantage of, and actually attracts "unfair" occurrences. It's a vicious cycle that never ends.

I'm sure we've all met these people who say, "If it weren't for bad luck, I'd have none at all," or "why does everything bad happen to me?" or, if you ask how they're doing, they respond, "hanging in there." Don't you want to run in the opposite direction when you see them coming? That's what a victim looks like.

Paul would never go that route. Never did, no matter what.

When he went off to Georgia Tech, with an empty bank account, and no one paying his tuition, he found a way. He applied to work as an assistant manager for the Georgia Tech basketball team, which took care of most of his expenses. It was basically a full time job and he did it well. I don't know how he managed it all, but it did take him an extra year to finish college. He never, ever complained. He knew my circumstances were also dire, newly divorced with no alimony or child support, with two children still living at home, while not only teaching full time but also a part time job to make ends meet. Paul moved forward, never blaming anyone for anything. Nor did my other sons for that matter. They all worked and chipped in. It's probably why they are all successful and independent today.

In writing this book, it forced me to look back on those difficult days. And they were difficult. But we all got through it with flying colors, I must say.

It was only recently that I had this conversation with my daughter-in-law, Erin, Frank's wife. I was crying on the phone thinking about how sad it was that Paul drove himself alone to Georgia to go to college, setting up his room, while everyone else had parents to help.

Erin calmed me down telling me that Paul talked about that first week at college, unloading and organizing. She said he wasn't bitter at all, but just laughed, shrugging his shoulders, saying it was fine, he got it done quickly, and it all worked out.

I'm hoping that he really didn't feel the sting of being alone. But, I have to say that visual in my head is painful, and I told her so. Once again, Erin reminded me it's what made Paul, Paul. Why he was so successful. So happy. So at peace. Because nothing was a big deal.

A mother, I guess, will always have a soft spot for her children, never wanting them to experience any kind of distress.

I don't know what I could possibly have done then with what I had to work with, but looking back, I wish I could have done something.

Why do we look back and regret things we can't change,

knowing, especially, there was little to be done? It's so unproductive!

In writing this chapter on forgiveness, maybe I need to forgive myself! Yes, maybe I do, even before I try to forgive anyone else!

It came down to accepting that we do the best we can at the time. I have to remember that, and finally let that go.

Here I would love to discuss all this with Paul. It's a conversation I always wanted to have, but something would come up, and it wouldn't happen.

Another regret I would think about and want to talk to Paul about was that I don't remember ever sending him home baked cookies or goodies. I was always cooking and baking before our world fell apart, and I wasn't baking like I used to anymore. Actually, it never crossed my mind to do that, until years later when I heard people would send certain foods to their college kids. Oh, the guilt!

What good does torturing myself with such thoughts now? None. Woulda. Coulda. Shoulda. Ridiculous words.

I actually know I was a very good mom. That horrific divorce and all that went with it, was a terrible distraction and energy zapper, to say the least, all going on around Paul's preparation for college. And, yet…Paul was happy.

Is it because he was a forgiving person to begin with?

Or, was it because he was intrinsically happy first, so being forgiving was easy? Seems like happiness and forgiveness are tied together.

I'm intrinsically happy, but find it hard to forgive. I know I could be happier if I did forgive more often, because there's negative residue when grudges exist.

My dear husband Manny lives like Paul in so many ways. He's always able to "move on" while I "hold on."

So, who's more at peace?

Who has more room in their brain for happier thoughts?

Grudge ruminations take up a lot of room!

Paul's "that's not that big of a deal" reaction to most disappointments seemed to work very well for him.

You never saw him without a smile on his face.

Grudges seem to give us the power we feel we didn't have in the hurt done to us.

But, to find out, in my reading many books on this subject, when you don't forgive, our grudges become lodged in our energy centers, and eventually, these emotional blocks can manifest in physical, mental ailments or diseases. Who wants that?

It's a spiritual lesson that has to be learned, and, if we don't learn it here on earth, in this incarnation, we'll have to deal with it again in the Afterlife. (See section on Afterlife).

So, what's this about forgiveness that makes it so necessary?

Steve Maraboli, author and motivational speaker, says "The truth is, unless you let go, unless you forgive yourself, unless you forgive the situation, unless you realize that the situation is over, you cannot move forward." He goes on to say it's not because they deserve it, but you do. Loving yourself enough to MOVE ON!"

Well, that about sums it up, doesn't it? There's no room to doubt the power of forgiveness in that quote!

Archbishop Desmond Tutu, Nobel Peace Prize winner, along with his daughter, the Reverend Mpho Tutu, wrote a manual on the art of forgiveness, helping us to realize that we are all capable of healing and transformation.

In *The Book of Forgiveness: The Fourfold Path for Healing Ourselves and Our World*, we learn that the quality of human life on the planet is nothing more than the sum total of our daily interactions with one another. Forgiveness is the way we set those interactions right. It is the way we mend tears in the social fabric. It is the way we stop our human communication from unraveling.

"When you forgive, you are free to move on in life, to grow, to no longer be a victim. When you forgive, you slip the yoke, and your future is unshackled from your past."

Tutu goes on to say each one of us has a deep need to forgive and be forgiven. He suggests there are four important steps to healing: admitting the wrong and acknowledging the harm; telling one's story witnessing the anguish; asking for forgiveness and granting forgiveness, and renewing or releasing the relationship.

Offering forgiveness prevents us from being destroyed by a corrosive resentment. It helps us grow in being magnanimous. We can't be dependent on the perpetrator to say "sorry." The victim needs to give himself that gift, letting go of resentment and anger.

Tutu says it's the only way to say "sorry." The victim needs to give himself that gift, letting go of resentment and anger.

Tutu says it's the only way to free ourselves of the endless cycle of pain. And, it truly is freedom. The freedom in a simple act of forgiveness saves the expense of anger and the high cost of hatred after being hurt.

I heard it once compared to the bite of a snake. You rarely die from the bite, but the real damage is done by the venom that continues to flow through your system. The venom is the bitterness you hold onto, long after you're hurt, which eventually destroys your peace.

The antidote for this "venom" is forgiveness, simply "letting go." It's getting free from the burden of having the venom forever pump through your veins.

"Forgiveness is the key that unlocks the door of resentment and the handcuffs of hatred. It is a power that breaks the chains of bitterness and the shackles of selfishness." —Corrie ten Boom (1892-1983)

CORRIE TEN BOOM WAS A DUTCH watchmaker and author of many books. In *The Hiding Place*, she writes about how she, along with her father and sister, helped many Jews escape the Nazi Holocaust by hiding them in her home during World War II.

They were ultimately caught, arrested, and sent to the Ravensbruck concentration camp in Germany. She recounts how she found hope while imprisoned. When released, she traveled the world as a public speaker, talking mainly about forgiveness.

As I mentioned before, I have been a recipient of *Guideposts* magazines for decades. I would always cut out and file any interesting articles.

Many years ago, *Guideposts* included an article by Corrie ten Boom where she talked about a Nazi prison guard who approached her on one of her lectures, asking for her forgiveness. She recognized him from all those years ago as one of the guards responsible for killing her sister.

She said she knew she had to do it, remembering that God's forgiveness has a prior condition: that we forgive those who have injured us.

"If you do not forgive men their trespasses," Jesus says, "neither will your Father in heaven forgive your trespasses." (ouch)

Corrie explains she knew this to be very true because of what she witnessed after the war when she housed Nazi victims in her home, rehabilitating them.

The ones that forgave their former enemies were able to eventually return to the outside world, but those that nursed their bitterness remained invalids.

So, after asking for God's help, she told him she forgave him.

However, she found she needed to ask God's help each day for the miracle of forgiveness and couldn't understand why it was so hard, even knowing how important it was.

A wise Lutheran pastor explained that up in a church tower, the bell is rung by pulling on a rope. But, after the sexton lets go of the rope, the bell keeps on swinging. First ding, then dong. Slower and slower until there's a final dong and it stops.

He said the same is true of forgiveness. When we forgive someone, we take our hand off the rope. But, if we've been tugging at our grievance for a long time, the angry thoughts might keep coming like the ding dongs slowing down.

But the force has gone out of them. It just takes time.

Hurts, disappointments, betrayals, etc. come in all shapes and sizes, requiring our forgiveness.

Dr. Wayne Dyer, who I have spoken about previously, overcame many obstacles having spent his childhood in orphanages, along with his brothers, because his alcoholic father left his family when he was very young.

His life was solidified in his early thirties when he searched and found his father's pauper's grave and forgave him. If you ever get a chance, read his detailed account in actually finding that grave, which was short of a miracle. Divine intervention once again. Dyer said his life was transformed in every way from that act of forgiveness. His relationships, health, and work blossomed, being free from the burden of having venom pumped through his veins.

Dyer would oftentimes recite the quote from Mark Twain, "Forgiveness is the fragrance the violet sheds on the heel that has crushed it". That visual, and the significance of it, is so powerful.

Somehow, Paul knew all this. He knew that being a forgiving person was beneficial for himself, as well as others.

Because this book is about Paul, this chapter on the benefits of the power of forgiveness had to be included. And, hopefully, at the final end of this book-writing journey, I also will be able to live in a life of forgiveness.

Getting there, little by little, since I know it's truly the only way to have peace.

"If we really want to love, we must learn how to forgive."
—Mother Teresa, Saint Teresa of Calcutta, 2016

— ✳ —

THE AFTERLIFE

*"But I guess death is like that. It takes away from you in an
instant the people you've cherished for a whole lifetime. Just
like that. As simple as that. And you are suddenly left with
two things: anger for having been deprived of your beloved for
no reason at all; and emptiness, a vacuum that grows right at
your heart where all the joyful moments once had been."*

—Jocelyn Soriano, *In Your Hour of Grief:
When Mourning the Death of a Loved One*

DID YOU EVER HAVE A DEFINING EXPERIENCE in your life
when you go over and over, in your mind, as to where you
were and what was said? Playing out the whole scene in complete
detail, since it's so embedded in your brain?

That's what I do when I go back to that phone call on Saturday,
November 17th, 2018, at around 10 am PCT, days before
Thanksgiving. The last time I would speak to my son, Paul.

I was in my kitchen, in my California home, making the last
dish to freeze, when Paul called.

Some people say that when we make plans, God smiles. Or
something like that.

I was to find out how my planning, no matter how carefully, does not always work out. I was completely ready for our Thanksgiving celebration, days away. I was so excited to have my sons, family and friends coming. But none of it would happen.

That Saturday morning phone call would change everything.

Paul, on the other end of the phone, was saying he would not be able to make it for Thanksgiving. He was supposed to arrive in San Diego on Monday. He went on to explain that he had been very sick, bedridden, since that Tuesday night. It was the word "bedridden" that got my attention. And, instilled fear. For many reasons. First of all, Paul was never sick. And, he would never be missing work. Bedridden? This had to be serious. He recounted how he went to his annual physical exam on Tuesday, and, before he left, the medical assistant suggested he get a flu shot. He usually never gets a flu shot, having only had one his whole life, but, since he would be traveling, he explained, he made the last-minute decision to accept one.

His next words were, "mom, I should never have gotten that flu shot."

From early that Tuesday evening, he started not to feel well and went to bed early. On Wednesday and Thursday, he could not get out of bed. Terrible pain. Vomiting. Fever. He could not use his right arm.

Upon learning all this, I started crying, begging him to go to the hospital immediately. I wanted to fly to Georgia right away. He said he called the medical office that Thursday, telling them his symptoms, and they said he had a very bad reaction to the flu shot, but he also made an appointment for the next morning, Friday, because of the pain he was in. He went that Friday morning, driven by his roommate, and all they did was give him a muscle relaxer and pain pill prescription. This was Saturday, and he was no better. I continued to insist he go to the hospital, and he consistently said no. He said he just needed to rest at home because they said he was having a bad reaction. He said, "please, mom, calm down. I'll be fine."

I then asked for his roommate to get on the phone. I told him the same thing, "Get him to the hospital!"

He said, "He won't go!"

I told his roommate something was very wrong. Paul should not be this sick. I told him to write everything down that he could remember from when he had the flu shot on Tuesday—all the symptoms each day, and to let me know how he was doing.

My next call was to my oldest son, Frank, who was very close to Paul. Once again, crying on the phone, I told him to call Paul to convince him to get to the hospital. He called, but got the same answer. Paul wouldn't go. He said he was told it was a bad reaction to the flu shot, and that we all should not worry.

I was so frustrated and anxious. Then, there was the thought that maybe I was overreacting. Maybe it was just a bad reaction, like he said.

I tried to put my mind at ease, but I was very concerned all that Saturday and night, so much so that I cancelled Saturday night plans. I just wanted to be home. I was in no mood to go anywhere.

I texted Paul the following Sunday morning, asking how things were going. He answered, "a little better."

Well, maybe I did overreact, but "a little better" still didn't sit right with me.

And, Sunday night would confirm a mother's intuition, while changing my life forever.

It was about 9:45 pm PCT when my cell phone rang. It saw it was his roommate's number. I also knew it was three hours later in Atlanta, Georgia, which couldn't be good news. Before I even answered the call, I found myself screaming Manny's name to come to me, and I answered the call by screaming, "What?!! What happened?!"

But all I heard was crying on the other end. I kept screaming, "Tell me! Tell me!"

No answer, just crying.

Oh please, I thought, let it just be that he did go to the hospital, and they're helping him!

Please let it be just that and not what I'm really thinking.

With no response to my asking what happened, I finally screamed out a question a mother should never have to ask. "Is my son alive?!" And with that, he screamed back, "NO!"

It's that question and that answer I try not to think about, because that's when it was over.

There was no going to the hospital, no blood work, no medical care, nothing to do. Over. I don't remember much after that. I gave the phone to Manny with the roommate on the other end. I don't know what was said. I just walked around in circles, knowing I had to call my sons.

Of course with it being so late on the East Coast, and their already being in bed, no one answered. They wouldn't know till the next morning.

I never went to bed that night. Just cried and cried, waiting for morning.

Manny went right into action, along with Frank, making all kinds of funeral, hotel, and plane arrangements.

It's all a blur.

All I know we were on a plane Tuesday morning headed for Atlanta, Georgia.

I was inconsolable. I just sobbed and sobbed the entire time, even on the plane. My dear Manny just held me. There's really nothing else to do or say. Fortunately, I was in the window seat, so not visible to many people. Not that I cared. At one point, I just looked at Manny and said, "I just want to scream and scream!"

With panic in his eyes, he said, very calmly, "Please, honey, don't scream right now while we're on the plane. That could cause a lot of fright for the other passengers." (Or something like that). Whatever he said made me burst out laughing (while still crying) realizing how ridiculous that would be.

Sometimes you just need some comic relief, however short-lived. In this case, seconds.

Upon our arrival in Georgia, we were to drive to the Southern Cremations and Funerals at Cheatham Hall, Marietta, Georgia.

There we would meet with several of Paul's close friends and my other sons for a private viewing. That afternoon, Paul was to be cremated into an urn and that urn would be at the funeral service the following day, Wednesday, the day before Thanksgiving.

But, all these original plans would change.

Everyone was waiting for us outside as we arrived straight from the airport, so we could all go in together. It was extremely emotional as Manny and I walked over to them.

We then all went inside, and followed the funeral director down a flight of stairs to the lower level of the building into a secluded viewing room. Paul was entirely covered with a white sheet, except for his beautiful face.

We all stood there together in a semi-circle in front of the casket, crying, and speaking out intermittently, taking turns to go over to Paul, kiss him, and say goodbye.

I don't know how I did it. I do believe I was still in shock and denial as I looked at him lying there.

And then it was time to go. Upon all of us leaving the room, Taiwan, one of Paul's closest friends, asked to speak to me and Manny privately.

He suggested that instead of cremating Paul that afternoon, we wait until the following evening so we could have the service with

Paul there. He explained, "you have no idea how many friends want to say goodbye. They want to see Paul—not an urn of ashes when they come. They need closure in seeing his face again."

It made total sense.

We immediately spoke to the funeral director and staff, requesting our new plans and they were incredibly accommodating.

We then had to choose a casket, Paul's clothes, etc. for viewing the next day.

I am so grateful to Taiwan for his advice. True to what he anticipated, there were literally hundreds of friends who attended, from all over the country, suitcases in hand, and even someone who flew from Israel!

Keep in mind, this was Wednesday, the day before Thanksgiving. Not the most opportune time to have a funeral service, but nothing was going to hold back these faithful friends.

Even the funeral staff asked, "Who was your son? We never had so many attend a service to begin with, but on the day before Thanksgiving?!"

I will never forget the love Paul was surrounded by on that day.

The venue was a huge, light-filled chapel with a gigantic stained-glass window behind Paul's casket. His friends set up an ongoing slide presentation on an immense screen with hundreds of photos representing Paul's happy life.

There was a constant stream of Paul's friends heading to where he lay. Many would congregate around him, talking to him. Many were sobbing. So was I. This went on for hours.

It was such a heartwarming demonstration of love and compassion. I see why Paul loved his "framily" so much. They truly loved him and he felt it.

Friends went to the microphone from time to time, giving their testimonies as to what Paul meant to them.

I even spoke, thanking everyone for their support, while also finding the strength to share Paul's childhood Hong Kong story, which I've included in detail somewhere in this book.

Truthfully, I still wonder how I was able to tell that story so calmly. It was like an out of body experience as I think about it now and had to be from some God-given source.

And, then, it was time to go. It would be the last time I would see Paul's face.

After the service, we all congregated at Paul's place, where his friends organized all kinds of catered food to be delivered.

His home was where everyone was welcome. Always filled with fun get-togethers.

A place where anyone could go and stay if they were out of options. No expiration date. You could live there until you were ready to go on your own. It was the hub of his *framily*.

I was so fortunate to have experienced all that camaraderie two months before Paul passed when I went to stay with him for his birthday. He had a huge party, all catered, mainly for me to meet his friends and to celebrate my visit. While he was getting ready for the party, he was telling me about all his renovation plans for his kitchen and living room areas—how he was removing the wall in between, picking out cabinets, adding another sliding door to the wraparound deck, facing the lake, etc.

What do they say about making plans and God smiling?

Meanwhile, who would think I would be with these same people two months later at his funeral?

Who would think that would be the last time I would see my son alive?

The next day, Thanksgiving Day, Manny and I went back to the funeral home where the amazing staff once again went above and beyond by opening their doors specifically for us to pick up Paul's wooden box of ashes, on our way to the Atlanta airport for our trip back to San Diego. They did whatever was needed to make all these last minute plans possible, without a glitch. So thankful for their part.

Carrying Paul's ashes through the airport was a challenge since it was extremely heavy. It was also heart wrenching knowing what was inside. It was very hard to wrap my mind around what was happening. We wound up getting a wheelchair to set the urn on, wheeling it through the myriad hallways getting to our gate. You could laugh or cry seeing this. I was sobbing. I was a total mess.

This crazy scene was just too much for me. Paul in an urn, on a wheelchair, on Thanksgiving Day, the day he was actually to be at our house. Only now he's in a box.

What's wrong with this picture?

For the next month, that urn would remain on our dining room credenza, surrounded by photos and flowers. Whenever anyone came to visit me to see how I was doing, we'd go in that room to include him.

His final destination is now in my office.

And there he stays.

There's a lot of comfort having him there, as opposed to being in some cemetery I may rarely get to. He's with me every day now.

But, then again, he'd be with me anyway, as I would become aware of after all my research, included in this chapter.

I spent a lot of my time in my office, where Paul was. Usually crying. Talking to him.

I tried not to cry so much around Manny, but I usually had to. There was really no controlling my tears or meltdowns.

He was so devastated for me and frustrated that he couldn't make my sadness go away. After all, Manny was always my problem solver. My protector.

There was nothing anyone could do, other than "be there," and so many of my friends were and are always there for me. For that, I am so grateful.

Little by little, I made my way through the piles of sympathy cards on my desk, Paul's urn neatly on the shelf.

I felt it appropriate to open each one with his presence in close proximity. The cards remain in a basket on the adjoining shelf, and, any correspondence I receive concerning Paul gets added to the same basket, right by Paul.

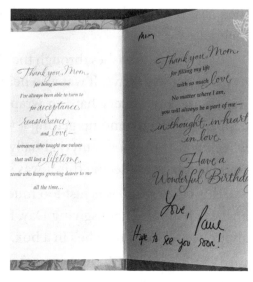

A Birthday Keepsake

On one of those days, I decided to torture myself some more by going through all the cards Paul ever sent me through the years. Yes, as I previously mentioned, I kept everything the boys ever gave me or sent me.

One particular birthday card from Paul had a detachable keepsake bookmark that I never originally noticed.

I removed it, and read the words that put me into a complete meltdown. It was almost prophetic.

It said: "Mom, no matter what I do today, or where the future takes me tomorrow, I promise to remember all the things you've taught me and how much you love me. And, in case I don't always say it, and sometimes I forget to show it, I wanted you to have this so you know I love you, too, Mom."

Finding that bookmark, after years, that I never noticed before, was, without a doubt, Paul reaching out to me.

It would be, as I would get to learn, a "sign."

It would be the first of many "Paul signs" to come.

And, it's why, after observing these unexplainable happenings, that I decided to examine, research and consider the possibility of knowing about the Afterlife.

Who really ever thinks about the Afterlife? Or if there is one?

First of all, no one ever talks about death if they can help it.

There's so much fear surrounding the subject.

As a Catholic, my fear was going to hell after I died so I tried to lead the perfect life to prevent these fires of damnation. Heaven was my goal.

My heaven visual was a place that went up, as opposed to a downward direction. There, high up, I would be greeted by St. Peter at the pearly gates, along with the saints and God. It would be a peaceful, happy place, where you would remain for eternity, in company with the angels. That was it.

I had no other ideas on the subject of death, nor did I think about it. Once someone died that I knew, it never occurred to me that I could, or might, hear from them again.

They were gone, with nothing but memories left behind.

I lost all my beloved relatives that I was so close to many years ago. As an only child, they were everything to me. Most recently, five of my longtime good friends also passed away.

Never did I think that there could be "something" more going on once they left this earth.

That maybe they would still be able to be reached or spoken to, or, that they could reach out to me!

It was the farthest thing from my mind.

However, I must admit, on a different level, I marveled at the practice of tarot card readers.

That interest began in 1989 when some teachers at my school were talking about this one particular tarot reader they would go to. I was shocked at all the predictions she correctly made, and the whole idea of it really piqued my curiosity. It was also a time in my life that I really could have used some guidance or "answers."

My first reading left me speechless. As I sat there, without saying a word, she talked for one solid hour explaining and even predicting things that made perfect sense.

Without going into all the details, I went to this lady for 10 years and all I can tell you is that she predicted every single thing that happened to me. It was all taped so you could go back to listen. She gave a "present-day" card reading and a future one. The information was 100% correct.

It all unfolded as she said it would, detail for detail.

I purposely never gave her any particulars so her reading would be as pure as possible. I could fill a book with these 10 years of readings, but the one I will mention was so incredible, there are no words. She warned me that a situation was in the making at the present time and that I should be aware of it. She gave the exact details of what was happening, and how it would be a financial disaster for me unless it was brought to the surface. She was protecting me in this disclosure. Trusting her as I did, I listened to her and proceeded to find out if it was true, through people who I thought I could trust, but I kept hitting dead ends, being told "it did not happen," and "there were no problems." (Of course, never saying I was told by a tarot card reader!)

But, one year later, the truth did come out big time. It was exactly what she said. The exact location and amount. And, yes, it was a financial disaster for me, precipitated by the person she said a year earlier.

But, as usual, I survived it, along with all the other circumstances I was put into.

And, if I say so myself, not only did I survive those heartaches, betrayals, and losses, but I blossomed. Looking back, those were my earthly lessons. I needed to be more alert, vigilant and not so trusting. More independent. And, all these experiences brought me to where I am today, almost 30 years later. I'm the happiest I have ever been, married to the man of my dreams. I lead a full, fun-filled life. Of course, losing Paul has altered my life, but I am finding the lessons in there too in order to move forward. Because, as I've learned, if we allow it, there are always rainbows after hardships if we learn the lesson that's hidden somewhere. If we can change the way we look at things, the things we look at change. That's a quote Dr. Dyer used all the time.

So, getting back to my tarot card reader, I do believe people are given gifts (by God) as messengers to those who seek it.

A few people frowned when they heard I was seeing this reader, as perhaps people are frowning now. Everyone has their own opinion, and that's fine. There was nothing sinister about my readings—only messages. And, if we believe there are angels on earth who guide us, when we ask (as in my children's book *"What Is An Angel?"*), why is this any different or strange?

I tell you all this because it wasn't therefore unusual to open myself up to consider other possible psychic abilities some people might have, after my times with the tarot reader.

The prospect of being able to reach those who have passed, or their reaching out to me was literally put in my path.

Finding that "keepsake bookmark" was only the beginning.

Soon, the most mysterious and yet beautiful sign would occur.

Our home was filled with magnificent orchid plants sent by

our friends in sympathy. They were dispersed throughout the first level of our home.

One plant was so enormous that I decided to place it on the middle island in our kitchen, and then, for some reason, arranged tiny seed lights amongst the green leaves, after surprisingly finding an unopened package purchased many months before from Home Goods. I found them in a drawer, added batteries, and switched them on only a couple of times.

Eventually, after about four weeks, the flowers fell off, but the green plants themselves remained so I just left them there in the pot on the middle island, but never switched the lights on again.

At night, I would sit in the den, reading, knitting or half watching TV. It was a time I didn't want to do anything at all. Just really laid on the couch, needing to be quiet. Most of the time crying on and off until I went to bed.

This particular night was unlike any other, except for what happened next.

Having one of my especially sad nights crying, all of a sudden, from the corner of my eye I saw blinking lights coming from the kitchen area. I then realized it was coming from the plant!

But, how can that be?!!! That switch was "off" for quite a while!

Believe me, I quickly stopped crying to see what was going on. Pulling the leaves apart to find the switch, it was shocking to see it was truly on "off"!

Standing there motionless, I could hardly breathe because immediately the thought came that this was a sign from Paul. He was trying to comfort me.

Some of you might have a hard time believing any of this, but what transpired for months following this night would make you a believer.

These "lights" would be my communication with Paul for the

next six months until we had to leave for Southampton, NY for the summer.

In telling my close friends about this phenomenon going on, they were as excited as I was. I even videotaped the lights when they would go on, which was usually when I felt extremely sad.

But, there was more.

The timing was incredible.

Every morning I would come downstairs to make coffee and the lights from the plant would be off. I had my back to the plant, fixing the coffee, and when I turned around, the "lights" would be blinking as if to say, "Good morning!"

They would stay on for a minute or two and then go off.

One time, the lights stayed totally off for about a week. I was actually keeping a log of the lights going on and off.

There was nothing.

It seemed this whole communication thing might be over after all. Perhaps Paul had other things to do rather than twinkling lights—like maybe getting some friends together into some concerts! Haha!

But, then, one night, I had what I would find out to be a visitation from Paul. It was very different than a regular dream. Paul was so real that I said to him, Oh! Paul! I thought you were gone! But you're here! He took my arm and smiled at me. He looked so young and happy and even had hair! I said, " Paul, those lights that blink were from you, weren't they?"

He smiled, shaking his head, "yes".

He didn't speak at all but responded by his facial expressions.

And then it was over.

Waking up very confused, my eyes were wet from crying the tears of happiness in this dream (visitation).

Going downstairs that morning to make coffee as usual, I

was very overtaken by what happened and, looking squarely at that plant, which remember, had not gone on for about a week. I actually said out loud, "Paul, if that was you reaching out to me last night in that dream (visitation) put those lights on right now!"

And, so help me, they started blinking like never before!

You can't make this stuff up!

Can it be our loved ones are still with us, in spirit, even though our bodies are gone?

It was so upsetting to leave my "twinkling light plant" behind when we had to leave for the summer.

I gave it to our cleaning lady after taking the lights off. The lights went in the kitchen drawer. We would not be back until October.

There were continuous signs all summer which I will share, but before I do, I want to share an update that happened months after we returned to California. I have the opportunity to do that because of my final editing before going to print next week. I am writing this right before going to press and am so glad I have the opportunity to tell of the most recent "sign".

So, we came back to California in October 2019. Some time after returning, I saw those same seed lights in the kitchen drawer and decided to take them out and make a centerpiece with a glass bowl and angel candle. The seed lights were wrapped inside around the glass bowl surrounding the candle and the switch was at the bottom of the bowl covered with colorful stones. So, if I were to put on the lights, I would have to move those stones and put on the switch. I never did. Instead, I said a prayer and "talking" to Paul, asked that he put those lights on someday as a miracle when I really needed it.

Months went by and nothing. One day a friend asked me to lunch and asked me to tell her about Paul since she was a new friend and knew about my upcoming book. I talked all about Paul, crying on and off, but it felt good talking about him. On the way home, which was only about eight minutes, I sobbed by myself in the car. I was just missing him so much. I walked in the kitchen and, you guessed it. The lights in that glass bowl were going crazy! I nearly fell down and sobbed some more, but those were tears of gratitude.

Now, how many unbelievers are still out there?

Now, back to the experiences in Southampton last summer. One morning, I was having coffee by myself on the patio under the umbrella, after Manny left for the gym (where I should have been going) and was thinking about Paul and how I was missing his "signs."

So, I started talking to him in my head.

"Paul, I need a sign from you somehow and please do it right away. You will figure out how."

Within three seconds, a tiny white feather fell right by my hand on the table. It came from nowhere!

Completely covered with the table umbrella, it was hot, humid, with no breeze and not a bird in sight.

Sitting there, staring at this tiny feather, I said, "If that's your sign, move the feather," and it moved immediately, as if there were a breeze, which there wasn't.

This might all sound crazy to many, but, to those who believe, these are definitely signs.

I used to play WORDS WITH FRIENDS with Paul and on two separate occasions, he reached out to me through that game.

One night, I had four letters left to work with, and, you guessed it, the letters appeared PAUL all in a row. Another night, Play with Paul popped up out of nowhere on my screen!

My other sons have come to me with their uncanny stories as well.

On Richie's birthday, we all had dinner in Southampton at a popular restaurant. Richie went into the men's room to wash his hands and heard a song playing. For some reason, a song called *Heaven* came to his mind. It's an old song by some group and he knew Paul liked it (the title alone is interesting here). All of a sudden, Richie said, the song that was playing stopped, and *Heaven* came on! It was as if to say, "Happy birthday Richie, I heard your thoughts and you'll know it's me."

The stories go on and on. Paul's friend Maryelle from Georgia put her Paul experience on Facebook and I included it in the Georgian Tales and Testimonies chapter.

So, when life is over, where do we go? What happens to us after we die?

Is it an end?

Or a beginning?

Is it possible that we live in just one plane of a multidimensional universe?

I think we have difficulty in coping with anything suggesting otherwise because Western culture predisposes us to disbelieve experiences that are unique, unusual, or hard to categorize.

I suddenly realized that these "signs" from Paul had therapeutic value in my grief, so why can't believing there is more to come when we die, be an acceptable part of the bereavement process?

And, that's when I began my research into the Afterlife.

*   *   *

The Afterlife

> "Life and Death are one thread, the same line viewed
> from different sides."
> —Lao Tzu

IN GRIEVING THE TRAUMATIC LOSS of a child, you go in directions you never planned, looking for meaning and comfort.

Sometimes, these directions take you all over the place, looking for answers.

As what happened to me.

I think finding ways to connect with a loved one is a vital part of the grieving process. I saw how much it helped me.

Of course, it's different for everyone. I've heard that some grievers write letters to their loved ones that are gone, wanting to know if they are okay, while telling them they're missed.

When you love deeply, the absence of the one who is gone takes an enormous toll on the living ones left behind. Because of that strong love connection, that love never dies. I will always have an internal son that I carry wherever I go, our souls forever joined.

But, the question is always there. Where did you go?

Thinking about what happens when someone dies is a natural part of the grieving process and suddenly becomes part of the life process.

That's what happened to me, without even realizing it. It started with unexpected twinkling lights, which then led me on a quest for the Holy Grail, so to speak. You can say it definitely helped me heal in that this newfound obsession kept my mind busy, reading and looking for answers. My house was filled with books on these subjects, and I read constantly.

It also opened my mind to think outside the box which I am always willing and excited to do. It's the only way to learn, acknowledging there can be other ideas out there, other paradigms to consider.

It was a satisfying and informative journey with so many positive outcomes which is why I wanted to share them to help others.

Put quite simply for now, death is but a transition from one life to another. It's not over.

It's when I was exposed to the possibilities that our deceased loved ones are really still with us, in some mysterious energy field, that I pursued the means to those possibilities to make it happen.

I was looking for comfort in any way possible.

After the "twinkling light" occurrence(s) I read that unexpected electrical activity is a common way for those in the Spirit to reach out and get our attention.

Same thing with meaningful songs that just start playing!

Or feathers (white) that just appear!

Or dreams that are unusually real—called visitations!

Like finding that keepsake bookmark in an old birthday card, giving me that loving and timely message. That's synchronicity, which means, connecting the dots to events that happen, usually for a purpose, and planned.

I started to make myself more aware of what was happening around me, seeing connections.

Finding Paul's biography that he wrote himself as a 10 year old for a school essay, in one of the storage boxes, as I am writing his now??

And, then, finding his essay on Heaven? And what Heaven meant to him as a 10 year old? Found in that same box?

And what about Richie thinking of the *Heaven* song (that was quite old) on his birthday in a restaurant, and all of a sudden, other music stops and that song *Heaven* comes on?

I don't think anyone can brush these off as just coincidences.

So many times I've heard it said that people are actually souls having a human experience. Our bodies are temporary, and eventually die, but our souls live forever, as eternal energy. It's that soul energy of love that binds us.

It's that love that binds souls to others that are still living. The soul elevates in energy, returning to the Oneness of the Universe, no longer having worldly constraints such as time, suffering or pain.

A certified, legitimate medium can telepathically communicate with a soul, giving messages to a loved one.

I read countless books on how this communication has helped in the healing process of intense grief.

The stories were real and beyond comprehension. Just because something is beyond comprehension, doesn't make it untrue or impossible. There's so much we don't understand now. New realizations happen every day, whether in science, biology, neuroscience, etc. It's why we have to remain open to learning, even if it's "incomprehensible" right now.

In reading the actual accounts of those hearing from past loved ones, there was no way they were made up.

The details told by the medium to the sitter (person being informed of messages) could never have been known.

Of course, there will always be some "wannabe fake psychic mediums" out there and that's why it's important to go through reputable ones such as those vetted by the Windbridge Research Center. It's where each prospective medium goes through an eight step screening and training process for several months.

The Windbridge Research Center performs scientific research and creates educational materials focused on dying, death, and what comes next.

Dr. Julie Beischel cofounded this independent organization consisting of a community of scientists who investigate human potential in correlation to psychic mediums.

It focuses on people who report regular communication with the deceased (mediums) and those who receive mediumship readings (sitters).

Their findings are astonishing. For me, it gives absolute credence to a soul never dying, but living on, and, at times, able to be reached by the mysterious gifts of a certified psychic medium. There are composed lists of such mediums.

I will discuss more about psychic mediums later in this chapter.

The important thing to remember, not only in this particular subject, but, in any subject, is to keep an open mind.

Consider there could always be more to what you always thought possible.

Elizabeth Kübler-Ross (1926-2004) was a Swiss-American psychiatrist, and pioneered studies in near-death-experiences (NDE).

I had never heard about NDEs before. A near-death-experience happens when a person has clinically died, or nearly so. It's what they experience as they step toward whatever lies beyond their life. Thousands upon thousands claimed their out of body travels took them to an unnamed destination where they met with remarkable encounters, including deceased loved ones, tunnels of light, pure peace, and even receiving messages. Many of them claimed to see and hear what was going on from above their supposed dead body which seems impossible, but it was all confirmed later on by those who were in the room. There was no sensible explanation other than it being totally mysterious and thought-provoking.

Dr. Ross researched more than 20,000 people who had NDE. She found, in all those documentations, that we first enter a period of review which we are "responsible for everything we have done... and, how every thought, word and deed, and choice we have made in our entire lives affected others."

I can only smile when I think of Paul having his life review when the "concert wrist band" stories came up. I can see Paul making his case, saying, "but look at all the people that I made happy!" This side joke will only make sense to the people who personally knew Paul. According to Ross, everything we experience during our physical lives consists in a series of lessons we needed to learn on a soul level. Life is a school, where we choose our own major and minor, our own teachers and where all of us have to go through tests, trials and tribulations. And, when we have passed the tests, we are allowed to graduate and return back home where we all came from, and where we will all be reunited again one day.

Although Dr. Ross was the author of more than 20 books, I especially liked *On Life After Death* where she presents writings that encourage us to approach the end of life with compassionate love. She not only gives compassionate advice for those dealing with terminal illness, removing fear, but for those suffering from the death of a loved one. There is a compelling message of hope, helping one to become stronger from tragedy.

I found these essays so inspirational.

Raymond Moody, philosopher, psychologist and author of many books, also researched and wrote about NDEs. Dr. Moody found consistency in all reports. Once revived, people told what lies beyond death in their own words, and whatever people were chasing for before—fame, power or money, they came back knowing what matters is love and fearlessness of death. It was part of their life review.

People said they felt the pain they gave out to others, as well as the goodness, helping them to understand his or her purpose in life. And, it is in this understanding about who they are that helps them make significant life changes.

When playwright George Kaufman said "you can't take it with you," he was referring to material things, but, in a life review, researchers noted that one of life review's main lessons is that knowledge and love are two elements that we take with us when we die.

This part of the NDE, the life review, creates the greatest catalyst for change. One is able to evaluate themselves on their life performance in their mistakes and good deeds.

Dr. Moody's book, *Life After Life*, in 1975, sold more than 13 million copies making the subject of NDEs popular, while opening the way for other studies and others to share their stories.

Sometimes, people are hesitant to come forward with such information for fear they might be considered a bit nutty.

I can see now that not all questions or observations can be resolved by science, especially this idea of life after death. It has to be more philosophical for now. Philosophy deals with questions that are unintelligible. How can one ever set up an experiment to prove life after death?

I probably read hundreds of these NDE stories. Many books have been written by the ones who actually had these experiences, telling how their lives changed forever. Other authors were researchers in the subject.

One book, by Dr. Eben Alexander, entitled *Proof of Heaven*, was one of my favorites, although there were many.

Dr. Alexander was a neurosurgeon in North Carolina when he fell into a seven day rare meningitis-induced coma in 2008. During his coma, he experienced a spiritual awakening in visiting otherworldly realms of consciousness. He met angels and spirits, feeling a unifying love. There he also met and spoke with the Divine source of the universe. He "came back" after seven days, which was considered a medical miracle.

Before his journey into this other world, in his knowledge of neuroscience, he had no belief in God, heaven or the soul. But all that changed. He is now certain that God and the soul are real, and that death is not the end, but only a transition.

No scientist or person could not believe this after reading this compelling story.

Perhaps it's now becoming clear why reading such accounts can have healing effects in losing a loved one.

It's not really the end. There's so much more. Not only is our loved one not gone forever, but we will see them again, with possible signs in between.

Another book I devoured was by Dr. Jeffry Long, *Evidence of the Afterlife*, 2009. He became interested in NDE by accident one day after coming across it in a medical journal. He then became obsessed in gathering evidence of NDEs through questionnaires. He documented, referenced and corroborated with scores of prior studies supporting the validity of NDEs.

In the thousands of cases of NDEs, there is a consistency of the results of chosen life changes and beliefs. That what we do here on earth matters.

Peter Kreeft, professor of philosophy, says "Earth is not outside heaven. It is heaven's workshop. Heaven is our real home where we have always longed to be."

Karma, I love that word.

People use it more often these days, but many people think of it as punishment. Actually, it isn't.

It's much deeper and more meaningful.

It originates from an ancient Hindu belief, but it's part of various other religious ideologies, also found in the Bible.

"A man reaps what he sows" (Gal 6:7).

It is the simple and natural law of cause and effect of an act.

What you give, you will get back. No judgement. Just a tool for learning.

We choose from either love or fear. High energy versus low energy. While here on earth, we need to learn all different lessons. We are responsible for our actions and the results they bring.

Thich Nhat Hanh, in *No Death, No Fear*, says "every thought you produce, anything you say, any action you do, bears your signature. Action is called Karma. And, that's your continuation. When the body disintegrates, you continue on with your actions. It's like the cloud in the sky. When the cloud is no longer in the sky, it hasn't died. The cloud is continued in other forms like rain or snow or ice. Our nature is the nature of no birth and no death. It is impossible for a cloud to pass from being to non-being. And that is true with a beloved person. They have not died. They have continued in many new forms and you can look deeply and recognize them in and around you."

I can see that what one chooses to do, say, think or act can and will define what kind of experience he will have in this life or future lives, as in reincarnation.

Reincarnation. It's a word not usually spoken about, and the jury is still out for me as far as my acceptance on this, but I thought to include it in here to let you all decide for yourselves.

Christians used to believe in reincarnation until it was removed from Christian doctrine in 325 CE at the Council of Nicea. I found this out while reading one of Mark Anthony's books (*The Psychic Lawyer*).

It seems the Church fathers wanted their people to believe their sins could not be corrected in a another life.

Reading Dr. Brian Weiss' book, *Many Lives Many Masters*, gave me pause. A highly respected psychiatrist, he tells the true story of one of his patients who was suffering from phobias and anxieties and how he decided to use hypnosis in her treatment. He was astounded, when, under hypnosis, she recollected events from past lives spanning hundreds of years, which ultimately steered her recovery, while changing his life as well. I could not put this book down.

I never gave the idea of reincarnation any consideration, but this book alone opened my eyes to the possibility. Again, it's the thought that the soul never dies. It has cellular memory.

The thought that Paul's soul is still with us, brings me comfort every day.

This past life regression therapy is now extensively used with surprisingly positive results for many.

Most people are familiar, or heard of psychic mediums, many who are television personalities, such as *The Long Island Medium*, *The Hollywood Medium*, Tyler Henry, John Edward, etc. And, yes I went to see all of them at one point or another after Paul passed away, as part of an audience in both New York and California. Although not chosen to be read out of these audiences, I was amazed at the readings of those who were.

One time, I took my friend Trisha to a James Van Praagh event in California. His first words applied directly to her! He went on to give her messages from her recently deceased mother-in-law, who she was very close to. His "messages" were uncannily detailed and she was shocked, while being so comforted. It was a night neither one of us will ever forget!

I had two personal meetings as well. One with the famous George Anderson that I waited months for an appointment. I took my youngest son, Richie along with me that day. We were both astonished at what George Anderson said. There was no way he knew anything about us since I had my friend pay and made the appointment, using her name.

He described and named every single deceased relative I have and some names were unusual—like Esther! There were poignant messages from my parents and Paul for both Richie and I that would not make sense to anyone but us. Anderson even said Paul's name and he was also known as "Paulie," which he was!

There was so much more. So glad we have it on tape.

So, you ask, how can this be? I don't know, but all I can say is that it has helped me, along with all the other tools I found for surviving unimaginable grief.

I went down these roads for that one purpose—comfort.

I didn't plan any of this. It seems I was led in that direction initiated with these twinkling lights.

It was Paul's way of helping me because he knew, in his passing, I would be inconsolable.

That would be Paul, finding a way to help.

I know he had something to do with this journey I set forth on and that I would know he was at peace and happy—that he is but a thought away, having never really left me.

I may not have him in the way I would like, in his physical form, but his soul lives on forever. And I will be with him again.

—— ❋ ——

Lewisboro And Georgian Testimonials And Tales

"Don't spend your time asking, 'why isn't the world a better place?' it will only be time wasted. The question to ask is, 'How can I make it better?' To that there is an answer."

"Too often we underestimate the power of a touch, a smile, a kind word, a listening ear, and honest compliment, or the smallest act of caring, all of which have the potential to turn a life around."
—Leo Buscaglia, 1924-1988

Leo Buscaglia was another favorite author of mine, who was also a motivational speaker. He was often called Dr. Love. He was another human gone too soon.

In this final section of this book, I included many of the correspondences that I received after Paul passed away, through emails, texts, Facebook postings and phone calls. I printed out as many as I could and, unfortunately, there were many I didn't.

During phone calls, I tried to take notes of whatever they told me about their memories of Paul. It gave me something to do during those first few very dark weeks, as well as thinking I would go back and read them again. Not realizing they would serve as a great part of a book I didn't know I would be writing.

Again, there always seems to be a plan, even though we have no idea at the time.

Some friends said they started to write about Paul, but couldn't continue—it became too painful. People express and deal with grief in their own way.

These entries were so comforting to me, seeing all the good Paul passed on. They serve as a reminder that how we treat others has an everlasting effect.

It's why I included these as the perfect ending to this book.

Leo Buscaglia's quote above says it all.

* * *

Submitted by Seamus Brophy:
Childhood friend of Paul's from Lewisboro, New York

When we look at the beginning of Christianity, two figures come into play: Jesus and Paul.

While Jesus is viewed by many Christians as the founder of the religion whose life events laid the groundwork of Jesus' mission, arguably one of the most important and influential figures in our history, delivering that mission in a way no one had before. The doctrines of Christianity primarily come from Paul's teaching.

Jesus was a foundation, Paul a powerful witness-

St. Paul. A powerful witness indeed! Delivering that mission in a way no one had before. Paul was my brother. He was everyone's brother, spreading gospel of love. He was next level special human being. They just don't make them like that and never will again. One of a kind, a true gem. I am so thankful for all the time I got to spend with him. I feel so lucky. He was such a character. There is only one Paul! WE HAD SO MUCH FUN AND SO MANY LAUGHS! The town pool, sharks and minnows, Dags, the iceman, cheeseburgers in paradise, the Bedford Diner, the Meadows, devil sticks, dead shows, Van Gundy's seats, Rutgers Lax Camp, the Monte Carlo, Georgia Tech, the Hawks, ATL, GD50 etc. etc.

His Generosity and kindness knew no bounds. We shared such wonderful times he will always be a part of my heart. He loved his family and friends and would do anything for them. He taught us all so much about how to truly love and care about each other with nothing asked in return. Paul was an angel here on earth. My heart will never heal but Paul would want us all to keep on keeping on and carry on his mission of kindness, generosity, and love. LIVE LIKE PAUL!

Never let go on these three things:

Faith, hope, and love.

And know that the greatest of these will always be love.

Submitted by Lars Lungren:
Childhood friend of Paul's from Lewisboro, New York

Greetings,

Where to start, here are just a few short stories that stuck with me through the years.

Middle School / High School – John Jay Years

I owe it to Paul for graduating High School. Paul called me one night and asked me if I had finished my paper that was due tomorrow. I said no. Paul said that I needed that paper to graduate, so in true Paul fashion, he drove over to my house that night and typed my paper as I vaguely gave him some ideas about what I was going to write about. Basically, Paul did the entire paper for me and for that reason I graduated High School. I don't know what I would have done without him looking out for me.

Paul is responsible for everyone getting home safely throughout High School, College, and beyond, he was always responsible to be the sober driver and to drop everything and pick up and then drop off everyone safely. He would always make multiple trips in the Chrysler or Frank's White Jeep Wrangler. He would always give us candy from the Booster Club candy box he had in the back of the car that he was selling at the basketball games that night.

I have a thousand stories of all our good times together through the years and how he would find one, two or several things that would get you worked up and then tease you with them every chance he got, just to make you have a laugh.

Wilmington – July 2002

Visited on his way up north—Shared about himself.

Really was looking for reassurance that you still accepted him as a friend and that everything would be the same. It was almost as if he was reaching out because he valued our friendship and if he could convince you, he could convince others. Of course, he would always have our love, support and of course, he would always have our friendship.

He was traveling by his pictures of our JJ Football team that won along with videos of the team's games.

It was a time before cell phones and social media made a big impact on our lives so staying in touch was off and on, but he was always welcome.

Denver, CO – March 2003

Paul traveled and made it out to Colorado in March 2003 for our wedding, it just happened that it snowed 7 feet that week and the airport was closed for a few days before our wedding, but he made it. I wonder how many weddings Paul attended? Everyone he knew, I'm sure invited him to their own.

Denver, CO – January 2007

Paul came to visit me and Jack for one of his annual ski trips to Vail. Jacked rolled off the ottoman when he was 4 months old, Paul looked at me and said, "Is that supposed to happen?" I said, "no, it's the first time he's ever rolled over." Paul then began to laugh hysterically, as only Paul could. He loved sharing the story with Jack through the years and would always laugh.

Paul poured over the teacher salaries from each district and convinced us that it only made sense to move from Denver Public Schools to our current school district in Jefferson County. He analyzed all the numbers and created a spreadsheet with comparisons throughout the years based on the salary schedule. He was looking out for our best interests. He always mailed the kids Christmas presents and brought them gifts.

Denver, CO- November 2015

Paul came out on another visit and we went out to Sweet Tomatoes Restaurant, Paul wanted to go because he had a coupon for a free meal. The funny part was he forgot to use it that night and left it on the table.

He told us that he saved all his bicentennial quarters and said that one day he would give them to his............when he passed away because he would never have kids.

Denver, CO – 2018

Paul was out in Denver again and we went to an AVS game, where he bantered with a scalper to try and get tickets. We didn't buy the tickets from this one particular scalper but the same scalper saw us about 15 minutes later and started to try and sell us tickets, noticed Paul and said, never mind, I know you guys. Paul then told the scalper that he would have sold to us because he wasn't going to be able to get rid of his tickets. We all laughed, while he only had that one- night encounter with the scalper, he made an impression on him and made him laugh. I'm sure that scalper is still telling that story. Paul could make anyone laugh in any situation.

Denver, CO – August 2018

Paul was in Denver to hike the 14er not San Juan with his friend who hiked all of Colorado's 14ers. He wanted to come up here and hike the last one with him. Paul said it was his first 14er that he hiked and that is why everyone was so excited. Again, making everyone laugh.

Submitted by Maryelle St. Clare:
Atlanta, Georgia

To all my Paul Giaccio Family: I have to tell you what happened today. Sorry it's long but please read through.

First, the backstory is that about two months ago I lost my Live Like Paul bracelet. I was making flower arrangements for a wedding, and I had to keep putting on and taking off medical gloves, and at one point I left to go get something to eat and realized while I was out that my bracelet was gone. I was so upset, but when I returned to the shop, my bracelet was sitting right on top of a nearly full 55-gallon trashcan. I thought thank God it wasn't at the bottom or I never would've been able to get it! So back on my wrist it went.

Two days after that I lost it again. Only this time it wasn't on the top of the trash. I had filled up two 55-gallon barrels with flower and greenery waste, and there was no way I could dig through all that trash to find it. So, my bracelet was gone, definitely gone, this time.

That was two months ago at least. Today I was back at the shop making wedding arrangements again. And just this morning I bought tickets to see the band Collective Soul in November. Collective Soul is the show where my sister and I ran into Paul some years back. Paul had been a long-time neighbor, but we didn't really know him very well at that point. He saw us at the show and waived and I said to my sister "Hey that guy Paul from the neighborhood is here." He came over and that's where we discovered the he was a huge live music fan, as were we. We started attending lots of shows together. We became familiar with Paul's "shows spreadsheet" and he could tell us who was playing anywhere in Georgia through the entire next year and so on, but I always remember that first one, Collective Soul, as being the lucky day, we ran into each other.

So, as I said, I happened to buy Collective Soul tickets again this morning, and today I was at the shop making arrangements and going outside repeatedly while I was painting some boxes, with Pandora playing on my phone. At one point I looked down to see what song it was and saw that my email was open to the Ticketmaster confirmation message for the Collective Soul show. I thought, "Oh I must have hit that by accident." I hadn't opened that email for a few hours, since I sent a screenshot of it to my sister and had used my phone lots since then. That screen was not still open from having sent it to her earlier. So, I saw it, didn't think much. Within one minute, I had made at least 25 times between today and yesterday, taking the same 10-foot route from the table inside to my painting area outside. But on this last walk, just after seeing that email, I stepped outside looked down, and saw my bracelet sitting there on the pavement. Just there out in the open. I walked that path dozens of times since yesterday and hundreds of times since I lost the bracelet. But I didn't see anything until this last walk.

Adrienne Falzon, Bryan Van Vranken,
Christine Nelson, Evan Blum, Diana Medrano and
everyone else who believes in **#livelikepaul**. He is out there.
🖤🖤🖤

I don't believe in a lot of "woo" and I'm pretty much a hard core skeptic, but I do believe in the transformation of matter and energy and I can only assume that Paul visited me today. His soul or his astral being or whatever you want to call it. I don't know how I could have missed that bracelet until now. It was RIGHT THERE in my eyeline. I guess we can't explain some things in this universe.

I could have added the above story from Maryelle in the afterlife chapter as well as here. She continues to be faithful friend, wearing her livelikepaul bracelet, taking Paul along to her concerts.

I just love how she takes Paul to her concerts!

Maryelle St. Clare is with **Christine Nelson.**   •••
July 19 · 🌐

On the way to Jacksonville to see The Rolling Stones. We will be bringing **Paul Giaccio** with us in our hearts. We'll see about "upgrading" our seats once we scope out the place. LOL. **#livelikepaul**

Submitted by Matt Harpring:

Matt and Paul met at Georgia Tech. Matt played basketball for Georgia Tech and went on to play two seasons with the NBA. Through all the years, Paul considered Matt and his family to be his own.

Here we go.......

Paul was my true best friend. We clicked immediately when we first met in college. I think we gained respect from each other's work ethic. I loved how hard he worked to help and really asked for nothing in return. He was such a thoughtful person, a person that truly cared about other people's happiness. A very unique quality Paul had was his understanding of different lives people lived and how he could always see the bright side in people. I can't tell you how many nights we spent talking and how he became such a trusted and great friend to have. He became my roommate and a person I could always, always rely on. He became as close as family. I have three brothers and a sister but really Paul was my fourth brother.

He became family in my eyes and was the one person in this world that knew more about me than anyone. We went from a time we did basically everything together to an adult "out of college" friendship. It was tough but we transitioned our friendship from college seamlessly. Moving to Orlando never hurt our friendship. In fact, it made us tighter. We both had huge life changing moments going on and we would just talk it out. Never did we go without talking for years. He was such a great friend and we were so close that I was honored when he said yes to being my best man at my wedding. My wife Amanda adored him and I couldn't imagine moving on in my life again without Paul being right there with me. Just like he had always been. We had a deep connection that never grew apart. We just knew each other so well and we truly enjoyed talking and spending time when we could. In my years in the NBA, I could be on the road somewhere and call him at 3 am and he always answered the phone to listen. He was always so interested—or at least made me think he was. He would make sure to call every few days to check in.

What great memories and laughs over the years and I can't thank him enough for being there for me all those years. Only His understanding of how my brain works really helped me throughout my years. Whether it was sports or relationships, he seemed to always have the right things to say. Sometimes he could see my point of view. Sometimes it was just to be a great listener, and sometimes I needed stories to make me laugh. He just had a knack to know what was best. What a great friend. I never got off the phone with Paul in a worse place than when I got on the phone with him. I really miss us laughing and catching up with the heckling and locker room type fun we had. I wish I could hear more stories that would make us both laugh and laugh. I will never have another best friend like Paul. Never again will anyone be so interested in my life and how I was doing. I find myself now wanting to call and want to check in with him. I yearn for his advice, our fun arguments, but most his words of wisdom. He is missed by so many, no more than by me. He's uncle Paul to my kids and will always be uncle Paul with my family. I think about him all the time. The world lost such a great person that touched so many lives. I wish I can have another day with him. One day we will see each other again. I miss my best friend.

Submitted by Betsy and Eric Dietsch:
Originally met Paul in Georgia, then moved to the state of Washington.

I've been struggling with what to say to you beyond my condolences and how sorry we are this happened. Then it dawned on me that social media is telling the story before my eyes for me.

While Betsy and I only touched the surface of getting to know Paul before we left Atlanta, it is obvious through all my extended networks that your son touched so many hearts across not only his local community but worldwide. He provided so many positive memories for countless friends, family, and even strangers he would notice who simply needed someone to listen. He was a giver of life lessons for so many people of my personal friends in Atlanta and a role model so strong he was called "uncle" to their children. I can say without a doubt that Paul influenced many of my close friends to become better friends, companions, coworkers, and parents. Take comfort knowing Paul made wonders.

Submitted by Kay Callahan:
Fellow teacher from my teaching days at John Jay Junior High School, where we met and became close friends. We know each of our families and shared memories and stories. Kay was, and is, a faithful friend.

A month ago, you sent me a picture of the two of us. Our kids were just starting high school and we each were dealing with life's current crisis. I never thought that I would be writing to you to tell you that I know the pain you are in and I wish I could do something to take it away. I cannot, but I can tell you that you are one of the strongest, most courageous people I know and that the love is holding you up now. Manny, your family and all of us who care so much about you will be your strength to keep going until you are able to stand alone.

Losing your child is not something most have to face but I have had this experience and I know you cannot imagine that you will ever be able to quiet the aching in your heart. You will find a way to put one foot in front of the other and take a step into life again.

Paul was an exceptional person. Every word shared by his brothers and friends echo his life's purpose to bring love, joy, and friendship to all he met. Those qualities were instilled by you and will live on in those whose lives he touched.

Fill your heart and soul with the precious memories of Paul. I know you will find strength and peace of mind and heart.

Love you,
Kay

The story you are about to hear began with this email:

Hi Adrienne,

I got your email from Christine. My name is Jack and I was hoping to speak with you about my story regarding Paul. The circumstances of how we met and became friends is truly incredible and I think would make a great addition to the book you're working on. I'd love to set up a call so we can chat a bit. My number is xxx-

Shane, Jack and Paul

xxxx. Just let me know a time that works for you and a number to reach you and we can go from there.

Thanks!

Jack Lansky

Well, that phone call took place and lasted almost one and a half hours. He started by telling me how he and Paul met, only a few years ago, and all that happened after.

Jack said he advertised on Magnolia Miracle to attend the Grateful Dead's 50th anniversary concert at Soldier Field in Chicago which was totally sold out. He was looking for a ticket, as well as a ride from Atlanta, Georgia to Chicago since plane tickets were so expensive.

With these requests reaching thousands of people, Paul was the only one to respond, only days before the concert. Jack told Paul he might even have a connection to get them tickets if, in driving to Chicago, they might pick up this Shane Nelson, who was walking across America for a documentary. Jack said he knew of this Shane who may need a ride if he couldn't finish in time to get to the concert by foot and that he was the one having tickets for the one picking him up somewhere, no place determined yet. As you can see, there were a lot of moving parts, but none that would disinterest Paul. He was always in for an adventure. But Paul's friends thought he was "crazy" meeting up and driving to Chicago with this absolute stranger, so Paul met up with Jack at his office, and had him "cleared" before they left.

Now two strangers to each other were on their way to Chicago, and possibly three depending on Shane's situation.

Jack said they left with Paul driving and the two of them talked nonstop about everything for hours, while keeping in touch with "Shane" along the way to see if he would need to go with them. Jack said, at one point, out of nowhere, Paul said, "by the way, I'm gay." Jack responded, "ok that's cool, no problem, here." And that was that. They heard from Shane finally and they did pick him up in a park in Indianapolis, Indiana. He was there where he said he would be. Now, three strangers in a car, like they always knew each other, on their way to Chicago!

Once there, Jack said, Paul met up with the friends he had plans with, but Jack said he didn't leave him in the dust. He introduced him to everyone and included him. Through Shane, they had tickets to the concert and after the concert, when it was time to go back, the three of them decided to do some sightseeing together in Chicago before Shane continued his walking documentary. Jack said they went to all the main spots to see in Chicago—the Willis Tower, Museum of Art, etc., taking lots of photos of the three of them.

Then, Jack and Paul on their way back to Atlanta, did more sightseeing in St. Louis, Missouri with more photos. He also talked about a little people convention while there, and their fun times with everyone. Jack said it was a trip he'll never forget because of so many reasons—not only how it all came together, but he said, meeting Paul and getting to know him changed his life.

It didn't end with that trip. He explained that Paul always invited him to all his events, concerts, poker games parties, etc, introducing him to everyone, opening up a whole new world. He said going to the concerts that Paul arranged created magical moments he never experienced. He found there was peace of total acceptance for all.

Meeting Paul and all that happened after, in the few short years he knew him, left an everlasting impression.

Submitted by David Fiestal:
Childhood friend from Lewisboro, NY

This is David Fiestal, a friend of Paul's from High School. I'm not sure if you remember me. Lars forwarded your email to us earlier this week. In any event, I was very saddened to learn of Paul's passing. My parents send their deepest condolences as well. Paul was truly one of the nicest people I've met. But he wasn't just nice, he was fiercely competitive which may not have been immediately obvious. Whether anchoring our offensive line as the smallest center ever, or pushing himself to maintain his perfect school attendance record or committing himself to work at D'Ag's from an early age, or, perhaps most effectively establishing strong bonds of friendship lasting many years with so many people from every corner of life. Paul was always pushing himself forward to be the best that he could be. And for all intents, he succeeded.

Much love,
David Fiestal

Submitted by John Hurley:
Dean of students at John Jay Junior High School

First, John Hurley's email to me:

Hi, Adrienne,

I was so sorry to hear from Bea that Paul passed away. What a tragedy. It bothers me that someone so kind and caring would be taken from us at such a young age. I feel so bad for you and the family! Paul was such a great kid and after 34 years at John Jay, with all the students that passed my desk, he stands out as one of the most outstanding young students that passed through JJMS.

I remember a wonderful moment where Paul reached out to help a new student become acquainted with the school. I wrote a paragraph describing it below.

When I think of Paul in the middle school I think about his outgoing personality and compassion for others. I hope this helps. My regards to you, Adrienne, and, again I am so sorry to hear about Paul, but his legacy will continue to live! Please tell Frank I said hello—he was a great kid and football player.

His submission:

"Paul was such a great kid (thinking back when he was in middle school). His outgoing personality, his maturity, and his deep caring for others was rather unique for his age. Waiting outside my classroom door for my next class, you would always see other students gathered around Paul as he made his way to his next class. There was never a time when he walked by with this group, even with the hallway being so noisy and crowded, that I didn't hear him say, 'Hey, Mr. Hurley.' This is who Paul was, always going out of his way even to say hello. It was also common for Paul to come up to me while I was standing at the doors to the cafeteria watching the 8th graders during their lunch period to chat. We would share our weekend stories, talk about his classes and sports. One day I was standing in the doorway looking in the cafeteria and noticed a new student to our school who was sitting alone. I thought to myself, after lunch, I should give the boy's guidance counselor a heads up. A few minutes later Paul came up to me and said, 'What's up Mr. H?' After a little time chatting, he noticed me looking attentively at the student and he asked me if everything was OK and I said, yes but I told him it bothered me that our new student was sitting alone. Paul asked me what his name was, I told him and then Paul asked me a few questions about our new student. The lunch bell rang and off to the races went Paul and the rest of the 8th graders.

I will never forget it but, it was either the next day or day after that when I walked into the 8th grade lunch there was Paul, another friend of Paul's, and the new student sitting having lunch together. I never pushed or suggested to Paul to reach out to this student, but he did this all on his own. Even at this young age he was deeply concerned about others. His caring and compassion for others was special. It is something that cannot be taught, but comes from within. Paul always exemplified this through his actions."

Submitted by Mikey Dunworth:

Mikey met Paul back in 2002 at the Twisted Taco in Atlanta, Georgia, as a customer when Paul was working there, along with building up his finance business. Mikey said they became friends because Paul was "super outgoing."

Paul attended Mikey and Jana's beautiful wedding in the Dominican Republic and they recently had their first son, Zion.

Mikey is LA based and works in the film industry. He and Jana are world travelers and love to share on Instagram. Their handle is oneloveourlove.com check it out.

Here is Mikey's submission word for word:

When I was 25 years old, I used to live in Vail, Colorado half the year and in Dominical, Costa Rica the other half.

So, occasionally, when I came back to Atlanta, Georgia, Paul set up a way to allow himself to take time off from his bar-bac job at Twisted Taco and allow me to cover for him while he was gone. Let me make it clear that Twisted Taco almost never let Paul have a weekend off because he was too valuable. He had designed the most perfect and efficient way to have a bar run. He was so good at whatever he put his mind to. We were almost never in town at the same time, or if so, it was super brief, so he would leave me detailed maps and directions on how to run the bar. With his directions and my work ethics, they allowed us to continue the trade-off whenever I came to town. We both benefited from this arrangement. One of the times we were hanging out he asked, "Hey, man, are you saving money? With the awesome lifestyle you are living?" and, I was like, yeah, for my next surf trip! He asked me in a polite way how much I was saving and was I setting myself up for the future. I probably never considered saving up for my future at this point. So, he said he would come over to my house and we would go over some ways that would help me later on in life. He said, "You don't want to be 30 yrs old and say you can do flips and spins on a snowboard and not have any money to your name!

So, after a short session with Paul, I had set up a Roth IRA and a Mutual Fund. Fast forward six years later. I had both of my investments still gaining me money, but didn't have cash. So, I withdrew my mutual fund which allowed me to travel and surf the world for six months. Without that, I couldn't have had one of the best experiences of my life. I was between jobs and that money allowed me to do it. I still have my IRA gaining money and I plan to use it for my retirement. I feel so blessed that he selflessly helped me out to make sure that I was never broke and without options. He also set up my mom with a great retirement plan as well. My mom was just starting to teach yoga and Paul was having some sciatica pain. She gave him CD's and videos on ways he could mitigate some of the pain and work on his flexibility. He would even invite my mom to events and parties because he knew sometimes, she was lonely when I was out of the country or state.

Paul also set me up with another investment opportunity when he went into his ATM business. I really praised him for starting it, while others made fun of him. Instead of taking out loans from banks, he asked friends to invest so we could all make interest. That way, he said, everybody could win. This has benefitted me in so many ways.

Paul was, and always will be an angel. I must say for the 12 winter seasons I lived in Vail, Colorado, he was the only friend who came to visit every single year.

He really loved skiing and organized ski trips with his close friends. I honestly think having all his friends together in one place was one of his most favorite things in the world.

He loved skiing so much that he would even make his own sandwiches and pack them in his ski pants so he wouldn't have to stop for lunch. He would eat them on the chair lift between runs. It was so funny because by the time he would pull them out to eat them, they would look like a pancake. I used to challenge him so much taking him into unridden snow. He wasn't the best skier, but he always managed to have a smile on his face and find a way down the mountain. Every year he got better and better and would keep up and ski with anybody he wanted no matter what level they were at. He was great to have visit and I always looked forward to when Paul and his friends came.

In sharing all of this, it's a way to see the value he added to my life, not in the form of money or things.

It was immeasurable. He was my best friend. He made everyone feel

he was their best friend as well. He always placed his friends first and added his special way of enhancing their lives. He was always available in person or on the phone. He wasn't a "texter" he loved calling to catch up. He loved connecting friends with friends. No matter who, what, or where in my life, I always knew Paul would be there for me. He was and is, the most selfless person I've ever known.

I honestly believe he made everyone he knew into a better person. We can all learn from him. His impact will never be forgotten.

We love you Paul
#livelikepaul

Submitted by Roger Andresen:

Hi Adrienne,

I don't believe we ever met. I met Pauly at Tech. I was several years ahead of him. I started in 1991.

I wanted to take a moment to tell you how much Paul meant to me. I recently received a "Live Like Paul" band, and I haven't taken it off since I got it. And I have had a number of chances to spread what I feel 'living like Paul ' means to me when asked about the bracelet. So, the love is spreading.

You and I probably haven't met because I wasn't really one of Pauly's closer friends. We were great friends for sure, but the problem is he had too many friends. Although he would never rank the order of his friends, I would say if he were forced to, I would fit in around 100th place.

Yet, every time I saw him, he made me feel like the most important person in his life. He cared so much for everyone. There were numerous times that he went out of his way for me and my wife, Kate, doing ridiculously kind things for us and never asking a thing in return. Some were favors that we asked for, but some were just random acts of kindness towards us and even loving gestures towards our kids.

Strange part is that there were probably half a dozen times that I had a heart to heart with him just to tell that he was the true embodiment of what a good person is. The fact that I took the time to tell him how wonderful he was is not any reflection on me and how I go around spreading words of kindness. He just happened to literally be the only person I know that was just doing everything right as a human living to the full potential of happiness and kindness and love; he was the best person I knew.

He lived free from fear.

He lived free from anger.

He lived free from hate.

He lived free from sadness.

He lived free from judgement.

I feel that any human living without these toxic emotions frees them to live on a higher plane which is where he existed.

When one is not encumbered as such, they truly become liberated to start engaging in life, giving them the ability to thrive, and he did.

A few of his strengths came to mind: creativity, curiosity, bravery, persistence, vitality, humor, hope and gratitude.

And most importantly, LOVE: love for life, love for his tribe (his very extended tribe), love for this world.

And you could always tell he glowed with a sustained happiness that only a person living such a life could have.

He was a beacon of love and light, and he spread that light wherever he found darkness.

Reminds me of something Martin Luther King, Jr. echoed. "Darkness cannot drive out darkness; only light can do that. Hate cannot drive out hate; only love can do that." Pauly was the light and the love.

Yours truly,
Roger

Submitted by Denna Babul:

Heaven gained one of the best this week. Paul Giaccio you were such a beautiful light. I am so thankful for the time we got to spend together. You will be severely missed but forever cherished.

Hug your friends and family tight this week. Tell them how much you love them.

I know Paul is smiling ear to ear watching all of these tributes pour in. I sure hope he knew just how loved he really was.

RIP my friend.

Submitted by Casey Baca:

Paul, you are the kindest and most generous person I have ever known. You've opened your heart widely to all and have done so without ever asking for anything in return. You will be missed beyond words. I love you dearly and my goal is to live each day of my life like you would. Heaven has a new angel.

Casey Baca is with Paul Giaccio.
1 hr ·

Paul you are the kindest and most generous person I have ever known. You've opened your heart widely to all and have done so without ever asking for anything in return. You will be missed beyond words. I love you dearly and my goal is to live each day of my life like you would. Heaven has a new angel

Submitted by Autumn Coleman:

There are people that truly make the world a better place just by being in it. Paul Giaccio was definitely one of those people. He was someone that really lived and encouraged friends and family to live more, too. His big heart and zest for life were infectious.

Paul orchestrated outdoor adventures—camping, hiking, ski trips;

often grabbed concert tickets (or fun colored bands) for friends to see their favorite artists; and hosted annual friend gatherings at his home. Those are just a few of the ways that he touched my life personally. I have many special memories because of Paul. He had a knack for finding analogies between Sienfield episodes to specific life situations.

No one could match my love of the Avett Brothers except maybe Paul. We saw them play in Atlanta at least three times together. The best seats I've ever had to an Avett show were a gift from Paul.

Paul was a lot of things to those lucky enough to have him in our lives. He was a supportive friend, doting uncle(s) and godfather(s); proud son and brother. It's been difficult to process that he left us so suddenly Sunday evening. What a mark he left on our lives!

Losing Paul so young is heartbreaking reminder that we're not guaranteed tomorrow. Life is oh-so short. Hold you loved ones tight and express what they mean to you.

I will miss him dearly. He was a bright light that loved generously and openly. I'm grateful for our memories and his friendship. Sending love and light to Paul's family and friends that are mourning this heartbreaking loss.

This song is for you, Paul. *"I And Love And You."* Directed by Crackerfarm.

❋

Submitted by Chuck Carignan:

This was posted on Paul's wall by his friend Chuck Carignan.

This video was taken on 11/19, the day I learned you were gone. It was difficult to think about attending a concert with such a heavy heart, but I thought about how many shows we had seen together and decided you would've wanted me to go.

It was an extremely emotional performance—with every song, you were in my thoughts. This video in particular, which is the only video or pic I took the entire night. The message in Jim's story about how it's our responsibility to be there for each other to "heal a broken heart" really struck a nerve. Even the name of his tour manager—it was all a reminder that you were there with me that night and will always be with me.

I have always admired you, Paul. Thank you for being there for me when I needed you. Now it's my responsibility to #LiveLikePaul and be there for those that need to heal a broken heart. Love you always.

Submitted by Bobby Cremins:

Head Basketball Coach, at Georgia Tech 1981-2000

Part of Paul's legacy was his commitment, dedication and compassion for the Georgia Tech basketball team and its players. He served as manager of the team under Bobby Cremins from 1993-1997. Here's a quote from Coach Cremins:

"I was very saddened to hear about Paul Giaccio's passing. Paul served as our manager from 1993-1997. Paul met his responsibilities every day and was willing to help in any way. He often stayed after practice with our players rebounding and shooting. He was as reliable as they come. I enjoyed his personality very much and you could tell how much he loved Georgia Tech basketball. A Georgia Tech endowment has been set up in his name.

I encourage you to contribute what you can so Paul's memory can always be part of his legacy at Georgia Tech."

LIVE LIKE PAUL

Sincerely, Bobby Cremins
Georgia Tech Basketball 1981-2000

Submitted by Kevin Cantwell:
Assistant Coach of the Georgia Tech basketball team while Paul was manager.

My thoughts on Paul…

Adrienne, there are certain people in your life that leave you with very distinct memories and Paul was one of those young men.

First of all, my son Kevin Todd was 12 yrs old ball boy at the time and hung out with the managers specifically Paul and he would be a good contact for stories.

My son would always tell me stories in the car on the way home about Paul… they have to do with managing duties dealing with our opponents or ways he was thinking about making money. Kevin was fascinated with Paul, so it drew me to watch and converse with him…which was always a treat.

And just a side note…When my son was in the 8th grade he was looking into buying an ATM Machine. I was amazed that Kevin had this business intuition but years later when I heard what Paul was doing for a living…I then realized where my son got his idea about ATM's.

So many times, I would watch the managers walk through the locker room before or after practice laughing and I would ask Matt Judy what's so funny…as he started to tell me 90% of the time, Paul was the lead character.

Nothing any of them did was bad…just mischievous…a lot of the times it dealt with setting up our opponent's locker room and I would listen and then laugh along with them.

"Paul was special—God Bless Him."

Another submission by Mikey Dunworth along with Jana from his Facebook post:

Mikey Dunworth is with Paul Giaccio and Jana Lankova…

I can't believe it's already been three weeks. I haven't been able to put into words how much you meant to me. The way you've always been there for Jana and I as well as my mom means more that I can express in a Facebook post. And what I've come to learn is that you treated your giant ring of family and friends the exact same. You made us feel as if we were something special and I realize you made everyone feel that way. You were a best friend to so many people. I've never met anyone else to present, selfless and sincere. You never had an ounce of envy or jealousy; you always wanted the best for everyone you knew. I'm going to miss talking about all our travels and future plans with you. You were the only person who always got so excited to hear all about our travels. You always remembered to text or call for birthdays, anniversary, and more. Because of you we've made so many great friends. How did you do it Paul? Everyone you know expresses how hard of a worker you were at the same time you always had time for everyone. I have no idea how you did it. I don't want to believe you have left us physically, but I know you have a strong presence in everyone you've touched. We are all better people for having known and spent lots of time with you. I have lots of stories I'd love to share in your mom's upcoming book as well. I'm painfully going to miss your yearly snowboard/ski trip. You're the only friend that visited me in the snowy mountains of Vail, Colorado for at least 17 times in twelve years. Coming to Atlanta now won't be the same at all. I'm really going to miss hanging out with you and all your close ones. Thank you for also visiting us numerous times in California. Thank you for being you and seriously enhancing our lives and the vibration of the planet as a whole. It still doesn't make sense and we can't understand why this happened. Why, why, did you have to leave us? Our hearts are crying from pain. Wherever you are now, they must have needed a superhuman to take you so soon! The world needs more Paul Giaccio! You made this world a better place and we will all aim to #livelikepaul every day! We love you and know you will always be with us!

P.S. The value you added into my life is absolutely priceless in so many ways. Your friends who are now my friends because of you will be friends for life. Out of all the amazing things you've done for me I can only think of one thing that you ever asked in return and that was for some free lift tickets at Vail. Which is actually funny because the only reason you wanted them was to selflessly give them to your friends so that we could all be on the mountain together.

This beautiful note was written to me from my special friend in Southampton…Kristen Dehler

I had to include these heartfelt sentiments that so touched me, and still do.

Dearest Adrienne,

You are in my heart and prayers daily. When I learned about your beloved son Paul's passing, my heart broke for you. And after reading all the beautiful tributes from friends and family, my heart aches for them as well. I woke up thinking of you and praying that God and all of your angels bind your wounds. Last night I had a dream that I was in this house for a dinner and I was looking through a bookshelf. I got all excited when I came to find your Angel book (which I last read to the boys in September) among the collection and I was saying, "this is Adrienne's book, she's a friend of mine!"

I know when I dream of someone it's usually because I'm missing them and they're on my mind of course. But maybe there's something I need to say too. This morning I opened Maria Shiver's "Sunday News" as I do every Sunday. I felt like I had to send it your way (see below).

I know you are not sleeping well and sometimes the only comfort is feeling connected to those who love Paul and reading how they are so impacted by his life. That they breathed better because of his friendship and kindness.

To say that I'm so deeply sorry and saddened does not seem adequate. You love life with your whole heart Adrienne and I know you'll let that love surround you through this. I have been told by my childhood friend's mom and my high school boyfriend's dad, that the grieving doesn't end when you lose a child, but you grow around it.

Paul is someone I would have loved to have met. His smile in all the photos tell the story of who he is.

Let Manny hold you and practice small acts of self-care for yourself through this unimaginable pain.

With all my love and deepest sorrow,
Kristen

Submitted by Joe Fuller:

LIVELIKEPAUL, I am feeling your spirit today, Paul, and I can't help but shed tears. I'm sorry that I've been so consumed with medical school that I allowed time to slip by without our occasional meet up to catch up on life. You have taught me so much and I will treasure it all. I will also treasure all of our FUN and AWESOME memories: concerts, road trips, sneaking into movies, pro ball games, and ALL of the GENUINE individuals you introduced me to that embraced me as family and

Paul Giaccio - I'm grateful for the time we had. The impression you made on this world, especially those of us who knew you personally, will never be forgotten. I'm honoring your life, your generosity and your passion for live music by giving to the Do It For The Love Foundation and I invite others who got the gift of one of your wristbands to do the same. We love you ♥ 🌴 https://www.doitforthelove.org

friends (I love you guys). You are so missed my friend. Fly HIGH!
#LIVELIKEPAUL

Submitted by Amy Daniel Granetto:

Paul Giaccio—I'm grateful for the time we had. The impression
you made on this world, especially those of us that knew you
personally, will never be forgotten. I'm honoring your life, your
generosity and your passion for live music by giving to the *Do It
For The Love Foundation* and I invite others who got the gift of
one of your wristbands to do the same.

We love you — https://www.doitforthelove.org

Submitted by my son Bobby Giaccio (Paul's brother):

Paul's passing has certainly left a hole in our family.

It's with the heaviest of hearts that I have to inform everyone
about my bother Paul's passing late Sunday night. I've never felt
so heartbroken and helpless about anything in my 40 years.

It appears as if this is the result of a flu shot, but we don't have all
the answers just yet.

Anyone and everyone who's ever known Paul loves him and
knows he was an incredibly special person. Safe to say one in a
million and actually mean it.

From the time he was very young, it was obvious he was going
places. Back in grade school, he donated so much of his time and
single-handedly raised thousands and thousands of dollars for
both the town and his athletic teams.

He was "Most Likely to Succeed" as his senior year superlative.
Football all-county honorable mention when John Jay won the
state title in '93, his senior year (I never missed a game). From
blazing trails at Georgia Tech, to working in for the Atlanta
Hawks and then starting his own successful business. I could go

on and on about all his accolades, but no one would have the time to read it.

He worked all the time and traveled for leisure just as often. He made time for everyone, and he treated all his friends' children as if they were his own, giving him the name "Uncle Paul" to far more than his own niece and nephew.

None of this seems real to me. I'm trying to take it all in stride to get through it and I'm very grateful to have such amazing friends who've been in constant contact with me since the news broke. And also, to many others who've reached out to offer their condolences.

I'm also fortunate to have been surrounded by about 25 of Paul's friends at his house in Atlanta all day yesterday while the rest of my family was making arrangements to fly in.

I'm plenty guilty of taking things for granted, and I think we all do. Today, I kindly ask all of you to not let trivial things to annoy you or take any family members/close friends for granted. Because when they're gone, it feels like a huge piece of your soul has left with them.

Paul, I probably didn't tell you often enough, but I love you and I'll always remember our times together and will always appreciate the impact you've left on me.

❄

Submitted by Olivia Giaccio: Paul's niece, Frank and Erin's daughter, who he loved so much.

Thank you for being one of the kindest, most compassionate people I've ever had the opportunity to know. Witnessing the impact you've had on hundreds of individuals beyond my immediate family and I has been pretty amazing. I wish I didn't have to say that you are already incredibly missed.

Submitted by Erin Giaccio:

Paul's sister-in-law, Frank's wife.
Paul spent a lot of time with Erin, Frank, Olivia, & Frankie.

I love Thanksgiving. It is by far my favorite holiday and I love to prepare this meal and open our home to anyone who wants to join. Paul was always a part of our Thanksgiving every year, and would travel to be with us in whatever mountain town we were living in at the time. We have a tradition of skiing in the morning and then an afternoon/evening of football and feast. Back in the Vermont years, Paul started the ping pong Turkey tournament. In typical Paul fashion, it was pretty elaborate with him creating a complete tournament setup with teams and brackets. It was mandatory that everyone had to play. It was so fun (and funny!).

When we moved west to Vail and now Park City, Paul continued to join us for this holiday. Everyone is welcome to our Thanksgiving and of course Paul has friends in every town that we have lived in, therefore we have had the amazing fortune of meeting many of his friends over Thanksgiving dinner. And many of our friends got to meet Paul over Thanksgiving dinner. I am thankful today for all these Thanksgiving memories we created.

Happy Thanksgiving!

Submitted by Kevin Granetto:

I had one of those magical moments listening to a song today.

I was driving home from taking Arya to karate and we were both agitated with each other. Sometimes *Just Like This*, by Cold Play, came on and we both started jamming in the car. I pulled in the garage and the song was far from over. I have no plans of turning off the car, and my daughter said daddy please don't turn off this song.

So, we sat there singing and bouncing in the car. I had that tingle when you're at a concert with friends and you hear a song that takes you to a magical place. Right at the moment when I was thinking of my super awesome friend Paul that we unfortunately lost last week, my daughter hugged me. For that short moment in time I felt like the 3 of us were jamming out together, and somehow my 5-year-old daughter knew! I miss you brother.

Thank you for the love,
Kevin Granetto

Submitted by Juelz Jaden:

Paul loved this family of four little boys and a girl, and they loved him right back. He took them on all kinds of adventures like hiking and skiing. He would often send me videos when they were over. Paul was like a magnet for all children.

"You threw Kali's first birthday party and every year we celebrate at your pool, you have taken the kids on so many adventures and taught our boys and Chase (girl) how to ski. They asked if we can go to our annual ski trip and stay at the cabin you picked out for us…and we will because that's how we will celebrate you and the beautiful memories you created for us. We miss you Paul and the

kids miss you more. Photo cred to you for capturing these wonderful moments while they were with you!"

Submitted by Danielle Justiniano:

I've known Paul for a little over 5 years. We first really bonded at the Pearl Jam concert in Chicago back in August 2013. Zoe had just turned a year old, and I was finally getting back out and learning to have fun again! After that, I was impressed with how much Paul remembered about my life. He was always checking in with me about my career and would remember specific details about my job and things I was concerned or excited about related to it. Every time I saw Paul, he made me feel special. I am a bit of an introvert married to a real extrovert (Hugo) so sometimes our big group parties were a bit overwhelming for me. If Hugo knew Paul was going to be there, it was so much easier for him to convince me to come along. I would search Paul out and we'd catch up for as long as he'd let me.

Paul joined us in renting a mountain house for my 40th birthday in June. I'm so thankful for that weekend having fun with friends. Before Paul left, he shyly came into my room and gave me a bottle of perfume for my birthday. I thought it was so cute because it seemed kind of awkward about it, and I'd never really seen that side of him.

Paul, Evan, Hugo, and I went back to Chicago for Pearl Jam in August 2018. It was one of the best weekends I've ever had. We laughed so much together that weekend.

Words can't express how much I loved Paul. You raised a wonderful son and I will miss him every day. As he did with the rest of our group, Paul inspired me to be a better person and enjoy my life. I plan to do that in his honor as much as I can!

I wish you all the best and hope you can find some comfort knowing how special Paul was in the short time you shared him with the world.

Love, Danielle Justiniano

Submitted by David Miller:

Hi, I never met you but wanted to share how much Paul meant to me. I met him when I was 17 at Georgia Tech. He was our fraternity advisor. He served as a friend and mentor to me over the last 14 years. He was at my wedding, was there for me through a divorce, always checked up on me after I was diagnosed with MS, and recently

joined me to finish a lifelong goal of climbing mountains in Colorado. He never asked for anything in return. I will miss him greatly but will never forget the positive impact he had on my life and so many others. He was an amazing man and will be remembered by so many for his positivity and how he put his friends above himself.

I am so sorry for your loss and will keep you and your family in my thoughts and prayers.
Dave

Submitted by Christine Nelson:

A much loved stonewall neighbor and friend.

We are saying goodbye to this guy today, Paul Giaccio. An irreplaceable human being. Doesn't seem real…as someone else said, "I can't wrap my head around it." An incredible son, brother, partner, neighbor, and friend taken way too soon.

Submitted by Majid Malek:

Going to miss you Paul Giaccio. I don't know if I have ever come across somebody so willing to lend a hand. There must be thousands of stories of you going out of your way to take care of a friend without ever thinking twice about it. I will share one, from 1994, I think…a few of us headed out to Athens in Sean Crowley's car for a night of debauchery at UGA. Somehow, Sean's car went back to Atlanta at the end of the night without me and Sean. We were lucky enough to find a place for the night to crash, and the next morning we called you (because, who else would you call in a situation like that), and you immediately dropped everything and drove the 2 hour + round trip out of Athens to collect us and bring us back to Georgia Tech. That anecdote is a perfect example of who you were and how you treated your friends. Countless times you were there for me or whoever needed help. Always joking around and giving everybody just a little bit of shit. Always finding an angle to work the system.

Always taking care of people. Always with a smile.

Submitted by Tristain Yankosky O'Donnell:

LIVE LIKE PAUL – He gave his all to everyone everyday of his life (and that is not an exaggeration) and did with ease and a smile. Happiness to him was his friends, family, and people may have even met just once being happy and that's all he wanted. He worked hard, played hard and loved hard and just wanted to be around all his friends and family. He was a people person and a friend's person.

He is without a doubt one of the best people I have met in my life and no words without it being the length of a book could truly explain who he was and what he meant to me and my family and especially to Ryan.

I love you Paul and I hurt every morning when I wake up and realize this is all still true. I am grateful to have met you and for all the trips, talks, shared memories, and times we shared. We will never be the same without you, but I will make sure to be a better person for you and LIVE LIKE PAUL.

Submitted by Ryan O'Donnell:

Longtime wonderful friend.

Thankful.

I'm thankful for you, Paul.

I'm thankful for all you do for me. For all you do for my family. I'm thankful for the jokes. For the stories. For the laughs. I'm thankful for all the trips, the weddings, dinners, and late-night beers. I'm thankful for your loyalty, for your reliability, and for your integrity. I'm thankful for the opportunities you gave me throughout my life. I'm thankful for the faith you always have in me. I'm thankful for all you have taught me. I'm thankful for showing me how to be more kind, more patient. I'm thankful for your selflessness. But more than all these things, I'm thankful for your time. I'm thankful that we

shared nearly every day for the last 20 years together.

I'm thankful for you, Paul.

Thankful.

Submitted by Matt Shofman:

Hello Adrienne,

I want to convey my sincere condolences for the loss of Paul. I regret we were unable to speak at length at his memorial or get together later. I know he cherished you and would have wanted us to meet. I arrived from Israel that morning for the service and was a bit too jet lagged and emotional to introduce myself. I am so sorry for this. As you already know, Paul was loved very much by so many people. He made an incredibly powerful impression on others during his short years. Like so many of those you met, I considered Paul to be my best friend. I met him through a mutual friend on a ski trip 6 years ago, and we grew closer ever since.

When I needed a place to stay 3 years ago, of course he opened his doors to me. And ever since, during my work and travel intervals, his home was my home base. Not because I needed a place to stay, but because the energy and interest Paul showed in caring for the happenings of my life gave them more meaning than anyone else could have.

He exhibited what true friendship meant. It is difficult to put that in words or overstate his impact. Though we no longer have him in the physical form, he lives on in all those whose lives he touched. For me personally, and probably many others, because of Paul I have a clear road map of how to live and treat others for the remainder of my life. Live energetically, be passionate in whatever I do, whether I've known them 20 years or 20 minutes, show love and care for others, live in the details of others lives as this is where the true heart is. Paul lives on as those who loved him carry his light with them as they go.

390

Submitted by Carisa Powell Stringer:

This picture of Paul Giaccio, Shonda Gaskins Summers, and myself is just one of a many memories of our Georgia Tech days… this trip to New York, Summer cookouts at Mi Casa where Paul and Ryan graciously hosted us every night for dinner as Shonda and I roughed out our summer at the fraternity house, Paul treating a big group of us to dinner at Ruth Chris with his stash of NBA gift cards, and so many more. He was truly one of the most kind and giving individuals I've ever met and would do anything for his friends.

On a day of thanks, I'm very thankful for the time I had Paul Giaccio in my life, he is simply gone too soon!

Photo: Paul Giaccio is with Carisa Powell Stringer and Shonda Gaskins Summers, July 2, 2008.

Submitted by Ari Siesser:

Paul – I still don't want to believe this is real. I don't want to believe that someone who brought so much positivity to this world could be taken away so suddenly. It's not fair.

Thank you for your friendship, your guidance, and being someone, I could always trust and look up to. I will really miss you my friend.

Submitted by Mrs. Van Vranken:

Bryan's mom, from Lewisboro Elementary School days.

I have known Paul for many years, and as he grew older, I watched him mature and take leadership especially in High School years. At that age he already had a good sense of what to do, when to do it and how to run things and how to make them successful. He already had a good business sense, and I knew success was in his future. He did things with poise, humility and honesty always considering his schoolmates and later on his fellow workers, business acquaintances and his friends. Paul cared about people. He was very kind and loving. Every time I saw him, his greeting was loving and very genuine, and I could tell he was happy to see me. I will miss him, and I know he will be missed by so many who had the privilege of knowing him. Mrs. V

Submitted by Chris Yerbey:

Paul is one of the nicest, most caring, sincere and genuine people I know. And I use the present tense because he will live in so many people's hearts like mine for the rest of our lives. I'm going to try to be more like Paul. One of the most beautiful people I ever met. I love you Paul. I'm glad I got to say that to you a few times, gonna miss you brother. See you in the afterlife. Hopefully you'll be able to find a way to get us good seats to a Janet Jackson concert in heaven.

Submitted by Bea Kruchkow:

Seventh grade science teacher at John Jay Junior High School who was so loved by all. She contacted me immediately upon hearing of Paul's passing.

"When I think of Paul, I think of joy…not only mine at being fortunate to have him as a student, but his, which he brought with him to class every day.

I'd stand in the doorway of Science 2 greeting students as they came in and I'd see him walking down the hall with his ever-present smile. No matter what else I was feeling at that point, it brought a smile to my face.

Every morning, he'd say…"and how was your day, Mrs. K" in a way that I knew he genuinely cared. He was enthusiastic and interested in everything that was going on in class and respected and valued by his peers. I'll keep his memory in my heart always.

As I write that, my heart is still breaking, Adrienne. I still picture you writing in the boys' books and I admired you for being so diligent about keeping up with it. What an important and loving tribute that is to your sons.

Love you,
Bea

Submitted by Mark Reycroft:

Hi Adrienne,

Here are a couple of stories I wanted to share—pranks:

Paul loves pranks. This one was years in the making. In 2008, several of us, including Paul, were headed to Amsterdam for

Jason Farls' bachelor party. That was the plan anyway. Paul as he always does, over-planned, tried to do too much, and threw out his back while skiing the weekend before, so he had to cancel the trip to Amsterdam. The only good part of that was that for years we could give him crap for not making the trip and tell him stories about all the great times we had without him. Fast forward to 2012 and several of the same crew were heading back to Amsterdam for New Years Eve. Paul told us from the beginning he couldn't make the trip citing some legitimate family excuse. We spoke several times leading up to the trip, each time giving him crap for missing yet another trip to Amsterdam and meanwhile he's been there several other times with his other "real friends". As I'm walking through terminal E in Atlanta towards my connecting flight on route to Amsterdam, imagine my surprise as I see Paul walking towards me. I asked him what he's doing, and he said he was connecting as well to some other state. What a coincidence. I should have known at that point that something was up, but it wasn't until he joined us at the boarding area for the Amsterdam flight did he disclose he was on the flight and coming with us. What a shock. He totally surprised everyone and made the trip. We had a blast and the picture attached (sorry for poor quality of 2012 iphone at night!) shows a canal tour we took where we could see the lights on no less than 5 bridges down the canal.

Giving:

Paul is always so thoughtful and for that I'm extremely thankful. One November, I took my family my family to Denver so we could enjoy skiing in Vail, Breck, and go to the Patriots vs. Broncos Sunday night football game. Being Thanksgiving and in a place where I knew no one, Paul suggested we join him at his brother Frank's house for Thanksgiving dinner. Frank fried up one of the moistest turkeys I've ever had, and his wife Erin put together a great spread. Frankie was there but Olivia was in Europe, so we FaceTimed with her. It was a Thanksgiving miracle all made possible by Paul. Thanks

Submitted by Christian Suarez:

Hi Adrienne,

I got to know Paul and hang out with him only a limited time, but I can tell you that his generosity towards me (an unknown) was instant. We needed a ticket for a concert for my brother-in-law. Some suggested I reach out to Paul. Not only did he respond with willingness to help out but came through as if I was his number one priority. I will never forget how fast he came to me and provided us with a much-needed ticket to save the day. I appreciated how he conducted his life and treated friends and unknowns alike. You can officially mark me down as a person/ friend who was helped and touched by Paul instantly. We will all continue to miss him and honor him daily.

Thank you,
Cristian Suarez

Submitted by John Minnix:

Is this Paul Giaccio's mom? We were friends close to 20 years ago. I met him through a mutual friend, Oliver Campbell, when they were both at Georgia Tech and I was at Emory. I very much enjoyed the time we spent together and the energy and enthusiasm he brought to every occasion. We played a lot of cards and had a lot of fun at some Georgia Tech parties. I also reached out to him a couple of years ago for some business advice. He had a lot to offer there, as well. I appreciate his expertise, wisdom, and encouragement.

Paul was a great guy and someone that, even 20 years on, stands out in my mind. I was very sorry to learn of his passing. I am sorry for your loss. The book sounds like an awesome celebration of his life. Also, you must have been a great mom to raise such an outstanding son.

Sincerely,

John Minnix

※

Submitted by Mathew Fair:

Hi Adrienne,

I had the privilege of living with Paul my last year of college and having his friendship for 24 years. He was really such a special person and I think of him often. I keep thinking he is going to appear at a restaurant, mall, hike, etc. I guess I just miss my friend and have to remind myself that I cannot call him. I picture him walking through the airport with that great Paul shuffle, smile, hands swinging by his side, etc.

I am not much of a writer so you will have to deal with some of my ramblings.

Paul Traits

It was very important for Paul to get confirmation that what he thought or felt was right. He would come up with these ideas or preferences and then look for affirmation that he was correct. Whether it was food preferences, music, grooming, personal etiquette, etc., he would look for assurance. I find this endearing and comical as some of his preferences were not the norm. For example, "Matt, you cannot make gravy without having the right canned tomatoes from New York. Without it, you're just wasting your time" or "it's rude when people having a phone conversation in the car when driving with someone else, right?".

Friendship

Paul embodied everything that a true friend should be. I never met someone so generous, kind, enthusiastic, and just plain old fun. He personally bailed more people out of jail that I can count or drove

396

two hrs. to pick up friends that were stranded in Athens. You could always count on Paul for ANYTHING, and he would be there with a big smile, not expecting anything in return but your friendship.

Small Story that highlight his adventurous personality

A good friend of ours, Brian Below was hiking the Appalachian Trail for a few weeks when a mutual friend canceled last minute. Brian called Paul and asked if he would like to meet him on the trail and go camping the next day. With no notice and zero camping experience, Paul drove to REI, made the 4-hour trip to NC, and then hiked 8 miles by himself to meet Brian. He camped for two days and then he left early in the morning to honor a pre-existing commitment. How many people do you know that would drop everything at the last minute to do something they had never done before? This happened in 2018.

Family Pool Parties

Even though Paul did not have kids of his own, he was so fond of children and was very good to my three daughters. Besides taking Chris's kids on adventures, he organized pool parties that were centered on kids and families having fun, whether it was foods, snacks, games, water balloons, etc. He also had this magical way of connecting with kids through his sparking eyes, warm smile, and ability to put them completely at ease.

Hustler

Paul was going to be successful in anything he put his mind to. I remember when he left the Hawks and interviewed at American Funds, he impressed the hiring manager with his quick wit and ability to grasp concepts that most people couldn't comprehend. He then transformed into a hard-core Financial Advisor and quickly gained the business of his friends before transitioning on to be an entrepreneur. Every time you talked to Paul, he was working a new angle or opportunity and then would dive into it 150%. He has the most impressive work ethic (outside of schoolwork!) of anyone I had come across. Every time I would talk to him about his business, he was always solving problems (i.e. getting SunTrust to drop of millions of dollars in $20, buying new gaming business, prospecting ATM locations, etc.).

I will give some more thoughts on stories I can share. For example, he thought his clothes size was a large until he was 42. He really was the absolute worst dresser, but again it was endearing.

Submitted by Brian, Mark, & Kristen Bernasconi:
Childhood friends from birth.

Our families went on vacations together and spent many days and nights at each other's homes. Even had some Bernasconi-Giaccio reunions at Frank and Erin's home in West Redding, Connecticut. Nothing but the best memories.

Dear Adrienne,

We are honored that you asked if we wanted to write a testimonial for Paul. Some of our fondest memories of growing up included your home and your boys. Our note is below. Also attached is a picture of the boys…this is how I picture them in my mind; even though we are much older now, my mind takes me back to the good old days running wild at the Giaccio's.

Much love,
Brian, Mark & Kristen

Our friendship with Paul was the result of our parents being good friends. Nothing was better than going to spend the day at the Giaccio's house. We couldn't wait to go and never wanted to leave.

Days were filled with stick ball games, adventures in the woods (it always felt like we were doing something we'd get in trouble for), roughhousing, watching our moms laughing until they cried...What was Paul's role in the day? He documented everything by videotaping it. He worked to keep peace among his brothers. He was outgoing and made sure everyone was included. It's easy to remember his smile and his warmth. Looking back now as adults, it's no wonder the person he became. Welcoming. Caring. Loyal. It is who he was all along. We are lucky to have had Paul in our lives. Of our childhood memories, some of our favorite were those days spent with Frank, Paul, Bobby, and Richie. It's unfortunate that time and distance got in the way of Giaccio-Bernasconi visits over the years, but the memories we made and the laughs we shared will always be in our hearts and bring a smile to our faces when we think of Paul.

Submitted by Kevin Morris
Basketball player at Georgia Tech

Kevin called me to give his testimony on Paul. He said there was so much to tell that he didn't know where to begin, but he began by saying that Paul was the first person he met when he arrived at the airport in Atlanta when he came to play for the Georgia Tech basketball team. Paul, the manager, picked him up at the airport and made him feel right at home. Paul got him all settled in, introducing him to everyone and made him feel so welcomed. He said Paul was a "genuine dude". I laughed at that. He said Paul was never down, he helped everyone asking nothing in return. He never changed. They wound up being friends with Paul introducing him to all his friends, going to concerts, events, polka parties, etc. He even lived at Paul's house for about a year at one point later on along with two other friends.

He said one day Paul told him "I think I'm gay." He responded "you think you're gay? Either you are or you're not, and just accept whether it is because it doesn't matter. You are who you are, and we love you no matter what."

Kevin said Paul was thinking of suicide because he didn't want to be gay because of what people might think and Kevin convinced him along with other close friends, to just get that idea out of his head because no one cared. (Whatever they said worked, thank God).

He said he had spoken to Paul about two weeks before he died and didn't know he had passed in between. He would always call Paul with various questions about things and this one day which was about two weeks after his previous phone call, he called him to ask a question and when someone answered, he immediately started talking asking his question and the person on the other end wasn't Paul, and then told him he was gone. He said he was in total shock and called for his wife to hear the tragic news. He misses his friendship.

Submitted by Ari Siesser:

Ari contacted me by email and said he had a story for me about Paul that would make me very proud and he wanted a phone conversation. And he truly did have a story to tell!

Ari gave me some background about himself and his move to Georgia in 2009, attending college at a very young age. Lots of details in between but the bottom line is that he met Paul while he was a bank teller at Wachovia for a year. He said Paul would go to his window and ask for $40,000.00 in 20-dollar bills. It was a process for him to get that done at first, going into the main vault, security steps, etc., but then once it was established, the process went quicker with Ari knowing the drill. Ari always wondered "what is this guy doing?!" and finally asked one day.

When he heard of Paul's lucrative business, he asked if Paul would help him get started in his own ATM business. He said most people would just not want to help out or get involved in helping someone succeed or they would want something in return. Not Paul. He said he will never forget how Paul took his own time to set him up with everything and Paul was always available to help or give advice. He went out of his way every time.

He says he has the LIVELIKEPAUL bracelet in his bathroom to look at each morning as he gets ready for the day, reminding him to help others. His getting that ATM machine (and eventually another one) completely transformed his life, giving him a substantial income every month he never would have had without Paul's help and guidance.

It's all about paying it forward.

He never met anyone like him.

Submitted by Jose Corneil:

Paul's friend and business partner for many years. Phone interview.

Jose met Paul back in 1999. Through Scott, Paul's fraternity brother at Georgia Tech.

Scott would always talk about his "big brother" Paul and wanted Jose to meet him. Which he did along with Ballard, Ryan & Scott. They were the "north easterners" who would go to Paul's house where he would host pasta dinner nights. Jose said he got to understand why Scott would always be talking about "this Paul friend" of his, and Jose and Paul also became great friends.

When Paul left the Atlanta Hawks around this time, he started to work as a financial advisor and Jose became one of his first clients. Along with building up his financial investment business, Paul was working at Twisted Taco as bar manager, so Jose would also stop by and see him there to talk. They started talking about starting an ATM business together and suggested putting their first ATM machine at

Twisted Taco, which they did.

Through the next few years, Jose was working in corporate America while Paul was building up his investment business, but the conversation about an ATM business was also always out there as a possibility.

In 2009 Paul sold his portfolio and Jose and Paul went into the ATM business, seeing the potential.

They purchased ATMs from other retiring companies, signed up many gas stations and they were on their way. They were just finalizing a huge deal with many malls, when the unthinkable happened on August 2, 2011.

Jose was at a convenience store at 9:30 am when he was shot in the face during a robbery as he was filling in the ATM machine. The robber took off, dropping the cassette of tens of thousands of dollars and the money was flying everywhere, while another man helped Jose by putting his shirt on his bleeding face.

The police and ambulance came, and Jose was on his way to the hospital while having someone call Paul to tell him to go to the store to pick up the cassette of money from the convenience store. Jose also had a bag with him with $30,000.00 and gave it to the policeman who met him at the hospital. He told the policeman to make sure nothing happened to that bag and he told him to look inside.

After that Jose doesn't remember anything. He was in ICU for two or three weeks, after extensive surgery. (He would go on to have other surgeries throughout the years).

During his recuperation, Paul took the lead and quite remarkably went ahead with the big deal that they had in the making, even though they weren't sure where this business was going after this tragedy with Jose. Paul assured Jose he could do it and not to worry. Paul hired extra help and the business took off in a different way. There were lots of uncertainties because, understandably, Jose had been through a nightmare.

Paul assured him it would all be fine.

Then another opportunity came up that alleviated the stress on Jose. In 2013 they decided to go into the gaming business which was legitimized in Georgia.

Jose was more comfortable concentrating on that business, and Paul concentrated on their ATM business, which involved hundreds of machines throughout the states.

Jose loved Paul. He called him "his compass" he would always run things by him for his advice. Paul was by his side for all his life events. He said he would always encourage Paul to buy things, dress better, etc. Paul was not interested in material things. Knowing how Paul loved taking photos, he bought him a camera and even a new watch. He expressed his sadness of not seeing and being with him every day.

It's just not the same.

Submitted by Liz Lundgren De Busschere:

A week ago, I walked into a room that was overflowing with people that had come together to say goodbye to Paul Giacco. A room that was filled with only a fraction of the people that were lucky enough to be Paul's friend or family member. The words spoken at Paul's memorial all shared a common theme—they painted a picture of a guy that worked hard, enjoyed life, and would do anything for a friend. But how do you say goodbye to someone that was full of life and left this world too early?

Our family was lucky to have Paul in our lives. Paul was a great friend to Lars from when they met in junior high through high school and into adulthood. I can't imagine it was easy being friends with my teen -aged brother. I'm sure that Paul kept Lars out of trouble on more than one occasion and I know my parents are grateful for the times when Paul brought Lars home safe after a night of teenage shenanigans. Paul braved a major blizzard to attend Lars and Brooke's wedding in Denver. Like many other children in his life, Paul considered Lars' kids his family. Jack and Kate loved when "uncle Paul" would visit. The last time I saw Paul he told us about his latest business endeavors and his recent travel adventures. He was full of pride when he filled us in on what his brothers were up to, how his  niece and nephew were excelling and how his parents were doing. Of course, he asked about our family and we spent time reminiscing about the "good old days." It is hard to believe that Paul is no longer with us.

So, how do you say goodbye to a one-of-a-kind person who was always there for his friends and family? I'm not sure you can. I think you just remember the good times and think about all the wonderful moments that Paul experienced in his short life. You smile and laugh through the tears and keep his friends, loved ones, brothers and parents in your thoughts and prayers—with Lars Lundgren and Paul Giaccio.

Submitted by Erin Eberhard:

Hi Adrienne!

So nice to hear from you! First, most important I want to buy the book as soon as it comes out!! Please let me know.

My name is Erin Eberhard. My son is Ben Personett. Ben was a year behind Paul at Georgia Tech. They all called him Uncle Pauly. I always heard about the adventures they all had. Even Paul bailing them out of jail when they were singing too loud at a country bar and leaving Marta money (not my favorite story) I have heard about you and the Children's books you sent to all the kids.

My husband and I moved to Atlanta area in 2006. We finally got to meet Paul in person. There are not enough words to express "who was Paul". He came to Ben's 40th birthday party here at our house with all the crew. Most of them had kids (Ben has 3 now) and Paul brought 2 kids with him to have fun and swim. Such a kind heart and wonderful spirit. He was such an amazing friend to Ben, and he made me feel very special even though I was the mom.

My husband and I actually invested in the ATM business way back and we are still invested. We were very lucky enough to get invited to the Christmas parties. Paul was so special. Everyone he touched misses having him in this world and it is hard not be sad sometimes just thinking about him. I can't imagine how much you miss him. The world would be so much better with more people like Paul in it.

Thank you for contacting me and I am looking so forward to this book!! I may even get some for the grand kids so they can have them in the future to see what their dad had as a friend in Paul.

Thank you also for all the time and work of love you are putting into the book!

Sincerely,

Erin Eberhard

Submitted by Erin Eberhard:

Part of Facebook post

He was amazing! Paul passed away unexpectedly just before Thanksgiving and the loss is going to be felt for ever. What an amazing outpouring of love I have never seen before!! Here is how to live like Paul – LIVE LIKE PAUL

Description;

1. To be concerned with the needs of those around you, above your own, all the time, without judgement, without contempt, with pure love and respect;

2. To be present in life, to enjoy nature and life to it's fullest, to pick up others, connect people, and bring them along for the ride, TOGETHER;

3. To have a great sense of humor, to joke, to give and take crap from others, but to do it out of respect and love;

4. To be available, to be consistent, to listen, to love, to be a true friend, to be "uncle Paul";

5. To be and act like Paul Giaccio; #LIVELIKEPAUL

Submitted by Phil Marsicano:

I added the following even though it shows Paul's mischievous side. Yes, he loved getting in places—like concerts, games, etc. without paying. Not for himself alone but bringing in everyone else.

I'm making the disclosure here that living like Paul would definitely NOT include this behavior!

I don't know when he started to do these crazy things—but it was years after moving to Georgia. Harmless but not lawful!

I blocked out any names that could be incriminating.

I also could have not included this, but I did for a reason. He was human. Not perfect.

Hi Adrienne,

Sorry it's taken so long to get this to you. These stories were hard to write, but I'm glad I did because it really made me happy reliving them. Please don't feel obligated to use any of these in the book, but I hope you enjoy reading them!

Phil (Vinny)

Brad Green, VIP

Paul and I have been to quite a few Mets games whenever they come to Atlanta to play the Braves. As you know all too well, Paul loved to try to get into places where we weren't supposed to go. When it came to Braves games, it was the 755 Club at Turner Field. Paul had a friend that used to work there, so we would try to get up there even if we didn't have a ticket to get in ~~there~~. On one occasion, we were walking into the elevator that takes us to the 755 Club when we were stopped by security. Paul, calm as ever, said "I'm going up to see Brad Green". The security guard nodded and let us go up. When we got in the elevator, I asked Paul "Who the hell is Brad Green?" His response: "My buddy from high school. I just used the first name that came to mind". Just one of many stories of Paul working his magic.

The many missions of Paul Giaccio:

This isn't really a story but more of a private joke I had with Paul. One thing I noticed very early on with Paul was that he was always walking somewhere with purpose. You could see it not only in how he walked, but the look in his face. He was always walking somewhere to get something done. So, I started asking him: "Paul, what mission are you on right now?" The guy was always on some mission of some sort, whether it be filling up the vending machine in this Phi Sig House or going to get lunch. No matter where he was going, he was going there with conviction.

Pink Floyd

One thing Paul and I had in common was that we both loved Pink Floyd. When Roger Waters or a Pink Floyd cover band came to town, we were there. These were all great concerts, but two moments in particular stand out to me:

1. One-year, Australian Pink Floyd played at the Woodruff Arts Center. My wife (Kristin) surprised me for my birthday by getting me really good seats for the concert. Paul decided he wanted to go, but didn't have a ticket (I know, shocking). So, he did his thing and got into the theater. Not only did he get in, but he found a seat directly behind us so we could all hang out during the show. As people started to file in, every seat got taken except for Paul's. Somehow, he managed to find the one seat that nobody had. To this day I don't know how he

managed to do that, but it's clear that he had quite the talent for this.

2. The last Pink Floyd concert I went to with Paul was in June 2018 to see Brit Floyd at the Fox Theater. Was a great group, with Paul, Mike Pink, and myself. While at the concert, there was a guy about two rows in front of us that got really into the show. He was so into it that he started acting like a band conductor for the band. For some reason, Paul found this to be so funny, that it sent him into one of his laughing sprees. The laughing sprees were common with Paul, but this one took the cake. Pink and I agreed later on that we'd never see Paul laugh so hard.

It makes me very sad when I realize that I'll never go to a Pink Floyd show with Paul again, but memories like this make me realize how lucky I was to experience Floyd shows with Paul. No matter what, every time I hear Pink Floyd I think of Paul, and it puts a smile on my face.

Submitted by Lynn Falkowski:
Reiki Master and incredible friend.

Reiki and Prayers sent this morning.

And there is more.

I sat quietly as I usually do after Reiki.

I had a vision.

You were standing up front, bright and tall.

There was an uncountable number of people behind you.

The further back they were the smaller they got.

Thousands in the least.

Possibly more.

You clearly were the one of "influence and guidance" showing the way.

Everyone appeared on a soul level… way beyond just the physical.

Good grief girlfriend, I'm not sure what God is preparing you for, but it is clearly BIG!

Submitted by Pablo Ricatti:

Paulie was our best friend. He was there whenever we called, and he called whenever… just to remind us he was there. His stories were hilarious, and his laughter was contagious. No doubt, his perspective was one of a kind…and his schemes and abilities, legendary. His memory was near perfect and his navigational abilities unmatched by humans or machine. When he made plans, they were always all inclusive. His entrepreneurship inspired while his dedication created opportunities and abundance for all of us. Paulie was a campfire of the heart and as he walked through life carrying out his purely intended meticulously crafted plans, many people of many different walks of life gathered together around him and met. He was a promoter, progenitor, and connector of life. And though he was never a father, he had many children, all of whom he loved and who loved him. He was a son to parents he loved and a brother to everyone he ever befriended. The heart-centered wisdom of his approach to life helped us grow. And by the magnanimity of his heart, he was active in all of our lives, taking advantage of most of the minutes of the day, sleeping very little and enjoying us very much. Paulie always gave his all, to every one of us, in all ways. And all the while, he proved continuously, that we COULD (manifest whatever we want) and that we SHOULD (smile and laugh while we do it). Always keeping in mind that it's the family you build around you that creates the real wealth of life.

That's just some of what Paulie was… what Paulie now IS, is a spirit guide in each and every one of us who carry him in our hearts.

Submitted by Ben Personett:

Adrienne,

My apologies for not writing sooner, this was one of the stories that I thought illustrated the entrepreneurial side of Paul during our days at Tech:

We used to have a coke machine in the chapter room of the fraternity house that was run by the house manager. The house manager would stock it and empty the cash and the money went back into the operation of the machine and to the house funds. Well, the house manager at the time, John 'Pizza' Entrekin had been running the machine for a while and was not making any money...he was as I recall, losing house funds with Coke vending machine. During one chapter meeting where Pizza announced that the machine was again losing money, Paul offered to take over the operation and see if he couldn't make it profitable. So, after that meeting Paul set out to make the machine profitable and came up with several ideas. The first was to change up the product mix- no longer would it be just Coke products with the largest button being devoted to Coke. He figured out which soft drinks people would actually buy and put them consistently in the smaller slots, for the big slot that held more than 2x what any of the other slots held he put it in the "mystery slot" with a big "?". You never knew what would come out of the mystery slot—could be Country Time Lemonade (WIN!), could be Big K Cola (FAIL!), it could even be left over beers (EXTRA WIN!). People would try the mystery slot just for fun or in desperation on Sundays (hoping there were still some Natty Light's in there...) someone playing the mystery slot would typically buy three to four drinks in effort to find one of the good ones (the losers would end up on the rail along the chapter room windows, free to those that wanted them (or sometimes Paul would put them back in when no one was looking). The machine became profitable within one quarter once Paul took over and everyone loved the mystery slot, to the point where Paul had to fill it at night so people would not see the order that the random good drinks and beers were being placed into the machine. I think this story illustrates Paul's perseverance and business savvy during his years at Tech. He was able to take something that was not much fun and barely thought about and not profitable and turned it into something that people loved to play and made money as well. Everyone loved the mystery slot on the Coke machine, no one else on campus had one like it, I mean who does that other than Paul?

Thank you so much for this and still miss Paul,
Benjamin Personett

Submitted by Tim Dolnik:

Tim, his sister Tricia, Kelly, & Karen grew up with Paul enjoying many family gatherings.

Adrienne –

I hope all is well!

I only recall Paul visiting my wife and I once when he was nearby in Hilton Head Island (where I used to live). I remember him just as I do when we were younger. He was sincere, empathetic and most importantly compassionately engaged. Our conversations lasted into the late hours of the evening. While I cannot expand on or quite recall the exact conversations, I can say that they were wonderful and really comfortable.

I'm certain we reminisced about the days visiting your home in NY where we truly had such a blast and, of course, summer stays in Long Beach Island. Paul was such a wonderful man that was taken from us too early. My wife, Jessi, would continually inquire about him after she first met him. Unfortunately, we did not stay connected after that (I never subscribed to any social media) so it pains me that I never made more of effort. I will forever think of you and your boys with much love, respect and adulation. My condolences again.

Please tell the other boys I said hello and if any of them visit the Savannah/Charleston area to give me a call or email.

All my love (and best to Manny!),

Tim Dolnik

❉

Submitted by Dan Zitoli:
Hi Adrienne!

Thank you for sending out this reminder.

Now I don't have any real epic tales or stories, but there's one thing that always stuck out to me with Paul, and that over the years with too many get togethers and parties to count, the amazing thing is that Paul always seemed to be there at some point, no matter what work related stuff he had to do that day.

He could have been coming from helping somebody move, straight to a big party to make an appearance, then I'd see him much later that night at the same party and ask him where he's been. He would answer, "Oh I went to go check on a couple ATMs like 45 minutes away and fill up a couple more around town" of course he was back at the party after all that.

Or like many times, he'd slip away and go to a concert, and be back at the party later. I appreciated that he did what my mind wanted to do, but rarely ever be able to pull off myself.

I really admired that, and thought to myself, look how much we can all get done, but still have fun with friends, and make lasting memories.

Such a great mind-set that I hope and try to implement myself, instead of getting so caught up in one activity.

Another great aspect of that, was he was soo interested in whatever he missed, and talked to everyone to find out what happened while he was gone and later on, he could tell the story like he was there the whole time!

So great how much interest he could put into everyone and tell a story about something better than people who were there!

I hope this helps! Can't wait to read the book!
Dan Zitoli

※

Submitted by Bryan Van Vranken:

Faithful friend from Elementary school days in Lewisboro

I was 7 years old and had just moved towns. There I was, in 2nd grade with absolutely no relationships. It's hard to change schools, especially midyear. That is unless one of your new classmates is Paul Giaccio. All that worry, anxiety, fear...say goodbye.

Paul welcomed me like a longtime friend. He was selfless, caring, reliable, and compassionate. A true friend. From Day 1. Over the next 38 years my relationship strengthened with Paul. He never failed me, he never wavered, he always came through. He still does today and will forever. So many others are blessed to be canvassed by Paul's amazing love and friendship. In a world where we say we are too busy and other priorities take precedent, Paul finds the time. He listens, cares, loves, gives and gives even more. Today, tomorrow and forever we have the opportunity to #LIVELIKEPAUL. Let's seize it. TOGETHER.

※

Submitted by Jason Falzon:

In the contact I had with him, I always found him to be personable and sincere. As Noelle often recalled, he frequently asked about the kids and was genuine in that he cared about the answer. He was also a man of integrity. On a personal level, I always connected with Paul.

I saw a lot of similarities in his relationship with Adrienne as I had with my mother.

❋

Submitted by Jason Faris:

Adrienne,

My first real interaction with Paul was in the fall of 1993 at Georgia Tech. We were in the same pledge class of our fraternity.

Paul, being the person that everyone knows, decided to cook Spaghetti with Marinara for all of the pledges.

By the time I got to the apartment, the food prep was well underway.

I opened the door to the apartment and couldn't help but notice an overpowering smell.

I had to go check it out. I hurried into the kitchen and started grilling Paul. I went over to the pot to get a firsthand look.

I noticed several white objects floating throughout the red sauce.

I said "Paul, are these a bunch of potatoes in your Marinara?"

He said "No, it's garlic."

I asked him "How much garlic did you put in there?"

He replied, "My grandmother's recipe calls for 4 cloves."

I replied in not such a nice manner. "Paul, you put 4 bulbs of garlic in there?" (Approximately 40 cloves)

Needless to say, everyone that was there, except for me, ate it right up.

Just goes to show you if you are a starving college freshman, most people will eat anything.

I never got around to asking if his grandmother was Italian or Transylvanian.

Thank you,
Jason Faris

"When one door closes another door opens, but we so often look so long and so regretfully upon the closed door, that we do not see the ones which open for us."

—*Alexander Graham Bell*

Submitted by Matt Shofman:

Paul Giaccio entered my life in March of 2013 in Vail, Colorado, on one of his annual ski trips. Everyone knows Paul loves skiing. I had been invited on the trip by a mutual friend, Ashwin Rao, and during the course of that long weekend, I was warmly welcomed by Paul and several others. I am remembering being remarkably impressed by Paul's thoughtful and caring nature, he was so attentive to everything and everyone's needs. I had never met a human like him; and we grew closer immediately from this moment. It was impossible to know it at the time, but Paul would redefine my understanding of love and friendship in ways I will spend the rest of my life comprehending.

As I got to know Paul more, I watched with a careful eye at the way he carries the banner of friendship. In doing so, I challenged my own previously held notions of what it means to be a friend. I had been doing it wrong all along. Paul helped me realize what true friendship is all about. Not that he was trying to show me anything, it all came as naturally to him as breathing fresh air. His selflessness, his care and thoughtfulness for others, his attention to detail in the lives of others, is simply unparalleled. He embodies true friendship. It is difficult to put the full meaning of this statement into words or even begin to convey his impact. But I will try.

Paul is always making time for people. He is busier than the rest of us, his social calendar is always full, his business thriving; yet he possesses a people-first mentality I have never seen in anyone else. The remedy to escaping a melancholic snare can be as simple as someone caring enough about your life to ask about it. It can be a lonely world in a city full of people, but not with Paul Giaccio in your life. Whether he has known someone 20 years or 20 minutes, Paul jumps to assist anyone whose life he believes he can make a difference in.

And he is very confident he can help many people, and not just people he knew intimately. A stranger in the streets is just as likely to be a beneficiary of Paul's graciousness as any other. In being so fortunately lucky to know the passionate soul of Paul Giaccio, I realize many of the amazing qualities that make him a Superman. He wants to leave his mark by serving others, and that's exactly what he does. I often wonder in amazement at how many people he positively impacts, and so effortlessly and naturally.

When I needed a place to live in 2015, Paul opened his door before I even asked. Over the following years since, between my intervals of out-of-town work and out-of-country travel, his home became my home. He has never held a hidden agenda or credit system over my head, or implied I owed him anything in the future. It is completely selfless on his part. What he really enjoys is having me around, conversating, exchanging stories and ideas, bonding and expanding the quality of our lives through the knowledge we have great friends in one another. He elevates me in ways I can never thank him enough for.

I stayed with Paul not only because I needed a place to stay, but because the energy and interest Paul showed in the happenings in my life giving them more meaning than anyone else can. There is no superficiality with him, he is just so interested in the smallest details of what I have to say, of what everyone has to say; I can tell that he is listening, and he cares about me. I have never felt more important than when holding an audience with Paul. He makes me feel great about who I am and who I can be. And I am not the only one; like so many others, I consider Paul to be my best friend.

Paul cares deeply about understanding personal relationships and connections; and even more so, in creating them. In 2015, shortly after I moved in, we took a trip to his hometown in New York and up to Boston. I met several of his friends that week, but one in particular illuminated what may be Paul's greatest talent; the desire and ability to connect others.

When we arrived in Boston, Paul had plans to stay with one of his childhood friends. Despite Paul's efforts, this friend did not like the idea of "Randy's", or "random friends", and he did not want me staying at his house. This is completely understandable, but it left me in a predicament. No worries, Paul called up a former fraternity brother, who just happened to be starting his MBA in Harvard that weekend, and in came "Super Dave" Miller into my life.

I stayed with Dave Miller the entire weekend and we made great friends fast. Paul introduced us not only because I needed a place to stay, but because he felt our similar energies would connect well and we needed to know each other anyway. Paul has this uncanny strength for sensing complimentary traits or common interests in people and goes out of his way to connect them. It is a game of his to introduce as many people as possible. He thinks highly of humans and knows the power of having the right people in your life at the right time; he makes it his responsibility to be that connecting force. His senses were spot on with Dave and I, and we have remained friends since; so much that I will be at Dave's wedding in 2020.

Another connection that Paul made in my life was introducing me to "Old Man Ron", or just, "Ron" as I prefer. For nearly 6 months, I heard about this guy who went on wild adventures in the 1980's and 1990's—forays that sounded similar to the ones I take. We needed to meet each other, and Paul would make sure we did.

Paul was right again; Ron was someone I needed to meet. And he became an important part of my life as well. This meeting opened the door to great adventures for all of us. In 2016, several months after this fateful introduction, Paul, Ron, and I took a 10-day, 1,800- mile road trip across frozen landscapes of Iceland.

This trip was magical in many ways, not the least being Paul's heroic act in driving every single mile, navigating us safely through treacherous conditions that include nearly sliding off slippery mountain pass,

feeling like the wind was about to push us off the road as we crossed an open stretch of the Icelandic coast, and plunging confidently through impossible mud clogged pits.

Another vivid memory from that trip was watching the sunset from the top of a volcano. We raced down in the colorful twilight, deep scree underfoot. Paul won, of course. Another time we were hiking on a frozen slab alongside a 1,000 – foot cliff when we heard a thunderous crack in the ice. I panicked like a child waking from a nightmare and took off running down the trail. Unfazed, Paul calmly said, "yeah, I guess we should turn around". He really is Superman.

This trip delivered a new perspective on the power, beauty and awesomeness of mother nature, and, on the importance of friendship. This was my favorite trip with Paul, and some of the best hiking of our lives. Ron and I became great friends too and we have now been to 7 more countries together.

Paul is a visionary, seeing the myriad of ways to help and connect others so they can empower each other. He has a genuine goal of helping those he comes in contact with, maximizing their life experiences. He wants to elevate others any way he can and takes pleasure only in seeing the happiness he fosters. With this authenticity, Paul makes powerful impressions and is loved by many. He is a source of helpful enthusiasm, bringing positivity into the world; making the uncertain into the confident, the untrustworthy into a worthy confidant, the tired into the relentless, the helpless into helpers, the weak into the strong and the strong into the stronger. This is what friendship is, what a purposeful life is, this is what Paul embodies and exudes everyday of his life.

Because of Paul, I have a clear road map of how to live and treat others for the rest of my life. He is a beacon of positive energy, and by example, lights a path for all of us to see. This path can be followed one word, one action, one breathe at a time, day by day, year by year; consistent, unwavering, unmoving, solidly, and purely. Friendship and love towards those you know and to those you don't; to those you have met, and to those you will meet; doing good for the sake of good alone; acting as an example, as a role model, as a friend; always selflessly enhancing others with an unrelenting and passionate energy in life, for life. For me, this is Living Like Paul.

Paul lives in all those whose lives he touches, as those who love him carry his light as they go through life. When I think of Living Like Paul, I think of friendship and connections. I think of maximizing life's opportunities. I think of being fair and keeping others in mind as I make my ascent and elevating them along with me. I think of how, though I may not be perfect, this will not deter my pursuit. When I think of Living Like Paul, I think of accepting myself for who I am, and accepting those I know as well as those I do not. I think of oneness of life, how it's not just me in this world, but us. I think of togetherness and unity, I think of kindness, I think of laughter. I think I will never need to remember because I will never forget how to *LiveLikePaul*.

Matt Shofman

Submitted by Manny Falzon:

Over the 25 years of being married to Adrienne, I've had the wonderful experience of being with Paul on many family get togethers to include holiday dinners, family vacations and visits to various places where we lived. Losing Paul has been devastating to his many friends and his family, especially to his mom, my wife

Adrienne. Although there are countless stories and memories I have of Paul, it's my most recent trip to Atlanta, the last time I spent with Paul, alive, that I'll never forget. Being a big sports fan, there were two remaining Major League Baseball parks I needed to visit to complete this item on my bucket list, the Miami Marlins and Atlanta Braves stadium. A friend of mine and I scheduled back to back games in both cities in September 2018. Where to stay in Atlanta, so we could be within walking distance of the stadium and to get seats at the stadium under cover in the event of rain, were important to us. Since we were unfamiliar with the stadium, I reached out to Paul to help us in choosing our hotel and stadium seats. Paul came through beautifully! At his suggestion, we stayed at a hotel adjoining the Braves' stadium and after he physically walked around the stadium, he was able to tell me which seats in which section were under cover.

He took us both to dinner that night before the game and we had a wonderful time spending time with him. While the game was being played, as is usually the case, people leave before the end, leaving their seats empty. Paul told my friend, who came to the game with me, that he and some of his friends will be joining us at some point during the game.

Knowing we had very good, somewhat, expensive seats, with a stadium employee stationed at the top of each aisle (checking tickets), I said, lots of luck, implying there would be no way anyone was going to slip into the seats around us without a ticket. Paul has a history of getting people into events and sometimes even getting them the best seats in the house, without them having tickets to the event or certain seats. Sure enough, as the innings wore on, I found lots of Paul's friends and even Paul himself sitting next to us or close by. There was no harm done, the rightful ticket holders had already left. As with so, so much in his life, Paul would find a way...and he did!

Submitted Lauren Reese Candee:

When someone who means the world to your family leaves the world way too soon, you try to spend the time around the dinner table thinking about all the beautiful memories, because you know that's what he would have wanted. It didn't work, and tears came instead, but we tried.

Paul Giaccio, you were the best friend, the best Uncle, the most selfless and generous human being we have ever ever known. Thank you for the privilege of your friendship, the laughs, and the memories. We miss you dearly, always and always.

✻

Submitted by Julie McGuire Hogg:

For me, first he was Paul, then Paulie, and then with my growing family he became Uncle Paul. But I am not the only one. He was Uncle Paul to many lucky children. He was the guy who showed up at the adult BBQ with toys and bubbles for all the kids. In this picture, the day before

Julie McGuire Hogg
May 22, 2016 ·

Gotta love **Paul Giaccio!**

we moved to England, he specifically brought bread so he could take all the kids to feed the ducks.

Submitted by Bryan Van Vranken:

Living Like Paul, Family Style. Paul bringing out the best in us. We love you buddy!

Hey buddy. Love you so much. Was wearing your shirt yesterday and a guy thought it was for apostle Paul. Pretty cool. Happy Easter and here's a big hug. Thanks for continuing to inspire me—with Paul Giaccio.

Submitted by Ballard Johnson:

I met Paul shortly after I pledged Phi Sigma Kappa during my first week at Georgia Tech. We were fast friends. He helped me with everything that was inconvenient for most freshman, including taking me to do my laundry at the basketball arena and grocery shopping. Paul seemed to know a lot of extremely influential people on campus including football and basketball players, and coaches. He invited me to many social events, introduced me to everyone he encountered while simultaneously entertaining us all with his light-hearted humor. As our friendship grew, Paul became like a brother to me. He was someone that I anticipated would be in my life forever.

Pretty soon we both graduated and started working. During this time the highlight of each year was the ski trips we would take together. In true Paul fashion, he would invite just as many random people as he did close friends. The first year it was Paul, Jose and me. We stayed on a friend's floor and skied all day during that trip. Every year we planned ahead even more so than the year before and invited more and more people. The number of people grew to 20+ staying in one house. We would rent a cabin and invited numerous other friends and family that lived in the area to join us. These ski trips are some of the best times we had. Paul was up early to make lunches for everyone, he offered a trail mix for snacking and peanut butter and jelly sandwiches to eat on the mountain. Paul did this to save everyone money and to be more efficient on the mountain. Because Paul always intended to maximize his runs and vertical feet skied which was a point of pride that he made sure everyone was aware of at the end of the trip.

These trips were very special to me. Paul and I worked together for months planning them. We spent hours discussing the most optimal dates as we wanted to make it convenient for everyone to come and were dedicated to finding a house big enough to accommodate everyone. Paul always invited different sets of friends who were outside of each other's friend groups and were all connected by Paul. When you went on these trips you were always assured to meet a few new people.

As I developed a routine of going to work, raising kids and spending time with the same people doing the same things, I always looked forward to phone calls from Paul.

Occasionally he would call to invite me on one of the many adventures the he planned. He enjoyed traveling to interesting places with groups that included both old and new friends.

The stories and invitations from Paul kept my life from becoming ordinary. For me, this is what it means to live like Paul. My promise to Paul is that I will reach out to people, help people when asked, spend time with people that are important to me. Mix groups to hang out. Enjoy and introduce others to new adventures. Make the most of the time I have been given.

Submitted by Andrew Kronitz:

Paul represented many things to me in the relatively few years that I was blessed to have him in my life—most of our 'framily' have been friends with him for much longer—because once he enters your life you never want him to leave. Whereas, I wish I met him many years prior, I am appreciative of the quality and quantity of time spent together. To me, Paul was a brother, a best friend, and a matriarch.

Very much like, Paul was a wise-ass, brimming with confidence, prudent, street smart, savvy, a survivor—always figuring out a solution when one was needed. We both had a passion for music and shared many a concert together—from *Widespread Panic* to *Bassnectar* and everything in-between. We both appreciated the outdoors, festivals, and really took advantage of what life had to offer.

To my son, Brock Star, Paul was a brother, a father, an uncle, a teacher, a friend, an angel. Nothing stood out more than when Paul was around youth. As disappointing as it was for Brock to experience a limited number of years with both of his grandfathers, I can't begin to describe what a huge setback Paul's loss was, affecting Brock's life and future. However, as Paul suddenly graced heaven prematurely, Brock has been positively 'stained' by Paul's love for him, Paul's belief in him, and most fortunately, by Paul's very positive influence on him, and such shall remain forever and ever, as an angel in his life.

We miss and love you Paul more than words can suggest, though you are with us every single day—heart, mind, spirit and soul.

Love,
Andrew Kronitz

If I have additional time, I would love to work on this further, but I believe I am the at THE deadline.

Love you Adrienne.
Peace,
Andrew

Submitted by Michael Pink:

I have sat down numerous times trying to put into words my feelings about Paul Giaccio and I have struggled. It has been very hard to encapsulate everything that Paul was to me and everyone around him, because he was just that special.

I am lucky to be able to say that I have known Paul for 36 of my 41 years of life. I knew him as a five year old kid and in elementary school, I looked up to him as a high schooler (where he was voted most likely to succeed). I joined him and his fraternity during my college years at Georgia Tech, I became life long friends, post college, while we moved forward with our careers and into adulthood. My wife and kids accepted him into our family as a brother and uncle. Needless to say, he was very important to me.

Paul was someone that I can say, without a doubt, changed my life for the better. He had such a positive impact on my life, my wife's life, my kids life, and I know we all would have been worse off having not known him. There are only a handful of people that I can say this about.

The interesting thing is, Paul had the same effect on another 100+ people and families, at least! It truly is amazing looking back at it. He is like no one else I have ever met or ever will meet again. I know this.

So, to put into words what Paul Giaccio was, as a person, is simply an impossibility. It's almost unfair to him to even try—because he was so special, and such a great, great man. He put everyone before himself. His friends and family came first. He'd even put strangers needs in front of his—every day. He had a unique way of connecting with people, helping them, building a relationship and maintaining that relationship - and ultimately becoming important to those people. He did this with so many people and we all loved him for it.

Paul was a living breathing version of the Golden Rule and I personally believe Paul was a gift from God to show us all how life needs to be lived and how people need to be treated. I don't know why Paul was taken away so suddenly, but it has made me recognize that we all can be better people and will be better people if we *Live Like Paul*. And this will make the world a better place.

Michael Pink

❊

Submitted by Shane Nelson:

As Jack has surely told you, our chance meeting with Paul sprang forth from an event that took place in Chicago for the 50th anniversary of the Grateful Dead. Music has a way of bringing people together that is unlike any other avenue of existence. The common interest in an artist or genre kickstarts friendships in a way that many other things can't quite seem to accomplish.

Prior to meeting Paul, I was in midst of a 193 day walk across America. Over the series of seven months I walked from Tybee Island, Georgia to San Francisco, California. There were several events that I had planned to experience along the way and the Grateful Dead: Fare Thee Well shows was one such event. Due to significant weather and a few other hang ups, I was uncertain that I would make it to Chicago in time for the shows. I put out a blurb to Facebook trying to trade one of my tickets for a ride into Chicago. That's where Jack came in.

I had met Jack whilst at another event in Atlanta after he approached me in regards to my "I'm walking across America" sign. We talked for a while and a friendship had found roots. He was one of the first people to contact me in regards to helping me in my quest. These shows were primed to be the event of a lifetime for many people. The Dead are arguably one of the most influential bands in American rock history, creating a subculture and community that has lived beyond many of its' members. They gave fans new life through music and have created a legacy that heals and inspires. Their music and community speaks to people in a way that is unlike any other and friends become friends without having ever met one another. This was exemplified through my experience with Jack and Paul.

Jack reached out to facebook in order to find a companion for the long drive from Georgia and Paul was able to connect with him. As Jack and I continued to plan things out, I was excited to already have a new friend in tow.

Some rough weather pinned me down at a campground in Earl Park, Indiana. I was there for three or four days before Paul and Jack arrived. The entire storm had lifted upon their arrival and we made our way north to Chicago for what was sure to be an experience nothing short of incredible.

The night before the *Fare Thee Well* event was set to begin, we attended a show featuring *Keller Williams*, *The Infamous Stringdusters* and *Greensky Bluegrass*. As *Greensky* took the stage, their dobro player spoke into the mic welcoming us to "the greatest weekend of our lives." The three of us toasted our beer glasses and shared a group hug. The concert was nothing short of fantastic.

We spent the next day traveling around Chicago and met up with a friend of Paul's for lunch. His friend showed us around some cool spots in the city and we were able to view the entire Chicago skyline from across the river as well as some really cool art installations. We did some touristy things which included a trip to the riverfront and a stop at the Willis Tower, formerly the Sears Tower.

There are viewing booths at the top floor in which you can step out into a glass box and look down at the ground below through the glass floor. I'll never forget seeing Paul walk out into the box, joining a group of girls as they took a picture. He counted down from three and told them he was going to jump! The horrified looks on their faces were priceless as he lifted off the ground. We laughed at that one for a good while.

The rest of the weekend was a frenzy of good music and interactions. I was able to spend time meeting with friends that had made the trip from other parts of the country. I reconvened with Jack and Paul a few days after the shows were over and they dropped me off just outside of the city. As we parted, I knew I had gained two new friends that I would see again soon.

I would run into Paul from time to time throughout the following years. One such time, we met up at a *Radiohead* concert at Philips Arena in Atlanta. Paul seemed to have so many great connections and knew how to work the events to gain access to things like VIP and other off limit areas for general admission. He toured me and a friend around the arena and introduced us to all of the staff members. They all seemed to know him by name and his presence elevated everyone's mood.

I ran into a friend that I had met in the crowd in Chicago. Imagine my surprise when it turned out that Paul had gone to the same high school as him! Outgoing people like Paul make the world seem so much smaller, but in reality it is their infectious personalties that shrink such a big world down in such a way. We reminisced on our time in Chicago and then Paul pulled out a pack of wristbands he had snuck in. He passed them around and all of a sudden we were all VIP!

I remember that night fondly as the show was such a great time and I went to meet Paul at a bar down the street when the show was done. I told him I was going to bring him a DVD of the walk and he responded that I should bring at least five. Once I was able to link up with him, he bragged on me to all his friends and passed out my extra DVDs. It felt so good to be spoken so highly of, especially because I thought highly of him.

The last time I saw Paul was shortly before his passing when we met up before a show in Alpharetta. I met another group of friends who told me stories about Paul and some of his antics. It seemed to me as though no one was a stranger to him. I gave him a big hug before heading into the show and he said, "If I don't see you, I'll see you some other time."

Regardless of a physical presence, one can see Paul as often as they'd like in those good heartwarming memories. Our friendship was brief in the grand scheme of things, but the times shared can never be forgotten. A true and lovable energy emanated from Paul and everyone who was able to experience it was surely lucky. I know I am.

Submitted By Danielle Greenway Justiniano:

Over the summer when Hugo and I went to Chicago with Paul to see Pearl Jam, Paul got cute and hacked an ATM at the bar we were at: *Pearl Jam best band ever!* He was so funny and giggly about it. I loved it and we all laughed so hard and wondered how long it would stay like that! So last Saturday I was at dinner with  my husband and kids, and Hugo was wearing his Pearl Jam T-shirt from the concert. A family stopped us on our way out to compliment Hugo's shirt and asked if we were at the show. Then the mom said "Best band ever" and the dad stood up with the kindest smile, looked me in the eye, and said, "Happy Mother's Day." The mom said that exact phrase! No more, no less. That was Paul, and I cried for two days. I miss him so much. My heart aches for you.

This isn't my only story of feeling Paul's presence—just the most recent and obvious one. I truly feel he communicates with me often because he knows I need him right now. Actually, the last three days I've gotten in my car, the Pearl Jam song *Given To Fly* has been on. I mentioned the coincidence to Hugo (the true PJ fan) and he thinks it's Paul's way of telling me he's at peace. Maybe give it a listen and read the lyrics.

Submitted By Kristin Vadas Marsicano:

Paul, Uncle Paul, Paulie...

Gosh, I will never forget your mischievous smile and smirk. Thanks for pushing me to try things and live a little, even when they were way outside my comfort zone:

For example, hiking the gorge, crossing the water on slippery wet rocks. I had never really hiked before. I almost turned back. But you encouraged me to do it and I loved it, even though I got wet.

Or my favorite memory, sneaking into the Lady Gaga concert and sitting in the front few rows. You let me and my friend sit the closest and you sat a few rows back. I'll never forget that huge smile on your face whenever I turned around...you were so genuinely happy to offer this opportunity to me to see an artist I loved so up close. Whenever I looked back, you flashed me a big smile, nodded your head, and gave me a thumbs up. After the concert you were SO excited to hear what I thought and if I had a good time. Thank you.

Or even all the times you poked fun at some of my insecurities or probed in jest about a falling out I had with a friend. "Oh, that's hot." You always did it with that smile, and it always felt out of love and fun, never out of judgement.

You were so full of life. Thank you for sharing your joy for music and outdoors and instigating trouble with me. Thanks for being such an amazing friend to Phil. And thanks for making my kids laugh and sending them presents in the mail. They always celebrated those and looked forward to them every year. I hope I can live each day even half as full of love and connection as you did. I love you, Paul.

Kristin Vadas Marsicano

Social Media Posts

A Year Later

It's a little over a year since Paul died.

This book is about to go into publication, but before it does, I wanted to update my readers on what has transpired since.

Besides setting up the Georgia Tech LIVELIKEPAUL foundation, benefitting the Athletic Department and Fraternity, his friends conducted nonstop fund raisers in the way of poker tournaments, concerts, dinners, hikes, etc.

October 12, 2019 marked the first annual *Paulie Palooza*, which was a day long celebration in Atlanta, Georgia. A huge success in every way. They are already planning *Paulie Palooza* 2020!

Facebook posts are endless with his friends writing their sentiments either on Paul's wall or their own. I write there also. One of the benefits of Facebook is bringing people together for comfort.

I decided to include some of these on the following pages.

As for me I continue to heal with the utmost support of my dear husband Manny, who never leaves my side. My dearest and best friends are also there in every imaginable way. Of course, my sons Frank, Bobby, and Richie keep a close connection every day, as always. I have been so blessed with amazing loving sons, as well as the above-mentioned relationships, and for that I am grateful.

Grateful for it all. I'm grateful for being Paul's mom for 43 years. Yes, I would have wanted more, but I'm grateful for what I had, and I've recently come to a new understanding, which I'd like to share.

With all the research I have done and books I have read, probably the best influential one is entitled *Inside the Other Side* by Concetta Bertoldi. And, I only read it two weeks ago! It has really affected me in the most positive way in my quest for answers.

When a mom loses a child, she wants to know why.

I do believe this author nailed it for me.

Bertoldi calls certain souls *Mission Entities*. I see Paul as one of these *Mission Entities* by her definitions and explanations.

I am paraphrasing some of them!

"A *Mission Entity* is a soul who chooses to come here with a full plate...very advanced, and they know they will push forward the evolution of many souls. Out of love and sacrifice, they take on a life, sometimes with an early death. They have a power of influence upon many people, known and unknown during their short life... they are karmic teachers here to teach us lessons in many ways... come on a mission from God, with God's help, helping to change the world, our attitudes towards our differences, as well as all the ways we think about love and peace and hope, having a special influence on us... totally selfless beings."

She had to be describing Paul!

She also talks about moms who have lost a child.

"In most cases, the mom is the emotional head of the family. If she is brave, others will be affected by her bravery, inspiring and encouraging them. A mom can choose to be present and loving to those who need and love her, or she can focus on the loss, the hole in her life, destroying herself and everyone else, withholding love and energy from others. Consider instead, carrying forward the work her child has done!"

Thinking of Paul as a Mission Entity makes sense and is comforting. Seeing all those affected by him and continually affected by him, gives me peace.

And for that, again, I am grateful.

1st Annual Pauliepalooza

SATURDAY, OCTOBER 12, 2019

Midtown Atlanta

A family friendly 5K fun walk/run through beautiful Piedmont Park and the Atlanta Beltline, ending at Bar Mercado (Krog Street Market) where we'll present the 1st two #LIVELIKEPAUL scholarships and celebrate the late, great Paul Giaccio!

≡   🔒 gofundme.com   ↻

≡   gofundme   🔍

👥 **Bryan Van Vranken** would like you to join their fundraising team for this campaign.

Join Team

Live Like Paul Endowment

 Bryan Van Vranken is with **Christine Nelson** and **11 others**.   •••
Wednesday at 10:12 PM · 🌐

Paulie Palooza is 10 Days Away. REGISTER NOW. Come celebrate the late, great, amazing Paul Giaccio with friends and family. We'll send day-of details in the next few days. Here is the link below: **#LIVELIKEPAUL**

https://sites.google.com/view/livelikepaul?
fbclid=IwAR0jEVjoeE_juU23sFIvZ3ps4KYuiMoXFw_-unpLl-
uwwd4niKdzxT92Xug

🔍 Search   ↩

SUN, FEB 17 AT 8 PM

Live.Like.Paul. 2019
Variety Playhouse · Atlanta, GA

 Andrew Kronitz invited you to this.

    ❓
Going   Maybe   Can't Go   More

📍 Variety Playhouse
1099 Euclid Ave NE, Atlanta, Georgia 30307

🕐 Sunday, Feb 17 at 8 PM

🔍 Paul Giaccio   ↩

 elovate.us
January 12 · 🌐

1st order of LIVE LIKE PAUL shirts and sweatshirts just got in. Now it's time to embellish with Paul's love! **#livelikepaul #lovelikepaul #elovat...** Continue Reading

Q Paul Giaccio

Bryan Van Vranken shared a link to the event: **In Paul's Memory**.
1 hr · ✉

Bryan Van Vranken is with **Chris Yerbey** and **15 others**.
September 16 · 🌐

CHECK IT OUT!!! The 1st Annual Paulie Palooza official T-Shirt design. T-shirt and bracelets included in donation for this amazing fundraiser. All money goes to the Paul Giaccio **#LIVELIKEPAUL** endowment. Thank you **Dan Zitoli** for the incredible design. Less than 1 month to go. Register NOW!

REGISTER HERE: https://sites.google.com/view/livelikepaul

Hey everyone - if you are interested in donating to a charity on behalf of Paul the following would be perfect. Please read bellow. LIVE LIKE PAUL

Paul Giaccio - I'm grateful for the time we had. The impression you made on this world, especially those of us who knew you personally, will never be forgotten. I'm honoring your life, your generosity and your passion for live music by giving to the Do It For The Love Foundation and I invite others who got the gift of one of your wristbands to do the same. We love you 🖤🌈

DOITFORTHELOVE.ORG
doitforthelove
HOME

Q Paul Giaccio

Andrew Kronitz ▶ Paul Giaccio
October 4 · Atlanta, GA · 👥

#LLP. Playoff time!! — 🎟 attending **Atlanta Braves NL Division Series Home Game 2** at **SunTrust Park**.

👍❤ Christine Nelson and 12 others   1 Comment

👍 Like   💬 Comment

Q Paul Giaccio

Andrew Kronitz is eating **dinner with beloved family** 🖤 with **Alexita Klein** and **13 others** at **Galla's Pizza**.
September 25 · Chamblee, GA · 🌐

As you desire, **Paul Giaccio**, your Framily is together and having a "Happy Paulie's Birthday." 🎂 You will never leave our hearts nor our spirits..... and, of course, you are always on our minds. 🧡 We love you our friend, our brother, our inspiration. ☮

👍❤ 85   3 Comments   4 Shares

👍 Like   💬 Comment   ↪ Share

‹ Q Paul Giaccio

 Antonio Ochoa ▶ **Paul Giaccio**
September 25 · 👥

Happy birthday my dear friend. So many memories that I still and will forever hold onto. Nothing but smiles from my **Paul Giaccio**! I truly do miss you and there's not a day that goes by and i wonder if I'll ever see you again. You brought everyone together and always made everything ok. The good ones always end up back in the heavens to continue their conquest and you surely conquered it here! Such an amazingly loving person that could and would connect with everyone. What an honor to have been considered a friend to you. We love you and miss you dearly and can not wait till we meet again my dearest friend!

👍❤ Christine Nelson and 2 others

👍 Like   💬 Comment

Myra Koblentz Greene ▶ **Paul Giaccio**
September 25 · 👥

Miss that sweet smile

👍❤ Christine Nelson and 1 other

👍 Like   💬 Comment

 ‹ Q Paul Giaccio

 Catherine Bowen shared a memory.   •••
June 24, 2019 · 👥

Miss these fun times with you Paul! Sending love and #livelikepaul forever. 💚💜 Paul Giaccio. Julie McGuire Hogg Katie Noland Zegarelli

Catherine Bowen is with **Julie McGuire Hogg** and **3 others**.
June 24, 2015 · 👥

David Gray and Amos Lee! Thank you Paulie!!! It's a great night!

 ‹ Q Paul Giaccio

Jessica Kuss ▶ Paul Giaccio   •••
January 19, 2019 · 👥

I will try to put a little of your positive energy and zest for life into each day. You're an inspiration, Paulie. #livelikepaul 💚

 ‹ Q Paul Giaccio

Bobby Giaccio is with **Paul Giaccio**.   •••
September 25 · 👥

Today you would've turned 44 and I'm sure you're probably out for a hike with friends and enjoying the day as you always did.

It's been just over 10 months and although I've accepted the fact you're no longer here, it's still extremely hard to swallow. My acceptance comes from the fact that I know you were recruited to take on a much larger and more important role up there: guiding others who were also taken too soon.

One of the greatest (and worst) ironies is that, sometimes being healthy can be a bad thing....like when your auto-immune system kicks into overdrive to fight off an infection like Sepsis. More people should be aware of this because it can take a perfectly healthy person's life away in as quickly as a few days without even knowing what's hit you -- and it's very difficult to diagnose.

The night you passed, you were supposed to go see Sebastian Maniscalco in Atlanta -- the comedian I'd been telling you about for a while. You bought eight tickets -- one for yourself and seven for friends to join you, and you never asked for anything in return. It's no coincidence that he happens in be in Charlotte tonight and I'll be going to see him. I know you'll be looking down and laughing with me.

Happy Birthday, Paul.

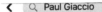

Tricia Hoory ▶ Paul Giaccio
January 13, 2019 · 👥

Cleaning out and came across this tiny diary I kept on a trip with **Paul** to **Julie** and **Darren**'s wedding in Scotland. We stopped off in Amsterdam to visit **Chris** and **Mariska** and celebrate his birthday. His gnarly hiccup scared the lady who checked us into our hotel. Feeling grateful for those good times. He was a most excellent travel companion. **#LiveLikePaul**

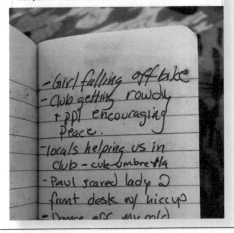

Andrew Kronitz checked in to **Paulie's Pizza** with **Paul Giaccio** and **Ryan O'Donnell**. •••
July 28, 2019 · Philadelphia, PA · 🌐

Live Like Paul - Philly Style .
BROTHERLY LOVE- what our Paulie is all about. 🙏💜🖤

facebook 🔍 ↻

Nöel Carignan ▶ Celise & Norie •••
4 mins · Greensboro, NC · 🔲

Service of Holy Baptism for Eleanor Paulina.

Uncle **Paul**, her namesake, is watching over her. — with **Chuck Carignan** and **7 others** at **First Lutheran Church, Greensboro NC**.

Maryelle St. Clare is with **Christine Nelson** and **Paul Giaccio**. •••
November 29 · 🌐

Heaven let your light shine down. Paul we miss you and love you. Thinking about you right now at Collective Soul. #livelikepaul

Cryshonda Kiser is with **Paul Giaccio** and **Crystal Alford**.
November 19, 2018 · 👥

Man NOT Paul!!! Very **#close** friend/family of bae 😔 This will be a hard one..a very very hard one... We bonded since day one he accepted me' my boys & my other loves into his circle of life! 🤍 Thanks for simply being you, thanks for being there, for everything thick & thin.. you showed us Family isnt just blood...you were the REAL definition of Family & a True Friend 🤍 you will truly be missed #youknowthat... 🕯️ 11.19.18 God Gained Another Angel #flyhighpaul 🙏🕊️

Denna Babul
Yesterday at 5:18 AM · 🌐

Heaven gained one of the best this week. **Paul Giaccio** you were such a beautiful light. I am so thankful for the time we got to spend together. You will be severely missed but forever cherished.

Hug your friends and family tight this week. Tell them how much you love them.

I know Paul is smiling ear to ear watching all of these tributes pour in. I sure hope he knew just how loved he really was.

RIP my friend.

Autumn Coleman is with **Paul Giaccio**.
January 2, 2019 · 👥

I'll live like you for the rest of my life, **Paul Giaccio**!! You are incredibly missed.

👍❤️😢 You, Bryan Van Vranken and 20 others

👍 Like   💬 Comment

Juelz Jaden ▶ **Paul Giaccio**
March 21, 2019 · 👥

Uncle Paul 🙏🙏 — with **Paul Giaccio**.

👍❤️ You, Ryan O'Donnell and 12 others   2 Comments

👍 Like   💬 Comment

Bryan Van Vranken is with **Bobby Giaccio** and **3 others**.
March 21, 2019 · 🌐

Social Media Posts

Bryan Van Vranken ▶ Paul Giaccio
3 hrs · 👥

Hey buddy. I know how much you like to keep 'stats' of things so here's an update. 200 LIVE LIKE PAUL bracelets are already on the wrists of your friends and family, across 10+ states and at least 2 countries so far. We just received 300 more (thank you Jason Faris) to keep spreading your love. You are alive within all of us. Love you.

👍❤️   1 Comment

👍 Like   💬 Comment

  Diana Medrano
#livelikepaul. Miss you Paul! Every day. 🖤💚

🔍 Paul Giaccio

 Diana Medrano   ...
July 27, 2019 · 👥

Such a beautiful song....it made me think of you today Paul Giaccio. #LLP.

YOUTUBE.COM
Queen Love Of My Life (Live Rock Montreal HD)
Queen Rock Montreal is a live album by English band Quee...

👍❤️ Christine Nelson and 6 others   2 Comments

👍 Like   💬 Comment   ↪ Share

< June Gumbel   ...
19 hrs · 👥

I now have my "Live Like Paul" sweat shirt and bracelet! He may be gone but he will never ever be forgotten ... we miss you Paul! #livelikepaul #paulgiaccio #gonebutnotforgotten

❤️ 💕 ❤️ 👏 😄 😃   ✕

< 🔍 Paul Giaccio

📝 Write Post   🖼 Share Photo

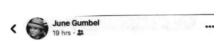 Ari Siesser is 😔 feeling heartbroken with Paul   ...
Giaccio.
Yesterday at 9:46 PM · 👥

Paul – I still don't want to believe this is real. I don't want to believe that someone who brought so much positivity to this world could be taken away so suddenly. Its not fair. Thank you for your friendship, your guidance, and being someone I could always trust and look up to. I will really miss you my friend 😢

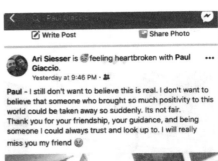

Katie Wise Brophy is with **Paul Giaccio**.
July 2, 2019 · 🌐

A friendship anniversary alert with you Paul...how bittersweet. Not a day goes by we don't think of you and smile...sometimes cry a little too because the world can feel so empty without you ...**#livelikepaul** 💚🫶🙏❓🤙

 Katie and Paul are celebrating 11 years of friendship on Facebook!
See Your Memories ›

 facebook 🔍 💬

 O'Donnell at Adair Park.
21 mins · 👥

Just realized I haven't posted on IG since you left @unclepaul.g . Getting these shirts today made me want to share something. To say I miss my boy is a gross understatement. **#livelikepaul** thanks @elovate.us , you made our day!

 Margaret Reynolds is with **Katie Reynolds Dahlen** and **Adrienne Falzon**.
Yesterday at 6:10 PM · 🌐

My three.. Learning to Live Like Paul..
Eastern Shore edition! 💜💜💜

 🔍 Paul Giaccio 💬

 Tristain Yankosky O'Donnell is with **Paul Giaccio**.
November 22 · 🌐

LIVE LIKE PAUL- He gave his all to everyone everyday of his life (and that is not an exaggeration) and did it with ease and a smile. Happiness to him was his friends, family and people he may have even met just once being happy and that's all he wanted. He worked hard, played hard and loved hard and just wanted to be around all of his friends and family. He was a people person and a friends friend.
He is without a doubt one of the best people I have met in my life and no words without it being the length of a book could truly explain who he was and what he meant to me and my family and especially to Ryan.
I love you Paul and I hurt every morning when I wake up and realize this is all still true. I am grateful to have met you and for all of the trips, talks, shared memories and times we shared. We will never be the same without you but I will make sure to be a better person for you and LIVE LIKE PAUL

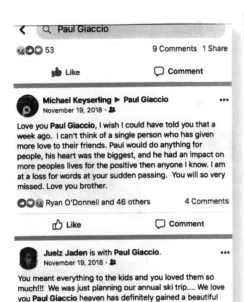

Q Paul Giaccio

😊😮👍 53   9 Comments   1 Share

👍 Like   💬 Comment

Michael Keyserling ▶ **Paul Giaccio**   •••
November 19, 2018 · 👥

Love you **Paul Giaccio**, I wish I could have told you that a week ago. I can't think of a single person who has given more love to their friends. Paul would do anything for people, his heart was the biggest, and he had an impact on more peoples lives for the positive then anyone I know. I am at a loss for words at your sudden passing. You will so very missed. Love you brother.

👍😮❤️ Ryan O'Donnell and 46 others   4 Comments

👍 Like   💬 Comment

Juelz Jaden is with **Paul Giaccio**.   •••
November 19, 2018 · 👥

You meant everything to the kids and you loved them so much!!! We was just planning our annual ski trip.... We love you **Paul Giaccio** heaven has definitely gained a beautiful Angel 😇

Home   About   Events   Photos   Videos   Commur

Stonewall Condominium   •••
November 20 at 3:39 AM · 🌐

Our little community is reeling at the sudden loss of our incredible director, neighbor and friend. Paul had lived here for about 13 years, championed the repaving of Stonewall Drive, loved our pool and included the entire neighborhood in his Pool Party and Poker Tournament every year. His kind and compassionate nature and infectious smile will never be forgotten. Rest in peace, Paul.. @unclepaul.g

Andrew Kronitz ▶ **Adrienne Falzon**   •••
December 19, 2018 · 👥

Paul has created a loving network of friends centered in Atlanta but with reaches throughout the world.
We will be sharing Paul's love as well as the love of Paul forever.
Although he is in our minds, hearts & souls daily, occasionally we are fortunate to gather and be together.... just as if **Paul Giaccio** orchestrated such himself.
#live.like.paul.

://www.facebook.com/events/382565155846262/?ti=icl

SAT, DEC 29, 2018
Live.Like.Paul. Celebration of Life & Love
Sidebar · Atlanta, GA   [GOING]

🔴 Andrew Kronitz invited you

Q Paul Giaccio

👍 Like   💬 Comment   ↪ Share

Diana Medrano is with **Paul Giaccio**.   •••
November 21 · 👥

Your life was a blessing, your memory a treasure, you are loved beyond words and missed beyond measure.
It's been a rough year since you left us.....forever in our hearts 😢🖤
#LLP

👍😮❤️ You, Christine Nelson and 115 others   4 Comments

Sending your amazing vibes and love out into the universe. Your incredible love, kindness, selflessness, sense of humor and friendship is as alive as ever. #livelikepaul

Olivia Giaccio is with **Paul Giaccio** at **Ruka Ski Resort.**
December 1 · Kuusamo, Finland · 🌐

We're just under a week away from the World Cup Opener here in Ruka, Finland, and I'm Living Like **Paul** every step of the way 🖤

👍 Like   💬 Comment

Cryshonda Kiser is with **Paul Giaccio.**
December 31, 2018 · 👥

I cant help but have him on my mind 😔 during this time! Still sooo #unreal to me... he should be HERE!!. 🙏 #livelikepaul Man we MISS you 🖤...i already know you would of stopped by and got LIT for a HOT sec...lol when you came thru' you ALWAYS had some up YOUR sleeve lol watch over us 🥃🖤..we NEED more people like YOU!! i swear i NEVER met a soul like yours!! #flyhighpaul 💯

Lauren Reese Candee
November 19 · 👥

One year without you. We love you Uncle **Paul!**

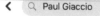

Lauren Reese Candee is with **Paul Giaccio.**
November 19, 2018 · 👥

When someone who means the world to your family leaves the world way too soon, you try to spend the time around the dinner table thinking about all the beautiful memories, because you know that's what he would have wanted. It didn't work, and tears came instead, but we tried.

Paul Giaccio, you were the best friend, the best Uncle, the most selfless and generous human being we have ever ever known. Thank you for the privilege of your friendship, the laughs, and the memories. We miss you dearly, always and forever.

Social Media Posts

Mark Reycroft ▶ **Paul Giaccio**
Sunday at 5:56 PM · 👥

Bella turned 18 yesterday, Paul. Here you are holding her. We had recently moved back to Atlanta and you always I opened your house to us. Always there. Always cared. She will be a better person because of you. We all are. Love you buddy. — with **Paul Giaccio.**

Kurt Karjalainen is with **Paul Giaccio.**
February 20, 2019 · 👥

Attending the show we first met at **#ATMIA2019** it's just not the same without you here Paul Giaccio. Had some great conversation about you with some mutual friend. You are missed! **#livelikepaul**

Amy Daniel Granetto is with **Paul Giaccio.**
November 19 · 👥

#livelikePaul we love you and miss you @unclepaul.g

> See that look on our faces? It's pure happiness! And you always felt that when you were with Paul. He shared so much love while he was here. He is so missed but we honor him when we **#livelikepaul** and keep spreading happiness.

Julie McGuire Hogg
Yesterday at 1:25 PM · 🌐

Hey **Paul Giaccio**- I realize you wouldn't have been here in person, but I started one of those "life adventures" today, and you were here in spirit and personality. Especially as we were soaking in the rain.... **#livelikepaul**

👍 Like   💬 Comment   ➤ Share

Catherine Bowen shared a memory. •••
June 24, 2019 ·

Miss these fun times with you Paul! Sending love and #*livelikepaul* forever. 💜💜 Paul Giaccio. Julie McGuire Hogg Katie Noland Zegarelli

5 Years Ago
See Your Memories ›

 Catherine Bowen is with **Julie McGuire Hogg** and **3 others.**
June 24, 2015 ·

David Gray and Amos Lee! Thank you Paulie!!! It's a great night!

 facebook 🔍 ◎

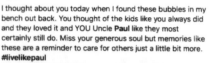 **Catherine Bowen**
5 hrs ·

I thought about you today when I found these bubbles in my bench out back. You thought of the kids like you always did and they loved it and YOU Uncle **Paul** like they most certainly still do. Miss your generous soul but memories like these are a reminder to care for others just a little bit more. #*livelikepaul*

 ‹ 🔍 Paul Giaccio ◉

 Lauren Reese Candee is with **Paul Giaccio.** •••
December 15 ·

Thinking about this man a lot this week. We miss you Uncle Paul. Oh to have one more hiccup!! 💜

 ‹ 🔍 Paul Giaccio

👍 Like   💬 Comment   ↪ Share

 Maryelle St. Clare shared a memory — with **Christine Nelson** and **Paul Giaccio.** •••
December 4 ·

Another memory of Paul. We went to this show and I don't remember where our real seats were, but Paul, with his Legendary Cloak of Invisibility temporarily extended to the rest of us, led us down to the floor and we ended up a few rows from the front. We never got asked to show our tickets and nobody ever came for those primo seats. Pat Monaghan from Train ended up going through our row during his offstage walk around the venue. Thanks for another great night, Paul. 💜

3 Years Ago
See Your Memories ›

 **Christine Nelson** checked in to **Infinite Energy Center** with **Maryelle St. Clare** and **Paul Giaccio.** •••
December 4, 2016 · Duluth, GA ·

Train at Jingle Jam!

444

<   Q   Paul Giaccio

Andrew Kronitz is 🎪 attending **Umphrey's McGee** at **Red Rocks Park and Amphitheatre.** •••
June 23, 2019 · Morrison, CO · 🌐

I didn't know when I'd be blessed to attend Red Rocks with **Paul Giaccio,**

But I always know that grin will always be in the heavens above,
still compassionate,
still Paul,
still Comforting us all. 🖤

<   Q   Paul Giaccio

Juelz Jaden ▶ **Paul Giaccio** •••
September 2, 2019 · 👥

We miss you **Paul Giaccio**

👍😮 Rich Giaccio and 17 others   3 Comments

👍 Like   💬 Comment

Bryan Van Vranken is with **Paul Giaccio.** •••
August 21, 2019 · 🌐

Love Day 22 - **Paul Giaccio.** Got a great big hug from you in

<   Q   Paul Giaccio

Andrew Kronitz ▶ **Paul Giaccio** •••
November 18 · 👥

Over the past 12 months, Brock & I have suffered so much from your absence, yet we have both grown greatly from your omnipresence.
We love you. 🖤

Author's Note

THANK YOU ALL FOR JOINING ME on this heart wrenching journey as I remembered my son Paul through his stages, stories and events.

I must say that although it was so difficult going through his photos, bringing up memories, it was both cathartic and healing to do so. It gave me a mission and occupied my troubled mind. I also learned so much along the way and for all that, I am grateful.

Yes, I may be the author of this book on the life of my son Paul, but I recently realized after the comment of a friend, that all of our lives are actual books, with a beginning, middle and end. True memoirs.

The Author of each of those books is God Himself. He is the Grand Author of all, deciding the birth, life, and death in each of our personal story books. Some books, as we know, are longer than others. The author knows when he or she has sufficiently told the story and therefore when it should end.

It's the same in the planning of our life. God knows when our story is done, despite our sadness, frustration and even anger in its final chapter. That final chapter may be too premature in our eyes, and usually it always is when we lose a loved one. We never want that chapter to end, no matter what.

But, when it truly is the end of a book we are cherishing, the end of a life story, the only comfort we can find is accepting that it is what it is and what had to be. It is all in the divine plan, and the question then becomes: "What is the message here? What now?"

Along with the sharing of his experiences through life, I hope the essential messages were made clear. Our daily words, actions and thoughts affect everyone around us, including our own destiny.

Paul genuinely loved and respected everyone as you consistently read in the testimonials. In turn, they now want to do for others.

To LIVE LIKE PAUL is simple and yet so powerful.

JUST BE KIND. The world needs this kindness more than ever now.

To celebrate and encourage such kindness, a LIVE LIKE PAUL Foundation was set up at Georgia Tech. Each year, scholarships will be given to two students displaying altruistic qualities.

If so inclined, donations can be made by check mailed directly to:

Georgia Tech Foundation, Inc.
For: LIVE LIKE PAUL ENDOWMENT
760 Spring Street, NW Suite 400
Atlanta, Georgia 30308

Or, online, go to http://development.gatech.edu.

Specify: LIVE LIKE PAUL FOUNDATION
Donations can also be matched by most Corporations.

I invite my readers to visit my website at: www.adriennefalzon.com

You can send me a message at any time, including any thoughts or reactions you may have after reading this or any of my children's books.

In the meantime, let's pray for peace throughout our world and we can help by just being kind to one another. *Live like Paul!*

Sincerely,

Adrienne Falzon

ABOUT THE AUTHOR

ADRIENNE FALZON LIVES IN RANCHO SANTA FE, CALIFORNIA and Southampton, New York, with her husband Manny.

Together they enjoy traveling, fun with friends, and being with their blended family of seven sons and nine grandchildren.

Adrienne participates in many local organizations such as Breast Cancer Angels, USO San Diego, various literary societies, and is a board member of the Rancho Santa Fe Garden Club.

Adrienne has also had her share of "unfair" times, but always concentrates on the positive, since she has found it always attracts more of the same.